Ergebnisse der Mathematik und ihrer Grenzgebiete

Band 37

Herausgegeben von
P. R. Halmos · P. J. Hilton · R. Remmert · B. Szőkefalvi-Nagy
Unter Mitwirkung von
L. V. Ahlfors · R. Baer · F. L. Bauer · R. Courant · A. Dold
J. L. Doob · E. B. Dynkin · S. Eilenberg · M. Kneser · M. M. Postnikow
H. Rademacher · B. Segre · E. Sperner
Redaktion: P. J. Hilton

Varieties of Groups

Hanna Neumann

Springer-Verlag New York Inc. 1967

Prof. Dr. Hanna Neumann
The Australian National University
The School of General Studies
Department of Pure Mathematics
Canberra, A.C.T. / Australia

Library of Congress Catalog Card Number 67 – 15 607
Printed in the United States of America

Title No. 4581

To Bernhard

Preface

Varieties of algebras are equationally defined classes of algebras, or "primitive classes" in MAL'CEV's terminology. They made their first explicit appearance in the 1930's, in Garrett BIRKHOFF'S paper on "The structure of abstract algebras" and B.H. NEUMANN'S paper "Identical relations in groups I". For quite some time after this, there is little published evidence that the subject remained alive. In fact, however, as part of "universal algebra", it aroused great interest amongst those who had access, directly or indirectly, to PHILIP HALL'S lectures given at Cambridge late in the 1940's. More recently, category theory has provided a general setting since varieties, suitably interpreted, are very special examples of categories. Whether their relevance to category theory goes beyond this, I do not know. And I doubt that the category theoretical approach to varieties will be more than a fringe benefit to group theory. Whether or not my doubts have substance, the present volume owes its existence not to the fact that varieties fit into a vastly more general pattern, but to the benefit group theory has derived from the classification of groups by varietal properties. It is this aspect of the study of varieties that seems to have caused its reappearance in the literature in the 1950's. Since then varietal methods in group theory have rapidly gained impetus and, as is wont to happen, they have thrown up their own problems and developed into a branch of group theory which is as much of intrinsic interest as it is powerful as a tool.

A course of lectures given in 1963 at the Manchester College of Science and Technology started the process of gathering and sorting the results on varieties of groups. Perhaps this very process has had some share in accelerating progress. In any event, when, after too long a time, the manuscript was ready for the publishers, it was also ready to be re-written. Experience shows that a report of this kind, delayed too long, becomes useless (if, indeed, it appears at all!). I therefore decided against re-writing which would have meant a long delay. It may then be in order to indicate briefly in this preface two of the points that I would have wanted to attend to.

The first is mainly, though not entirely, a matter of organization of material. Knowledge of metabelian varieties was scant until quite recently when it expanded so rapidly that, to do it justice, a separate chapter should now have been given to this topic. Instead I have merely added to the information provided in various contexts — a plan that was natural and adequate a short time ago. I have tried to ensure that these scattered references to the metabelian case are easily located by means of the index.

Secondly, I want to draw attention to an alternative development which has great advantages. ŠMEL'KIN's embedding theorem (22.48) should, I believe, be made the starting point of the treatment of product varieties. Its proof is direct, needing no more than basic facts and the construction of the verbal wreath product; but its use would shorten and simplify much of Chapter 2 and several other topics besides (for example in Chapter 4).

This report would not have been written but for the interest and active participation of my audiences in the lectures at Manchester, mentioned earlier, and in similar lectures given at the Australian National University, Canberra. JOHN P. COSSEY and IAN D. MACDONALD checked parts of the manuscript; so did L. G. KOVÁCS, and M. F. NEWMAN read most of it at some stage or other. KOVÁCS and NEWMAN contributed much more in the way of elucidation, simplification and correction than can be apparent from the text. B. H. NEUMANN and PETER M. NEUMANN read the proofs and, aven at that late stage, prevented a number of minor and major accidents. I wish to acknowledge in particular the efforts of the latter who seemed to interpret "proof reading" to mean "checking all proofs". I record here my gratitude to all of them, and affirm, as is usual but still important, that any errors that remain are mine. Last, but not least, I acknowledge SPRINGER's cooperation that was indeed all that one has come to expect of this name.

Canberra, November 1966 HANNA NEUMANN

Contents

Note XI

Chapter 1. The Basic Facts 1
1. Preliminaries 1
2. Words, Laws, Verbal Subgroups 3
3. Relatively Free Groups 9
4. Varieties 12
5. Varieties as Closed Classes of Groups 14
6. The n-Generator Groups and the n-Variable Laws of a Variety 20
7. Discrimination and Residual Properties 27
8. Verbal Products 32

Chapter 2. Product Varieties 38
1. The Algebra of Varieties 38
2. Wreath Products and Discrimination 45
3. The Uniqueness of Factorization 55
4. Some Classes of Indecomposable Varieties 58
5. Product Varieties Generated by a Finitely Generated Group 64
6. Residual Properties of the Free Groups of Product Varieties 73

Chapter 3. Nilpotent Varieties 77
1. Summary of Properties of Nilpotent Groups 77
2. Residual Properties 80
3. A Lemma on Words with an Application to Free Products 83
4. The Laws of a Nilpotent Variety and Related Topics 89
5. Generating Groups of Finite Rank 99
6. The Variety of All Metabelian Nilpotent Groups of Class c 104

Chapter 4. Miscellaneous Properties of Relatively Free Groups 110
1. Remarks on Automorphisms and the Hopf Property 110
2. Free Subgroups of Free Groups 114
3. Theorems Like Auslander and Lyndon's: the Schreier Property 126
4. The Splitting Property; Direct Decomposability 136

Chapter 5. The Laws of Finite Groups 145
1. Critical Groups and Cross Varieties 145
2. The Theorem of Oates and Powell 151
3. Critical Groups and Subvarieties 161
4. Critical p-Groups and Locally Finite Varieties; a Summary of Developments 174

References 181

Author Index 187

Subject Index 189

Note

The numbering is decimal; thus for example the statement numbered 34.12 refers to Chapter 3, Section 4, Subsection 1, Item 2. Subsections are not formally marked in any other way, and a subsection may contain no more than a single numbered item – such as 32.1.

The presentation is intended to be self-contained. Facts have been used without proof only if they are "known" in the sense that they have found their way into at least one textbook. For less familiar facts of this kind – here the choice is of necessity subjective – a textbook reference is given explicitly, and referring to one textbook does not mean that others may not also serve. Apart from this statements without proof occur, I hope, only on the fringe of the main development, in examples and in summaries of further results.

The textbooks referred to are the following; any reference containing merely the author's name and a page or section number is to these books.

COHN, P.M.: Universal algebra. Harper's Series in Modern Mathematics. New York: Evanston and London: Harper & Row 1965.

CURTIS, C.W., and I.R. REINER: Representation theory of finite groups and associative algebras. New York and London: Interscience Publ. 1962.

HALL Jr., MARSHALL: The theory of groups. New York: Macmillan 1959.

KUROSH, A.G.: The theory of groups, vol. I and II. Translat. from the Russian and edit. by K.A. HIRSCH, 1st or 2nd ed. New York: Chelsea 1956, 1960.

SCOTT, W.R.: Group theory. Englewood Cliffs, New Jersey: Prentice Hall Inc. 1964.

Since this report went to press, the book by W. MAGNUS, A. KARRASS and D. SOLITAR, Combinatorial Group Theory, Interscience has appeared. Had it been available earlier, reference to it would have been frequent, for example wherever commutator calculus is used.

Chapter 1

The Basic Facts

1. Preliminaries

The following *notation* will be adhered to throughout.

Groups: capital Roman letters.

Group elements: small Roman letters. But the identity of every group is denoted by 1.

Varieties of groups: capital German letters; these will also be used for more general sets and classes of groups.

Sets of group elements: small German letters.

Mappings and functions: small Greek letters.

However, small Roman and small Greek letters will also occur as exponents, and as subscripts and superscripts. In this context the capital Roman letter I will always denote the set of positive integers.

The order of a group, or the cardinal of a set, is indicated by vertical bars: $|A|$, $|\mathfrak{x}|$. If A and B are groups, and there exists a monomorphism of A into B, we often write $A \leqq B$: A is isomorphic to a subgroup of B. If it is relevant that A is actually a subset, we write $A \subseteq B$. If A is a normal subgroup of B, we write $A \lhd B$. The derived group of the group A is A'.

For any set S and any positive integer n, S^n denotes the cartesian product of n copies of the set S. If $T \subseteq S$, then $S \backslash T$ is the set of elements of S that do not belong to T.

Arrows denote mappings as usual. In the case of homomorphisms, a two-headed arrow ($\twoheadrightarrow$) indicates an epimorphism, an arrow with a tail ($\rightarrowtail$) indicates a monomorphism.

A *factor* of a group A is any factor group H/K where $\{1\} \leqq K \lhd H \leqq A$; the factor is *proper* unless $K = \{1\}$ and $H = A$.

We shall make frequent use of the following notation which is a slight modification and extension of that used by P. Hall: If $\mathfrak{X}$ is a class of groups, we denote by

s$\mathfrak{X}$ the class of subgroups of groups in $\mathfrak{X}$,

q$\mathfrak{X}$ the class of homomorphic images of groups in $\mathfrak{X}$ (q for quotient group!),

c$\mathfrak{X}$ the class of cartesian products of groups in $\mathfrak{X}$ (cf. Section 5 of this chapter),

D$\mathfrak{X}$ the class of finite direct products of groups in $\mathfrak{X}$ (where 'finite direct product' does, of course, not imply the finiteness of the group, but only that the product is formed with a finite number of factors). Thus, for example, QS$\mathfrak{X}$ consists of all factors of groups in $\mathfrak{X}$.

We summarise some simple facts on *free groups*. All that is used can be found in textbooks, for example those by A. G. KUROSH and by MARSHALL HALL.

The letter F will denote a free group of unspecified rank; we write F_n if the free group is of finite rank n, F_∞ if it is of countably infinite rank. A set of free generators is denoted by $\mathfrak{f}$; thus

$$F = \text{gp}(\mathfrak{f}), \quad F_n = \text{gp}(f_1, \ldots, f_n), \quad F_\infty = \text{gp}(f_1, f_2, \ldots).$$

Each element $\neq 1$ *of* F *has a unique representation in the form*

11.11 $$f_{i_1}^{\mu_1} f_{i_2}^{\mu_2} \ldots f_{i_l}^{\mu_l}, \quad i_\lambda \neq i_{\lambda+1} \quad \textit{for} \quad \lambda = 1, \ldots, l-1$$

and the μ_λ *are non-zero integers.*

Let $A = \text{gp}(\mathfrak{a})$ be an arbitrary group and $F = \text{gp}(\mathfrak{f})$ a free group whose free generating set $\mathfrak{f}$ has the same cardinal as $\mathfrak{a}$. Then there is a $1-1$ mapping $\alpha: \mathfrak{f} \to \mathfrak{a}$ of $\mathfrak{f}$ onto $\mathfrak{a}$.

11.12 *The mapping* α *can be extended to an epimorphism* $\alpha: F \twoheadrightarrow A$.

This extension is, of course, obtained by mapping $f_{i_1}^{\mu_1} \ldots f_{i_l}^{\mu_l}$ on $(f_{i_1}\alpha)^{\mu_1} \ldots (f_{i_l}\alpha)^{\mu_l}$. Note that the mapping of the free generating set and the homomorphism extending it are denoted by the same letter. Moreover we shall, unless otherwise stated, use the convention that if the generating set $\mathfrak{f}$ is indexed by the elements of some index set, then the set $\mathfrak{a}$ of images will be indexed by the same set in such a way that elements of $\mathfrak{f}$ and $\mathfrak{a}$ bearing the same subscript correspond under α.

Going beyond 11.12 we have more generally:

11.13 *Every mapping* $\alpha: \mathfrak{f} \to \mathfrak{f}\alpha \subseteq A$ *can be extended to a homomorphism of* F *into* A.

In particular

11.14 *Every mapping* $\vartheta: \mathfrak{f} \to \mathfrak{f}\vartheta \subseteq F$ *can be extended to an endomorphism of* F.

We go back to 11.12; it shows that $A \cong F/R$ where $R = \ker \alpha$. Put differently, we have a presentation $A = \text{gp}(\mathfrak{a}; R)$. Here every element $r \in R$ is called a *relator* of the generating set $\mathfrak{a}$ of A, and if $r = f_{i_1}^{\mu_1} f_{i_2}^{\mu_2} \ldots f_{i_l}^{\mu_l}$ according to 11.11, then $a_{i_1}^{\mu_1} a_{i_2}^{\mu_2} \ldots a_{i_l}^{\mu_l} = 1$ is a *relation* satisfied by the generators of A.

Next the subgroup theorems:

11.21 **Schreier's Theorem.** *Every subgroup of a free group is free.*

Moreover, if $H \subseteq F_n$ and if m is the rank of H and j the index of H in F_n, then

11.22 **Schreier's Formula.** $m+j=nj+1$.

The formula written in this way admits of a reasonable interpretation also when one or more of m, j, n are infinite; in particular, when j is infinite, m need not be. But:

11.23 *A non-trivial normal subgroup of infinite index in F_n has infinite rank.*

A normal subgroup R of F is said to *admit* the endomorphism ϑ of F if $R\vartheta \subseteq R$.

11.3 *If the normal subgroup R of F admits the endomorphism ϑ of F, then the mapping $fR \to (f\vartheta)R$ for all $f \in F$ is an endomorphism of F/R.*

We call it the endomorphism *induced by* ϑ on F/R and usually denote it by the same letter ϑ without risk of confusion.

In the case of a free group of finite rank the automorphism group is reasonably well known. We shall need only:

11.41 *If F_n is freely generated by $\mathfrak{f}=\{f_1, \ldots, f_n\}$, then the automorphisms given by the following mappings of the generating set into F_n generate the automorphism group of F_n:*

(i) *the permutations of* $\mathfrak{f}$,

(ii) $f_1 \to f_1^{-1}, \quad f_i \to f_i \; (i \neq 1)$,

(iii) $f_1 \to f_1 f_2, \quad f_i \to f_i \; (i \neq 1)$.

Comparison with the automorphism group of the free abelian group of rank n shows:

11.42 *Every automorphism of F_n induces an automorphism of the (free abelian) factor group F_n/F_n'; conversely, every automorphism of F_n/F_n' is so obtained.*

Neither of these two statements remains true for factor groups F/R in general, even if R admits the automorphism.

2. Words, Laws, Verbal Subgroups

We introduce an alphabet $\mathfrak{x}$ of letters $x_1, x_2, \ldots$ and denote by X_∞ the free group freely generated by $\mathfrak{x}$. For each $n \geqq 1$ the free group X_n freely generated by $x_1, \ldots, x_n$ will then be embedded in X_∞ in the natural way. The letters y, z, sometimes also indexed, will stand for letters of the alphabet $\mathfrak{x}$ when convenient.

This free group X_∞ is reserved for the special purpose to provide 'words': a *word* is an element of X_∞. The letters u, v, w are usually used for words. An element of the derived group X'_∞ is called a *commutator word.*

If A is a group, α: $\mathfrak{x} \to \mathfrak{x}\alpha \subseteq A$ a mapping of the free generators of X_∞ into A, then the image of the word w under the corresponding homomorphism α: $X_\infty \to A$ is called a *value* of the word w in A. In general many homomorphisms $\alpha \in \mathrm{Hom}(X_\infty, A)$ determine the same value of w, namely certainly all those that agree on those letters that occur in the representation 11.11 of w in terms of $\mathfrak{x}$. If the letters $x_{j_1}, \dots, x_{j_n}$ occur, then $w\alpha$ is computed by substituting the images $x_{j_1}\alpha = a_{j_1}, \dots, x_{j_n}\alpha = a_{j_n}$ for the letters x_j in the representation

$$w = x_{i_1}^{\mu_1} \dots x_{i_l}^{\mu_l} \quad (l \geqq n).$$

We usually indicate this procedure by writing

$$w\alpha = w(a),$$

where $a \in A^n$ stands for the ordered n-tuplet $(a_{j_1}, \dots, a_{j_n})$. If the detailed correspondence between the x_j and the a_j is relevant, we may even write

$$w(x_{j_1}, \dots, x_{j_n})\alpha = w(a_{j_1}, \dots, a_{j_n}).$$

As a rule, the letters occurring in w may be assumed to be $x_1, \dots, x_n$ without loss of generality.

In this situation the letters x_i are described as variables, and w is referred to as a *word in n variables.* We shall use this convenient language although the domain of these 'variables' is not defined: it is sometimes one group, sometimes another.

The following abbreviations for special words are used: $x^y \equiv y^{-1}xy$ and $[x, y] \equiv x^{-1}y^{-1}xy$ for the y-transform of x and the commutator of x and y respectively. From the latter we get inductively *left-normed commutators of weight* $c+1$:

$$[x_1, \dots, x_c, x_{c+1}] = [[x_1, \dots, x_c], x_{c+1}], \quad c \geqq 2.$$

The word w is a *law* (or *identical relation*; or, in German, *Regel*) in the group A if the only possible value of w in A is 1: $w\alpha = 1$ for all $\alpha \in \mathrm{Hom}(X_\infty, A)$, or equivalently

$$w(a) = 1 \quad \text{for all} \quad a \in A^n.$$

Let $\mathfrak{w}$ be a set of words. The word u is a *consequence* of $\mathfrak{w}$ if u is a law in a group A whenever every word $w \in \mathfrak{w}$ is a law in A. The sets $\mathfrak{w}_1$ and $\mathfrak{w}_2$ of words are *equivalent* if every word in $\mathfrak{w}_1$ is a consequence of $\mathfrak{w}_2$ and vice versa. In particular:

12.11 *Two words obtained from each other by re-naming the variables are equivalent.*

The following example of equivalence is basic:

12.12 **Theorem** (B. H. NEUMANN [*1*]). *Every word w is equivalent to a pair of words, one of the form x^m, $m \geqq 0$, the other a commutator word.*

Proof. By 12.11 we may assume that the representation 11.11 of w involves the letters $x_1, \ldots, x_n$ precisely. Then we rewrite w in the form

$$w = x_1^{m_1} x_2^{m_2} \ldots x_n^{m_n} c,$$

where c is a commutator word. If all exponents m_i are zero, $w = c$ and we have finished. Otherwise assume $m_1 \neq 0$. If w is a law in a group A, substituting 1 for $x_2, x_3, \ldots, x_n$ and an arbitrary element $a \in A$ for x_1 shows that $a^{m_1} = 1$ for all $a \in A$, that is x^{m_1} is a law in A. Similarly x^{m_i} is a law in A for $i = 1, \ldots, n$, and so x^m is a law in A where m is the greatest common divisor of $m_1, \ldots, m_n$. But if x^{m_i} and w all take only the value 1 in A, so does c; hence c is a law in A.

Conversely, if x^m is a law in A, so are the words $x_i^{m_i}$; therefore, if x^m and c are laws in A, so is w. //

12.21 **Definition.** *The verbal subgroup $\mathfrak{w}(A)$ of a group A corresponding to a set $\mathfrak{w}$ of words is the subgroup generated by all values in A of the words of $\mathfrak{w}$:*

$$\mathfrak{w}(A) = \mathrm{gp}(w\alpha \mid w \in \mathfrak{w}, \alpha \in \mathrm{Hom}(X_\infty, A)).$$

If $\mathfrak{w}$ consists of a single word w, we write $w(A)$.

We have:

12.22 *All the words $w \in \mathfrak{w}$ are laws in A if and only if $\mathfrak{w}(A) = \{1\}$.*

Let ϑ: $A \to A\vartheta$ be any homomorphism of A, $\alpha \in \mathrm{Hom}(X_\infty, A)$, then $\alpha\vartheta \in \mathrm{Hom}(X_\infty, A\vartheta)$; thus $w(a)\,\vartheta = w(a\vartheta)$.

Hence we have

12.31 $$\mathfrak{w}(A)\,\vartheta = \mathfrak{w}(A\,\vartheta).$$

We remark as an aside that 12.31 permits us to state:

12.32 *If $\mathfrak{w}$ is a set of words, then the mapping $A \to \mathfrak{w}(A)$ defines a functor on the category of all groups and homomorphisms of groups.*

Moreover, taking ϑ as an endomorphism of A in 12.31:

12.33 *Every verbal subgroup of a group is fully invariant in that group.*

The converse is not true in general. But we have:

12.34 **Theorem.** *Every fully invariant subgroup of a free group F is verbal.*

Proof. Let $V \subseteq F$ be fully invariant in F; then $V = \mathfrak{w}(F)$ where one may take $\mathfrak{w}$ to consist of all those words

$$w \equiv x_{i_1}^{\mu_1} \dots x_{i_l}^{\mu_l}$$

with the property that the corresponding expression $f_{i_1}^{\mu_1} \dots f_{i_l}^{\mu_l}$ belongs to V. This is easily checked. //

A set of words is *closed* if it is, qua subset of X_∞, a fully invariant subgroup of X_∞. We use the letters U, V, W for closed sets of words. Explicitly:

V is closed if and only if

(i) $v \in V \Rightarrow v^{-1} \in V$,

(ii) $v_1, v_2 \in V \Rightarrow v_1 v_2 \in V$,

(iii) if $v \in V$ is a word in n variables, and $(u_1, \dots, u_n) \in X_\infty^n$ an n-tuplet of words, then $v(u_1, \dots, u_n) \in V$.

One is tempted to believe that condition (i) can be dispensed with. I have not been able to prove or disprove this. Although this is of no great consequence, we state:

Problem 1. *Are* (ii) *and* (iii) *sufficient to ensure that a set is closed? In other words, is a fully invariant subsemigroup of a free group of rank* $\aleph_0$ *necessarily a subgroup?*

The definition gives at once:

12.41 *The intersection of any number of closed sets is closed.*

12.42 *The product* UV *of two closed sets is closed.*

We may introduce the *closure* of an arbitrary set $\mathfrak{w}$ of words as the intersection of all closed sets containing $\mathfrak{w}$. Since the set of all words is a closed set containing $\mathfrak{w}$, this definition is reasonable. Then, as usual:

12.43 *Every word in the closure of* $\mathfrak{w}$ *is obtainable from the words in* $\mathfrak{w}$ *by a finite number of applications of the operations of inversion, multiplication and substitution.*

The significance of the closure operation to us lies in:

12.51 *If every word of a set* $\mathfrak{w}$ *is a law in each one of a given set of groups, then so is every word of the closure of* $\mathfrak{w}$. *The set of all laws satisfied in every one of a given set of groups is closed.*

12.52 *If* $\mathfrak{w}$ *is a set of words,* V *its closure, and* A *an arbitrary group, then the verbal subgroups* $\mathfrak{w}(A)$ *and* $V(A)$ *coincide.*

Both 12.51 and 12.52 follow from 12.43 in conjunction with the fact that the values of $w(u_1, \dots, u_n)$ in A are, for a fixed n-tuplet $u_1, \dots, u_n$ of words, a subset of the set of all values of w in A.

We need to have a closer look at the relation between the verbal subgroups of the free group F_∞ and those of F_n. We denote the natural mapping of X_∞ onto F_∞ by ξ; it is given by

$$\xi:\ x_i \to f_i \qquad (i \in I),$$

and is, of course, an isomorphism between the two free groups which, restricted to $X_n \subset X_\infty$, maps X_n onto $F_n \subset F_\infty$.

Let V be a closed set of words, that is, a fully invariant subgroup of X_∞. The words in V that involve only the letters $x_1, \ldots, x_n$ are given by $V \cap X_n$. One checks easily:

12.61 *If V is a closed set of words, then $V_n = V \cap X_n$ is fully invariant in X_n.*

The corresponding fully invariant subgroups $V\xi$ and $V_n\xi$ of F_∞ and F_n respectively are verbal by 12.34. We show more precisely:

12.62 *If V is a closed set of words, then $V(F_\infty) = V\xi$ and $V(F_n) = V_n\xi = V(F_\infty) \cap F_n$.*

Proof. By the proof of 12.34 we have $V\xi = V(F_\infty)$ and $V_n\xi = V_n(F_n)$. As $V_n \subset V$, one certainly obtains $V_n\xi = V_n(F_n) \subseteq V(F_n)$.

Now denote by π_n the projection of F_∞ onto $F_n \subset F_\infty$ given by $f_i\pi_n = f_i$ for $i = 1, \ldots, n$ and $f_i\pi_n = 1$ for $i > n$. Then $F_n = F_\infty\pi_n$, and as π_n is an endomorphism of F_∞, 12.31 gives:

$$V(F_n) = V(F_\infty\pi_n) = V(F_\infty)\pi_n = V\xi\pi_n \subseteq F_n \cap V\xi,$$

the latter because $V\xi\,\pi_n \subseteq F_\infty\pi_n = F_n$, and $V\xi\,\pi_n \subseteq V\xi$ as $V\xi$ is fully invariant in F_∞. But

$$F_n \cap V\xi = X_n\xi \cap V\xi = (X_n \cap V)\xi = V_n\xi,$$

and the second part of 12.62 follows. //

Finally:

12.63 *Let Y be a set of words involving the letters $x_1, \ldots, x_n$ only, such that Y represents a fully invariant subgroup of X_n. If V is the closure of Y, then $V_n = V \cap X_n = Y$.*

Proof. By 12.34 $Y\xi = Y(F_n)$; by 12.52 $Y(F_n) = V(F_n)$; by 12.62 $V(F_n) = V_n\xi$. Hence $Y\xi = V_n\xi$, that is $Y = V_n$. //

This plausible fact 12.63, which says essentially that the closure of a fully invariant subgroup of X_n intersected with X_n leads back to the original subgroup, is important later on. By contrast, the closure of $V \cap X_n$ may well be properly contained in V (cf. Hanna Neumann [*1*]).

From given fully invariant subgroups of X_∞ new ones may be obtained by two further processes:

12.71 *If U, V are fully invariant in X_∞, then so is the mutual commutator group* $[U, V]=\mathrm{gp}([u, v] \mid u\in U, v\in V)$.

Proof. For every endomorphism ϑ of X_∞, $[u, v]\,\vartheta=[u\vartheta, v\vartheta]$. //

12.72 *If V is fully invariant in X_∞ and U is fully invariant in V, then U is fully invariant in X_∞ and, for some closed set of words W, $U=W(V)$.*

Proof. $V\vartheta\subseteq V$ for all endomorphisms ϑ of X_∞, and ϑ induces an endomorphism on V. As U is fully invariant in V, it admits this induced endomorphism of V, that is $U\vartheta\subseteq U$. By 11.21 V is a free group, hence by 12.34 U is a verbal subgroup of V. //

Note that not every fully invariant subgroup of X_∞ contained in a fully invariant subgroup V of X_∞ is fully invariant in V. For example the derived group $[x, y]\,(X_\infty)$ is not fully invariant in $\{x^m, [x, y]\}\,(X_\infty)$.

We conclude this paragraph with a list of important closed sets of words — or, equivalently, fully invariant subgroups U of X_∞. In view of 12.62 these are faithfully represented by the verbal subgroups of F_∞. For later convenience we list the latter, giving also, for many of them, a single word that defines the verbal subgroup. For simplicity of notation we write F for F_∞.

12.81 *The group of n-th powers:*

Put $nF=x^n(F)$ for $n\in I$. Then $1F=F$ and, as is well known, $2F\supset F'$.

12.82 *The lower central series:*

Put $F_{(1)}=F$, $F_{(c+1)}=[F_{(c)}, F]$ for $c\geqq 1$. $F_{(c)}$ is the c-th term of the lower central series, and $F_{(c)}=[x_1, x_2, \ldots, x_c]\,(F)$ for $c\geqq 2$.

12.83 *The derived series:*

Put $F^{(0)}=F$, $F^{(l)}=[F^{(l-1)}, F^{(l-1)}]=[x, y]\,(F^{(l-1)})$ for $l\geqq 1$.

$F^{(l)}$ is the l-th term of the derived series, and is for $l\geqq 1$ the verbal subgroup corresponding to the single commutator s_l where $s_1=[x, y]$, and if s_{l-1} is defined and involves 2^{l-1} variables, then s_l is the word in 2^l variables obtained by setting $s_l=[s_{l-1}(x), s_{l-1}(y)]$.

12.84 *The iterated lower central series:*

Put

$$F_{(c_1+1,\, c_2+1,\, \ldots,\, c_l+1)}=(F_{(c_1+1,\, \ldots,\, c_{l-1}+1)})_{(c_l+1)}.$$

This is a verbal subgroup of F obtained by applying the process 12.72 repeatedly. We shall usually abbreviate this by using the notation $P(F)$.

Clearly, $F^{(1)}=F_{(2)}$ is the derived group, and $F_{\underbrace{(2,2,\ldots,2)}_{l}}=F^{(l)}$, so that $P(F)$ generalizes both the lower central series and the derived series.

3. Relatively Free Groups

We use the important property 11.14 of free groups to define a more general class of groups.

13.11 **Definition.** *A group is called relatively free if it possesses a generating set such that every mapping of this generating set into the group can be extended to an endomorphism.*

13.12 *A generating set with the property specified in 13.11 is called a set of free generators.*

Relatively free groups are also called *reduced free* or *Hall-free**, free generators are also known as *canonical* generators. We give other characterizations of these groups:

Theorem. *The group G is relatively free if and only if it has one of the following properties:*

13.21 *G possesses a set of generators such that every relator of these generators is a law in G.*

13.22 *G has a representation $G \cong F/U(F)$ as the factor group of a free group by a verbal subgroup of F.*

13.23 *G has a representation $G \cong F/R$ such that every endomorphism of F induces an endomorphism of G.*

Proof. 13.11 ⇒ 13.21. Let $\mathfrak{g}$ be a set of free generators of G and r a relator of that set, involving m letters, say. Then there exists an m-tuplet $g \in \mathfrak{g}^m$ such that $r(g)=1$. But an arbitrary mapping $\gamma\colon \mathfrak{g} \to \mathfrak{g}\,\gamma \subseteq G$ defines an endomorphism of G, hence

$$1 = r(g) = r(g)\gamma = r(g\gamma).$$

As the images under γ of the components of g can be prescribed in G this means that every value of r in G is 1, that is r is a law in G.

13.21 ⇒ 13.22. Choose a generating set $\mathfrak{g}$ as specified in 13.21 and let F be a free group whose free generating set $\mathfrak{f}$ has the same cardinal as $\mathfrak{g}$. Then the mapping $\varphi\colon \mathfrak{f} \to \mathfrak{g}$ leads according to 11.12 to a representation $G \cong F/R$ with the property that $r(f) \in R$ for some $f \in \mathfrak{f}^m$ implies $r(f\vartheta) \in R$ for every endomorphism ϑ of F. Thus R is fully invariant, hence by 12.34 a verbal subgroup of F.

13.22 ⇒ 13.23. This is immediate from 11.3.

13.23 ⇒ 13.11. The given representation $G \cong F/R$ gives us the natural generating set in F/R, namely the cosets $fR, f \in \mathfrak{f}$. We show that this generating set has the property required in Definition 13.11. Take any

* After P. Hall who introduced the concept; cf. P. Hall [2].

mapping ϑ of the elements fR into the group. Every element of F/R can be expressed in the form $w(f^* R) = w(f^*) R$ where w is some word and $f^* \in \mathfrak{f}^n$ for some n. Choose a fixed such representation for every image $(fR)\,\vartheta, f \in \mathfrak{f}$, and define the mapping $\vartheta_1 : \mathfrak{f} \to \mathfrak{f}\,\vartheta_1 \subseteq F$ by $(fR)\,\vartheta = (f\vartheta_1)\,R$ for $f \in \mathfrak{f}$. By 11.14, ϑ_1 determines an endomorphism of F; this – by assumption – induces an endomorphism on F/R, which – by definition of ϑ_1 – coincides with ϑ on the chosen generating set of F/R. Thus the mapping ϑ can be extended to an endomorphism of F/R. //

We note two corollaries of the proof:

13.24 **Corollary.** *Every endomorphism of a relatively free group G is induced by an endomorphism of F, where $G \cong F/U(F)$ according to 13.22.* //

13.25 **Corollary.** *Every relator of a set of free generators of a relatively free group G is a law in G.* //

We can now extend the property 12.34 of free groups to all relatively free groups:

13.31 **Theorem.** *A fully invariant subgroup of a relatively free group is verbal.*

Proof. Use the representation 13.22 of G in the form $G \cong F/U(F)$. Let N be the complete inverse image in F of the given fully invariant subgroup of G. Then $N/U(F)$ is fully invariant in $F/U(F)$. By 11.3 every endomorphism ϑ of F induces an endomorphism of G so that both $U(F)$ and $N/U(F)$ admit ϑ. It follows from the definition of the induced endomorphism that also N admits ϑ. Thus N is fully invariant in F and so by 12.34 is verbal in F: $N = \mathfrak{w}(F)$. But then $N/U(F) = \mathfrak{w}(F/U(F))$. //

13.32 **Corollary.** *The verbal subgroups of $G \cong F/U(F)$ correspond precisely to the verbal subgroups of F between F and $U(F)$.* //

It remains to extend the gist of the properties 12.61 and 12.62 to relatively free groups. We extend the notation used for free groups of finite or countably infinite rank, writing G_∞ and G_n for relatively free groups isomorphic to $F_\infty/U(F_\infty)$ and $F_n/U(F_n)$ respectively, and $\mathfrak{g}$ for a set of free generators. It is immediate from the definitions 13.11 and 13.12 that in G_∞ the subset $\{g_1, \ldots, g_n\}$ of $\mathfrak{g}$ generates freely a relatively free group. However, we have more precisely:

13.41 *In $G_\infty \cong F_\infty/U(F_\infty)$ the subset $\{g_1, \ldots, g_n\}$ of $\mathfrak{g}$ generates freely the group $G_n \cong F_n/U(F_n)$.*

Proof. We may assume that $\mathfrak{g}$ is the image of a set $\mathfrak{f}$ of free generators of F_∞ under a homomorphism φ: $F_\infty \twoheadrightarrow G_\infty$ with kernel $U(F_\infty)$ such that $f_i\varphi = g_i$ $(i \in I)$. The restriction of φ to $F_n \subset F_\infty$ maps F_n onto

$\mathrm{gp}(g_1, \ldots, g_n) \subset G_\infty$ in the natural way; but

$$F_n\varphi \cong F_n U(F_\infty)/U(F_\infty)$$
$$\cong F_n/U(F_\infty) \cap F_n = F_n/U(F_n),$$

by 12.62. //

13.42 *If V is a closed set of words, G_n a relatively free group embedded in the natural way in G_∞, then*

$$V(G_n) = V(G_\infty) \cap G_n.$$

Proof. $V(G_n) \subseteq V(G_\infty) \cap G_n$ is obvious. To obtain the reverse inclusion, we use again the projection π_n defined by $g_i\pi_n = g_i$ for $1 \leqq i \leqq n$, $g_i\pi_n = 1$ for $i > n$. The endomorphism of G_∞ so defined is retractive, that is $G_\infty \pi_n = G_n$ and the restriction of π_n to $G_n \subset G_\infty$ is the identity. Hence:

$$V(G_\infty) \cap G_n = (V(G_\infty) \cap G_n)\pi_n \subseteq V(G_\infty)\pi_n \cap G_n\pi_n.$$

Using 12.31 and $G_n\pi_n = G_n$, we have:

$$V(G_\infty)\pi_n \cap G_n\pi_n = V(G_\infty\pi_n) \cap G_n = V(G_n) \cap G_n = V(G_n),$$

giving the required inclusion. //

The abelian relatively free groups are familiar. To relate terminology usual in abelian group theory to the present set-up, we state, as an immediate consequence of 12.12:

13.51 *An abelian relatively free group freely generated by the set $\mathfrak{g}$ is either 'free abelian' with 'basis' $\mathfrak{g}$, or it is the abelian group of exponent m every element of whose basis $\mathfrak{g}$ has order m for some $m > 0$.* //

We accordingly simplify our terminology by speaking of a *free abelian group* or a *free abelian group of exponent m*, dropping the word 'relatively' in these cases. We also use the term *absolutely free* group for the free groups F when we want to stress the distinction.

13.52 **Theorem.** *If G is a relatively free group, freely generated by $\mathfrak{g}$, then the factor commutator group G/G' is a free abelian group freely generated by $\mathfrak{g}$ taken modulo G'. The group G has exponent zero or $m > 0$ according as G/G' is free abelian or free abelian of exponent m.*

Proof. Let $G = F\varphi$ with $\ker\varphi = U(F)$; then $G/G' = F\psi$ with $\ker\psi = F'U(F)$. By 12.42 $F'U(F)$ is a verbal subgroup of F; it contains F', hence G/G' is relatively free and abelian. Also, $F/U(F)F'$ has exponent zero if and only if $U(F)F' = F'$, that is $U(F) \subseteq F'$, and G satisfies commutator laws only. Finally $F/U(F)F'$ has exponent m if and only if $x^m \in U$ in which case G has exponent m.

Let $\mathfrak{f}$ be a set of free generators of F, then the image $\mathfrak{f}\varphi$ freely generates G, and $\mathfrak{f}\psi$ freely generates G/G'. As $\ker\psi \supseteq \ker\varphi$ the set $\mathfrak{f}\psi$ is the image of $\mathfrak{f}\varphi$ under the natural mapping of G onto G/G'. //

The cardinal of the basis of a free abelian group, of exponent zero or m, is an invariant of that group; hence we have:

13.53 *If* $G \neq \{1\}$ *is relatively free, freely generated by* $\mathfrak{g}$, *then the cardinal* $|\mathfrak{g}|$ *is an invariant of* G. //

We call $|\mathfrak{g}|$ the *rank* of G. Then the notation G_n, G_∞ introduced on p. 10 indicates the rank of the relatively free group just as F_n, F_∞ indicates the rank of the absolutely free group.

4. Varieties

14.1 **Definition.** *A variety of groups is the class of all groups satisfying each one of a given set of laws.*

We say the variety is defined by the set of laws. By 12.51:

14.21 *A set of laws and its closure define the same variety.*

The variety defined by the closed set V will de denoted by $\mathfrak{V}$. Then, restating 14.1 by means of 12.22:

14.22 *A group* A *belongs to the variety* $\mathfrak{V}$ *if and only if* $V(A)=\{1\}$.

Hence

14.23 **Theorem.** *A group* A *belongs to* $\mathfrak{V}$ *if and only if it is (isomorphic to) a factor group of* $F/V(F)$ *for a free group* F *of suitable rank.*

Proof. Let $\mathfrak{a}$ be any generating set of A, $\mathfrak{f}$ of the same cardinal as $\mathfrak{a}$ and $F=\mathrm{gp}(\mathfrak{f})$ the corresponding free group. The canonical epimorphism α of F onto A as introduced in 11.12 gives, using 12.31:

$$V(F)\alpha = V(F\alpha) = V(A) = \{1\}.$$

Hence $V(F)$ is contained in the kernel of α. //

Moreover, there is a group in the variety $\mathfrak{V}$ defined by V which satisfies precisely the laws of V and no more. For consider $F_\infty/V(F_\infty)$: if w is a law in this relatively free group, then $w(f)\in V(F_\infty)$, and by 12.62 this means that $w\in V$. Thus:

14.31 **Theorem.** *There is a* $1-1$ *correspondence between the varieties* $\mathfrak{V}$ *and the fully invariant subgroups* V *of* X_∞ *(or the closed sets of words* V*), namely: if* $\mathfrak{V}$ *is the class of all groups satisfying the laws of* V, *then* V *represents the set of all laws that hold in every group of* $\mathfrak{V}$. //

14.32 **Corollary.** *If two closed sets of laws U, V define the varieties $\mathfrak{U}$, $\mathfrak{V}$ respectively, then $U \subset V$ implies $\mathfrak{U} \supset \mathfrak{V}$ and vice versa.* //

We say $\mathfrak{V}$ is a *subvariety* of $\mathfrak{U}$.

We call the relatively free groups $F/V(F)$ the *free groups of rank ... of $\mathfrak{V}$* or the *$\mathfrak{V}$-free groups*, and write $F(\mathfrak{V})$, $F_n(\mathfrak{V})$, $F_\infty(\mathfrak{V})$ for the $\mathfrak{V}$-free groups of unspecified rank, or of finite or countably infinite rank respectively. Normally the letters G, $\mathfrak{g}$ will be reserved for the $\mathfrak{U}$-free groups and their free generating sets, H and $\mathfrak{h}$ similarly for the $\mathfrak{V}$-free groups, and K for free groups of other varieties that may occur.

We can now prove another analogy between relatively free groups and absolutely free groups F, generalizing 11.12 to relatively free groups:

14.4 **Theorem.** *The $\mathfrak{U}$-free groups are Bates-free* in the variety $\mathfrak{U}$, that is: if $\mathfrak{g}$ is a free generating set for $G = F(\mathfrak{U})$, and $A \in \mathfrak{U}$ arbitrary, then every mapping of the free generators $\mathfrak{g}$ of G into the group A can be extended to a homomorphism.*

Proof. Let $\gamma\colon \mathfrak{g} \to \mathfrak{g}\,\gamma \subseteq A$ be an arbitrary mapping of the generators $\mathfrak{g}$ into A. It can be extended to a homomorphism precisely if $r(g)=1$ for $g \in \mathfrak{g}^n$ implies $r(g\gamma)=1$ in A. By 13.25 $r(g)=1$ implies r is a law in G, hence $r \in U$, and so r is a law in A and $r(g\gamma)=1$. //

14.5 **Theorem.** *Every relatively free group G is the free group of appropriate rank of some variety $\mathfrak{U}$.*

Proof. By 13.22, $G \cong F/R$ for the free group F of rank determined by G and some fully invariant subgroup R of F. The latter is, by 12.34, a verbal subgroup: $R = \mathfrak{w}(F)$ for some set $\mathfrak{w}$ of words. The closure U of $\mathfrak{w}$ determines the same verbal subgroup by 12.52, and $G \cong F/U(F)$ is thus a free group of the variety $\mathfrak{U}$ corresponding to U. //

Finally we list some important varieties and fix the notation at the same time. Amongst them are in particular those corresponding to the verbal subgroups mentioned in Section 2.

14.61 *The variety $\mathfrak{A}$ of all abelian groups, defined by the word $[x, y]$ whose closure is $F_{(2)} = F^{(1)} = F'$.*

14.62 *The variety $\mathfrak{A}_m$ of all abelian groups of exponent m (that is, m or dividing m), defined by the words $[x, y]$ and x^m.*

14.63 *The variety $\mathfrak{B}_m$ of all groups of exponent m, defined by the word x^m whose closure is mF, and called the Burnside variety of exponent m.*

---

* Cf. Bates [*1*] where the property stated in the theorem is used to define free algebraic systems of different kinds.

Clearly $\mathfrak{A}_2 = \mathfrak{B}_2$.

14.64 *The variety* $\mathfrak{N}_c$ *of all nilpotent groups of class* c *(that is, of class* c *or less), defined by the word* $[x_1, x_2, \ldots, x_c, x_{c+1}]$ *whose closure is* $F_{(c+1)}$.

14.65 *The variety* $\mathfrak{S}_l$ *of all soluble groups of (solubility) length* l *(that is,* l *or less), defined by* $s_l(x)$ *(cf. 12.83) whose closure is* $F^{(l)}$.

Clearly $\mathfrak{N}_1 = \mathfrak{A} = \mathfrak{S}_1$.

14.66 *The variety* $\mathfrak{P}$ *of all polynilpotent groups of class row* $(c_1, \ldots, c_l)$, *corresponding to the verbal subgroup defined in 12.84**.

We introduce no more specific notation for it, as a natural expression will emerge in the next chapter.

The free groups of the varieties defined in 14.63–14.66 will respectively be called *free Burnside groups* of exponent m, *free nilpotent groups* of class c, *free soluble groups* of length l, and *free polynilpotent groups* of class row $(c_1, \ldots, c_l)$.

It is important to realize that each of these varieties contains other relatively free groups, partaking of the defining property of the variety, namely the $\mathfrak{V}$-free groups of subvarieties $\mathfrak{V}$ of the variety in question. We shall distinguish between them, for example by speaking of a nilpotent relatively free group of class c as distinct from the free nilpotent group of class c.

5. Varieties as Closed Classes of Groups

We recall the definition of the *cartesian product* of a family $\{A_\lambda \mid \lambda \in \Lambda\}$ of groups: it is the group of all functions φ defined on Λ such that $\varphi(\lambda) \in A_\lambda$, with multiplication defined componentwise:

$$(\varphi\psi)(\lambda) = \varphi(\lambda)\psi(\lambda) \quad \text{for all} \quad \lambda \in \Lambda.$$

We denote this cartesian product of the groups A_λ by $C\Pi A_\lambda$.

The *support* of a function φ is the subset $\sigma(\varphi)$ of Λ defined by:

$$\lambda \in \sigma(\varphi) \quad \text{if and only if} \quad \varphi(\lambda) \neq 1 \quad \text{in} \quad A_\lambda.$$

The functions of finite support in $C\Pi A_\lambda$ form a subgroup which is the *direct product* ΠA_λ of the groups A_λ. The functions whose support consists of just one element, $\sigma(\varphi) = \{\lambda\}$, form a subgroup isomorphic to A_λ, the *factor* or *constituent* or *coordinate subgroup* corresponding to λ.

If all the groups A_λ are isomorphic, $A_\lambda \cong A$ say for all $\lambda \in \Lambda$, then the cartesian product of the groups becomes the *cartesian power*, denoted by A^Λ, which consists of all the functions $\varphi: \Lambda \to A$. The *direct power*,

* I have slightly modified the terminology of GRUENBERG [*1*].

written $A^{(\Lambda)}$, consists of all the functions $\varphi: \Lambda \to A$ with $|\sigma(\varphi)| < \infty$. Note that we use the notation, taken from set theory, for the set of functions from Λ to A also for the group of functions obtained by introducing the obvious multiplication.

The most important property of a cartesian product in our context is:

15.1 *The cartesian (direct) product* $C\Pi A_\lambda$ (ΠA_λ) *satisfies the law* w *if and only if* w *is a law in every constituent* A_λ.

Proof. Let $\varphi_1, \ldots, \varphi_n$ be elements of the cartesian product, then $w(\varphi_1, \ldots, \varphi_n) = 1$, the identity function on Λ, if and only if for each $\lambda \in \Lambda$, $w(\varphi_1, \ldots, \varphi_n)(\lambda) = w(\varphi_1(\lambda), \ldots, \varphi_n(\lambda)) = 1$ in A_λ. Thus, if w is a law in A_λ for each λ, then w is a law in both, the cartesian and the direct product. Conversely, if w is a law in the cartesian or direct product, then clearly also in the constituent subgroups isomorphic to the A_λ. //

Now let $\mathfrak{X}$ be a class of groups; we define closed classes of groups as follows:

15.21 **Definition** (BIRKHOFF [*1*]). *The class* $\mathfrak{X}$ *of groups is closed if* $\mathrm{Q}\mathfrak{X} \subseteq \mathfrak{X}$, $\mathrm{S}\mathfrak{X} \subseteq \mathfrak{X}$, $\mathrm{C}\mathfrak{X} \subseteq \mathfrak{X}$.

15.22 **Definition.** *The closure of an arbitrary class* $\mathfrak{X}$, $\mathrm{cl}(\mathfrak{X})$, *is the class of all groups obtainable from* $\mathfrak{X}$ *by a finite number of applications of the operations* Q, S, C.

Then clearly the closure is closed. In fact we shall see that three operations are always enough to obtain the closure:

15.23 **Theorem.** *For every class* $\mathfrak{X}$ *of groups,*

$$\mathrm{cl}(\mathfrak{X}) = \mathrm{QSC}\mathfrak{X}.$$

We shall not prove this now, but obtain it as a corollary of the proof that closed classes of groups and varieties are the same thing. This fact was first established by G. BIRKHOFF (loc. cit.) for more general systems. A proof for such general algebras can be found in B. H. NEUMANN [*5*]. We proceed to the proof for groups, which will be given in several steps.

15.31 *A variety of groups is closed.*

Proof. If $\mathfrak{U}$ is a variety, then it is immediate from the definition that $\mathrm{Q}\mathfrak{U} \subseteq \mathfrak{U}$ and $\mathrm{S}\mathfrak{U} \subseteq \mathfrak{U}$; and by 15.1 also $\mathrm{C}\mathfrak{U} \subseteq \mathfrak{U}$. //

From 14.23 we have:

15.32 *If* $\mathfrak{X}$ *consists of all* $\mathfrak{V}$*-free groups, then* $\mathfrak{V} = \mathrm{cl}(\mathfrak{X})$; *in fact* $\mathfrak{V} = \mathrm{Q}\mathfrak{X}$. //

Now let $\mathfrak{C}$ be a closed class of groups. Let V be the set of all words that are laws in every group of $\mathfrak{C}$, and let $\mathfrak{V}$ be the corresponding variety. Then obviously

15.33 $$\mathfrak{C} \subseteq \mathfrak{V}.$$

The reverse inclusion will follow from the following two results:

15.34 *There exists in $\mathfrak{C}$ a group whose laws are precisely the laws given by V.*

15.35 *If the set of all laws holding in a group A is V, then the closure $\mathrm{cl}(A)$ contains every $\mathfrak{V}$-free group.*

For 15.32 and 15.35 give at once:

$\mathfrak{V} = \mathrm{cl}(\{F(\mathfrak{V})\}) \subseteq \mathrm{cl}(A) \subseteq \mathfrak{C}$, as $A \in \mathfrak{C}$; therefore $\mathfrak{V} = \mathfrak{C}$ and besides $\mathfrak{V}$ is the closure of a single group. //

Proof of 15.34. As the set of all words is countable, we can enumerate those that do *not* belong to V: let them be denoted by w_i, $i \in I$. By definition of V, there is to each $w_i \notin V$ a group in $\mathfrak{C}$ in which w_i is not a law, so that there exist elements $a_1^{(i)}, \ldots, a_{n(i)}^{(i)}$ in that group such that $w_i(a_1^{(i)}, \ldots, a_{n(i)}^{(i)}) \neq 1$. Put $A_i = \mathrm{gp}(a_1^{(i)}, \ldots, a_{n(i)}^{(i)})$; as subgroup of a group in $\mathfrak{C}$ it also belongs to $\mathfrak{C}$, it is finitely generated, and w_i is not a law in it. Then the group $A = C\Pi A_i$ belongs to $\mathfrak{C}$; by 15.1 every word of V is a law in A, but by the choice of the constituents A_i no other word is a law in A. //

Note: We have constructed A from finitely generated groups in $\mathfrak{C}$ which is unnecessary for the proof, but relevant later on.

The proof of 15.35 will be contained in the following theorem which gives explicitly the construction of all $\mathfrak{V}$-free groups from one group whose laws are precisely V.

15.4 **Theorem.** *Let A be any group, V the set of all its laws. Let Λ be an index set and $A^{(\Lambda)}$ the set of all functions of finite support defined on Λ, taking values in A. Put*

$$A^* = A^{A^{(\Lambda)}},$$

the cartesian power of A with $A^{(\Lambda)}$ as index set. To each $\lambda \in \Lambda$ define an element $h_\lambda \in A^*$ by

$$h_\lambda(\varphi) = \varphi(\lambda) \quad \textit{for each} \quad \varphi \in A^{(\Lambda)}.$$

Then $H = \mathrm{gp}(h_\lambda) \subseteq A^*$ is isomorphic to the free group of rank $|\Lambda|$ of $\mathfrak{V}$, freely generated by the elements h_λ.

Proof. By 13.21 we need only show that every relation between the generators h_λ is a law which belongs to the set V of laws of A. Assume

$w(h_{\lambda_1}, \dots, h_{\lambda_n})=1$; this holds if and only if for every $\varphi \in A^{(\Lambda)}$

$$\begin{aligned} w(h_{\lambda_1}, \dots, h_{\lambda_n})(\varphi) &= w(h_{\lambda_1}(\varphi), \dots, h_{\lambda_n}(\varphi)) \\ &= w(\varphi(\lambda_1), \dots, \varphi(\lambda_n)) \\ &= 1. \end{aligned}$$

But to given elements $a_1, \dots, a_n \in A$, there exists $\varphi \in A^{(\Lambda)}$ such that $\varphi(\lambda_i)=a_i$, $\varphi(\lambda)=1$ for $\lambda \neq \lambda_i$, as $A^{(\Lambda)}$ consists of all functions of finite support. This shows: $w(h_{\lambda_1}, \dots, h_{\lambda_n})=1$ implies $w(a_1, \cdots, a_n)=1$ for arbitrary choice of $a_1, \dots, a_n \in A$, and so $w \in V$. //

Thus we have established:

15.51 **Theorem.** *Every closed class $\mathfrak{C}$ of groups is a variety, namely the variety $\mathfrak{V}$ defined by the set V of those laws which hold in every group of $\mathfrak{C}$.*

15.52 **Corollary.** *The set of all laws satisfied by every group of a class $\mathfrak{X}$ is the same as that satisfied by all groups of the closure of $\mathfrak{X}$.* //

The proofs of 15.34 and 15.35 contain further information which we shall make explicit. First the assertion 15.23:

Proof of 15.23. Denote by V the set of words that are laws in every group of $\mathfrak{X}$; choose to every word $w_i \notin V$ a group $A_i \in \mathfrak{X}$ in which w_i is not a law (A_i will in general not be finitely generated now!). Then $A = C\Pi A_i$ is a group whose laws are precisely the words of V, and $A \in \mathrm{C}\mathfrak{X}$. By Theorem 15.4, all the $\mathfrak{V}$-free groups are obtainable as subgroups of cartesian powers of A; as $\mathrm{CC}\mathfrak{X} = \mathrm{C}\mathfrak{X}$, the $\mathfrak{V}$-free groups are contained in $\mathrm{SC}\mathfrak{X}$. By 15.32, $\mathfrak{V} = \mathrm{cl}(\mathfrak{X}) \subseteq \mathrm{QSC}\mathfrak{X}$. As the reverse inclusion is trivial, $\mathrm{cl}(\mathfrak{X}) = \mathrm{QSC}\mathfrak{X}$ follows. //

Remark. S. P. Kogalovski [*1*] points out that taking subcartesian products (cf. p. 30) may replace the two operations C and S:

15.53 *The class $\mathfrak{X}$ is a variety if and only if it is closed with respect to taking subcartesian products and epimorphic images.*

Proof. 'Only if' is trivial. To prove the sufficiency one needs to show that every subgroup B of a group A of $\mathfrak{X}$ is obtainable from $\mathfrak{X}$ by means of these two operations. Consider the *diagonal* of A^I, that is the subgroup consisting of all constant functions from I to A; it is clearly isomorphic to A, hence contains a subgroup B^* isomorphic to B. Moreover the subgroup of A^I that is generated by B^* and the direct product $A^{(I)}$ is a subcartesian power of A and it can be mapped epimorphically onto B as $A^{(I)} \lhd \mathrm{gp}(A^{(I)}, B^*)$. //

We now replace 'closure of $\mathfrak{X}$' by *variety generated by* $\mathfrak{X}$, and we write var $\mathfrak{X}$ for the variety generated by a set or class $\mathfrak{X}$ of groups and var A for the variety generated by a single group A.

As an immediate consequence of the note to the proof of 15.34 we have

15.61 **Theorem.** *Every variety is generated by its finitely generated groups.* //

As every one of these is a factor group of the free group of rank $\aleph_0$ we have:

15.62 **Theorem.** *Every variety* $\mathfrak{B}$ *is generated by its free group* $F_\infty(\mathfrak{B})$. //

We add one further remark in this context:

15.63 *If* $\mathfrak{B} = \operatorname{var} A$ *then there exists a countable subgroup* $B \subseteq A$ *such that* $\mathfrak{B} = \operatorname{var} B$.

Proof. If A is countable, there is nothing to prove. Otherwise, enumerate again the words that are not laws in A; to each one, w_i say, there are elements $a_1^{(i)}, \ldots, a_{n(i)}^{(i)}$ in A such that $w_i(a_1^{(i)}, \ldots, a_{n(i)}^{(i)}) \neq 1$; the set of all these elements $a_j^{(i)}$ is countable, and the subgroup $B = \operatorname{gp}(a_j^{(i)})$ generated by them satisfies the same laws as A, so that var B = var A. //

An important and much used consequence of the construction in Theorem 15.4 is

15.71 **Theorem.** *The free groups of finite rank of a variety generated by a finite group are finite. In fact*

$$|F_n(\operatorname{var} A)| \leqq |A|^{|A|^n} \quad \text{for} \quad n \geqq 1.$$

Proof. By 15.4, $F_n(\operatorname{var} A)$ is obtainable as subgroup of the power $A^{A(n)}$, where $A(n)$ is the set of all n-vectors with components in A, so that $|A(n)| = |A|^n$. //

The estimate for the order of $F_n(\operatorname{var} A)$ can in general be much improved (cf. B. H. NEUMANN [*1*] for some further details).

As the variety generated by a finite set of groups is the same as that generated by their direct product, we have

15.72 **Corollary.** *The free groups of finite rank of a variety generated by a finite number of finite groups are finite.* //

And as a finite group of a variety is a factor group of one of its free groups of finite rank, application of 15.23 gives further

15.73 **Corollary** (HIGMAN [*2*]). *If* A *is a finite group in the variety generated by a finite set* $\mathfrak{X}$ *of finite groups then* $A \in \mathrm{QSD}\mathfrak{X}$, *that is* A *is a factor of a finite direct product of groups in* $\mathfrak{X}$. //

The varieties just considered in 15.71 – 15.73 are special instances of *locally finite varieties*, that is varieties consisting of locally finite groups.* By 15.61 such a variety is generated by its finite groups but the converse is clearly wrong: The set of all distinct finite cyclic groups generates the variety $\mathfrak{A}$ of all abelian groups which is not locally finite.

15.74 (KOVÁCS [*1*].) *The class of locally finite groups of exponent m is a variety if and only if the order of a finite group of exponent m that can be generated by n elements is bounded in terms of n (and m).*

Proof. Let $\mathfrak{K}$ be the class of locally finite groups of exponent m. If $\mathfrak{K}$ is a variety, then every n-generator group (that is, every group that can be generated by n elements) is a factor group of $F_n(\mathfrak{K})$, itself a finite group. Its order provides the required bound.

To obtain the converse note that $\mathsf{s}\mathfrak{K} \subseteq \mathfrak{K}$, and that, for every integer $n \geqq 1$ the subclass $\mathfrak{K}_n$ of n-generator groups of $\mathfrak{K}$ contains, by assumption, only a finite number of non-isomorphic groups. We want to deduce that every finitely generated group of var $\mathfrak{K}$ is finite; for then var $\mathfrak{K}$ is locally finite, hence var $\mathfrak{K} \subseteq \mathfrak{K}$, and var $\mathfrak{K} = \mathfrak{K}$ follows.

It suffices to show that $F_n(\text{var}\,\mathfrak{K})$ is finite for every n. By 15.4 and its proof, this free group is a subgroup of a cartesian product of groups K_λ in $\mathfrak{K}$; it is freely generated by functions $\kappa_1, \ldots, \kappa_n$ defined on the index set Λ whose values $\kappa_1(\lambda), \ldots, \kappa_n(\lambda)$ in K_λ generate an n-generator subgroup of K_λ, that is a group of $\mathfrak{K}_n$. Thus we have in fact: $F_n(\text{var}\,\mathfrak{K}) \in \text{var}\,\mathfrak{K}_n$. Now $\mathfrak{K}_n$ contains only a finite number of non-isomorphic groups which moreover are finite; hence, using 15.72, we see that every finitely generated group in var $\mathfrak{K}_n$ is finite and so in particular $F_n(\text{var}\,\mathfrak{K})$ is finite. //

The result 15.74 gives an interesting alternative formulation of the *restricted Burnside problem:* Do the locally finite groups of exponent dividing m form a variety? According to A. I. KOSTRIKIN [*1*], the answer is positive when $m = p$ is a prime. Hence we add to the list of varieties given at the end of Section 4:

15.75 *The variety $\mathfrak{K}_p$ of all locally finite groups of exponent p, called the Kostrikin variety of exponent p.*

A result announced by P. S. NOVIKOV [*1*] may then be used to give:

15.76 *The variety $\mathfrak{K}_p$ is a proper subvariety of the Burnside variety $\mathfrak{B}_p$ for all sufficiently large primes p.*

On the other hand the Burnside variety $\mathfrak{B}_m$ has been proved to be locally finite for a number of small values of m (for details see Chapter 18 of the textbook by MARSHALL HALL).

---

* Generally we say a variety has property $\mathscr{P}$ if it consists of groups having property $\mathscr{P}$.

We turn to the *lattice of varieties:* The closed sets of laws, that is the fully invariant subgroups of the free group X_∞, are countable subsets of a countable set. Hence they form a set that is partially ordered by inclusion. Moreover, restating and slightly extending 12.41 and 12.42, we see that any subset $\{U_\lambda \mid \lambda \in \Lambda\}$ of the set of all fully invariant subgroups possesses a least upper bound and greatest lower bound in this partial order:

15.81 *The intersection* $\bigcap U_\lambda$ *and the 'union'* $\bigcup U_\lambda = \mathrm{gp}(U_\lambda \mid \lambda \in \Lambda)$ *of a set of fully invariant subgroups* U_λ *of* X_∞ *are fully invariant subgroups of* X_∞. //

The one-one correspondence between closed sets of laws and varieties reverses the inclusion relation: $U \subset V$ if and only if $\mathfrak{U} \supset \mathfrak{B}$.

15.82 *The varieties of groups form a set partially ordered by inclusion which is a complete lattice by means of the following definitions of greatest lower and least upper bound:* $\mathfrak{U} \wedge \mathfrak{B}$ *is the variety whose set of laws is* UV, $\mathfrak{U} \vee \mathfrak{B}$ *is the variety whose set of laws is* $U \cap V$. //

In fact, by means of 15.81, the least upper and greatest lower bound of any subset of varieties is defined. We write $\bigvee \mathfrak{U}_\lambda$ and $\bigwedge \mathfrak{U}_\lambda$ for the varieties corresponding to $\bigcap U_\lambda$ and $\mathrm{gp}(U_\lambda) = \bigcup U_\lambda$ respectively.

In the case of two varieties $\mathfrak{U}$, $\mathfrak{B}$ we have

15.83 (i) *The variety* $\mathfrak{U} \vee \mathfrak{B}$ *is the variety generated by* $\mathfrak{U}$ *and* $\mathfrak{B}$: $\mathfrak{U} \vee \mathfrak{B} = \mathrm{var}\,(\mathfrak{U}, \mathfrak{B})$.

(ii) *The variety* $\mathfrak{U} \wedge \mathfrak{B}$ *is the intersection of* $\mathfrak{U}$ *and* $\mathfrak{B}$.

Proof. (i) The variety $\mathfrak{U} \vee \mathfrak{B}$ is defined as the variety corresponding to the intersection $U \cap V$ of the corresponding sets of laws. But the laws satisfied by every group of $\mathfrak{U}$ and by every group of $\mathfrak{B}$ are by 15.52 the laws of the closure $\mathrm{cl}\,(\mathfrak{U}, \mathfrak{B}) = \mathrm{var}\,(\mathfrak{U}, \mathfrak{B})$.

(ii) A word belongs to UV, the set of laws of $\mathfrak{U} \wedge \mathfrak{B}$, if and only if it is a consequence of the words in U and the words in V. Thus every word in UV is a law in a group A if and only if every word of U and every word of V is a law in A, that is if and only if $A \in \mathfrak{U}$ and $A \in \mathfrak{B}$. //

The lattice of varieties has a least element, the variety $\mathfrak{E}$ consisting of the trivial group only and corresponding to X_∞ as its set of laws; it has a greatest element, the variety $\mathfrak{O}$ of all groups, corresponding to the trivial group as its set of laws.

6. The *n*-Generator Groups and the *n*-Variable Laws of a Variety

The term '*n*-generator group' will always mean that the group can be generated by *n* elements, but may in fact need less. The term '*n*-variable word' will refer to a word in $x_1, \ldots, x_n$; thus the *n*-variable words of V

form the set $V_n = V \cap X_n$ defined in 12.61. This convention relies, of course, on the fact that in a law involving n variables the name of these variables is immaterial.

16.1 **Lemma.** *An n-generator group belongs to the variety* $\mathfrak{V}$ *if and only if it satisfies the n-variable laws of* $\mathfrak{V}$.

Proof. 'Only if' is trivial. Conversely, if A is generated by n elements, it is a factor group of F_n; and if it satisfies the n-variable laws of V, then – as $V(F_n) = V_n$ by 12.62 – it is a factor group of $F_n/V(F_n)$; that is, $A \in \mathfrak{V}$. //

16.21 **Theorem.** *The variety* $\mathfrak{V}^{(n)}$ *defined by the set* V_n *of n-variable laws of* $\mathfrak{V}$ *consists of all those groups whose n-generator subgroups belong to* $\mathfrak{V}$.

16.22 **Corollary.** $\mathfrak{V}^{(n)} \supseteq \mathfrak{V}$, *and* $\mathfrak{V}^{(n)} = \mathfrak{V}$ *if and only if* $\mathfrak{V}$ *can be defined by n-variable laws.*

Proof of 16.21. If the n-generator subgroups of B belong to $\mathfrak{V}$, then they clearly satisfy the laws given by V_n, and so $B \in \mathfrak{V}^{(n)}$. Conversely, if $B \in \mathfrak{V}^{(n)}$ then B, and therefore its n-generator subgroups, satisfy the laws of V_n; so the n-generator subgroups of B belong to $\mathfrak{V}$ by 16.1. The corollary is immediate: the laws of $\mathfrak{V}^{(n)}$ are given by the closure $\mathrm{cl}(V_n)$ of the set V_n; this is contained in V as $V_n \subset V$ and V is closed. Also $\mathfrak{V}^{(n)} = \mathfrak{V}$ if and only if $\mathrm{cl}\,(V_n) = V$. //

Clearly $\mathrm{cl}\,(V_{n-1}) \subseteq \mathrm{cl}\,(V_n)$ for all n; moreover V is the union of the closure of the sets V_n for all n. Thus:

16.23 $$\mathrm{cl}(V_1) \subseteq \mathrm{cl}(V_2) \subseteq \cdots \subseteq \mathrm{cl}(V_n) \subseteq \cdots \subseteq V = \bigcup \mathrm{cl}(V_i);$$

and

$$\mathfrak{V}^{(1)} \supseteq \mathfrak{V}^{(2)} \supseteq \cdots \supseteq \mathfrak{V}^{(n)} \supseteq \cdots \supseteq \mathfrak{V} = \wedge\, \mathfrak{V}^{(i)}.$$

These inclusions can be proper:

16.24 **Example** (B. H. Neumann [*2*] to which we also refer for the proofs of our statements).

Take $\mathfrak{V} = \mathfrak{S}_2$, the variety of all metabelian* groups. It is defined by the law $[[x, y], [z, t]]$; hence $\mathfrak{V}^{(4)} = \mathfrak{V}$. Also $\mathfrak{V}^{(1)} = \mathfrak{O}$ trivially. There exist 3-generator non-metabelian groups all whose 2-generator subgroups are metabelian: the 2-Sylow subgroup of the symmetric group of degree 8 is an example. Thus $\mathfrak{V}^{(2)} \supset \mathfrak{V}^{(3)}$. Similarly, there exist 4-generator non-metabelian groups all whose 3-generator subgroups are metabelian; thus

* The term 'metabelian' will always mean 'soluble of length two' in agreement with current English usage; note however that in much of the Russian literature the term is used in the sense of 'nilpotent of class two'.

$\mathfrak{B}^{(3)} \supset \mathfrak{B}^{(4)}$. Therefore for the variety of all metabelian groups:

$$\mathfrak{B}^{(1)} = \mathfrak{O} \supset \mathfrak{B}^{(2)} \supset \mathfrak{B}^{(3)} \supset \mathfrak{B}^{(4)} = \mathfrak{B}.$$

It is not known whether the chains 16.23 can be properly infinite:

Problem 2. *Can every variety be defined by laws in at most n variables for some integer n depending on the variety only?*

This is a special case of the following problem, though equivalent to it for varieties whose finitely generated groups are finite on account of Schreier's Formula 11.22 (cf. also Chapter 5):

Problem 3. *(The 'finite basis problem'). Does the maximum condition hold for fully invariant subgroups of* F_∞*?*

Equivalently: can every variety be defined by a finite set of laws? Or, at least: is the set of varieties countable?

Partial results will be reported in various contexts; nevertheless a brief summary of the present state of the problem may not be out of place here. The earliest significant result is due to R. C. Lyndon [*1*] who proved that the laws of every nilpotent variety are finitely based (34.14). The proof was generalized by Graham Higman [*2*] to yield the finite basis property for certain product varieties (34.24). Recently work by D. C. Cross led to a successful attack on the problem in the case of finite groups: Sheila Oates and M. B. Powell [*1*] proved that the laws of a finite group have a finite basis (52.12). For metabelian varieties the finite basis property was established by D. E. Cohen in 1965 (36.11) and M. F. Newman extended the proof to some more general varieties (36.13).

Clearly if two varieties $\mathfrak{U}$ and $\mathfrak{B}$ satisfy the minimal condition for subvarieties, then so does their intersection. That the union also does, is non-trivial:

16.25 (R. A. Bryce, unpublished). *If the subvarieties of* $\mathfrak{U}$ *and of* $\mathfrak{B}$ *satisfy the minimal condition, then so do the subvarieties of* $\mathfrak{U} \vee \mathfrak{B}$ *and* $\mathfrak{U} \wedge \mathfrak{B}$.

Proof. To prove the non-trivial part, consider the verbal subgroups U and V of $X = X_\infty$. The assumptions mean that the set of verbal subgroups containing U and the set of verbal subgroups containing V both satisfy the maximum condition. We want to establish the same for the verbal subgroups containing $U \cap V$.

Consider an ascending chain $U \cap V \subseteq W_1 \subseteq W_2 \subseteq \cdots$. Then the verbal subgroups $(U \cap W_i)\, V$ of X form an ascending chain all whose terms contain V. By the assumption this chain will be stationary after a finite number of steps: there exists an integer k such that $(U \cap W_i)\, V = (U \cap W_{i+1})\, V$ for $i \geqq k$. Let $w_{i+1} \in U \cap W_{i+1}$; then $w_{i+1} = w_i v$ for suitable elements $w_i \in U \cap W_i$ and $v \in V$. Hence

$$w_i^{-1} w_{i+1} = v \in V \cap U \cap W_{i+1} = U \cap V \subseteq U \cap W_i,$$

hence $w_{i+1} \in U \cap W_i$ and so $U \cap W_{i+1} = U \cap W_i$ for $i \geqq k$.

Next consider the chain $U \subseteq U W_1 \subseteq U W_2 \subseteq \cdots$; as all terms contain U, it also becomes stationary, that is $U W_j = U W_{j+1}$ for $j \geqq l$, say. Take $m \geqq \max(k, l)$ and consider an element $w_{m+1} \in W_{m+1}$. Then $w_{m+1} = u w_m$ for suitable elements $u \in U$, $w_m \in W_m$; and

$$u = w_{m+1} w_m^{-1} \in U \cap W_{m+1} = U \cap W_m, \quad \text{since} \quad m \geqq k.$$

Therefore $w_{m+1} \in W_m$ and so $W_{m+1} = W_m$ as required. //

While 16.25 is useful, it does of course *not* mean that if the laws of $\mathfrak{U}$ and $\mathfrak{B}$ are finitely based then so are those of $\mathfrak{U} \vee \mathfrak{B}$; but again the corresponding fact is trivially true for the intersection, since a basis for its laws is provided by the union of the bases of the laws of $\mathfrak{U}$ and of $\mathfrak{B}$.

We add one further remark: Because in the Kostrikin variety $\mathfrak{K}_p$ (cf. 15.75) finitely generated groups are finite, the very special case of the finite basis problem, whether the Kostrikin variety $\mathfrak{K}_p$ can be defined by a finite number of laws, now assumes the following intriguing form:

Problem 4. *Given a prime p such that $\mathfrak{K}_p \subset \mathfrak{B}_p$, does there exist an integer $n = n(p)$ such that a group is finite (and of exponent p) provided all its n-generator subgroups are finite and of exponent p?*

Next we consider the subvariety of $\mathfrak{B}$ generated by its n-generator groups. As these are factor groups of the free group of rank n of $\mathfrak{B}$, it is the variety generated by $F_n(\mathfrak{B})$. The following fact is useful:

16.31 *If $\mathfrak{U} = \text{var } A$, then the subvariety of $\mathfrak{U}$ generated by the n-generator groups of $\mathfrak{U}$ is generated by the n-generator subgroups of A.*

Proof. As the subvariety of $\mathfrak{U}$ in question is generated by $F_n(\mathfrak{U})$ which, by 15.4, is a subgroup of a cartesian power of A, it is also generated by the projections of $F_n(\mathfrak{U})$ into the components of this cartesian power. But these are n-generator subgroups of A; these therefore also generate this variety. //

Obviously from 15.52

16.32 *The variety* var $F_n(\mathfrak{B})$ *is defined by the set of all laws that hold in $F_n(\mathfrak{B})$.*

To find this set, represent $F_n(\mathfrak{B})$ as a factor group of F_∞. To do this we think of $F_n(\mathfrak{B})$ as naturally embedded in $F_\infty(\mathfrak{B}) = \text{gp}(h_1, \ldots, h_n, h_{n+1}, \ldots)$. Now $F_\infty(\mathfrak{B}) \cong F_\infty / V(F_\infty)$, where $F_\infty = \text{gp}(f_1, \ldots, f_n, f_{n+1}, \ldots)$. We use again the projection π_n of F_∞ given by: $f_i \pi_n = f_i$ $(i = 1, \ldots, n)$,

$f_i\pi_n=1$ $(i>n)$, with ker $\pi_n=E_n$. Then $F_\infty\pi_n=F_n$, and π_n induces the corresponding endomorphism on $F_\infty(\mathfrak{V})$. Thus:

16.33 $F_n(\mathfrak{V})\cong F_\infty/V(F_\infty)\,E_n$ *and the set of all laws of* $F_n(\mathfrak{V})$ *is given by the greatest fully invariant subgroup of* F_∞ *contained in* $V(F_\infty)\,E_n$. //

Further, as $F_{n-1}(\mathfrak{V})\subseteq F_n(\mathfrak{V})$ for each $n>1$, and these free groups together generate the whole variety $\mathfrak{V}$, we have:

16.34 $$\operatorname{var} F_1(\mathfrak{V})\subseteq \operatorname{var} F_2(\mathfrak{V})\subseteq \cdots \subseteq \operatorname{var} F_n(\mathfrak{V})\subseteq \cdots \subseteq \mathfrak{V}$$
$$\textit{and}\quad \mathfrak{V}=\bigvee \operatorname{var} F_i(\mathfrak{V}),$$

with the corresponding descending chain for the sets of laws.

Again, the inclusions can be proper:

16.35 var $F_1(\mathfrak{V})=\mathfrak{V}$ *if and only if* $\mathfrak{V}$ *is abelian.*

Proof. 'Only if' is obvious. Conversely, if $\mathfrak{V}$ is abelian, then $F_1(\mathfrak{V})$ is cyclic and $F_\infty(\mathfrak{V})=F_1(\mathfrak{V})^{(I)}$ is a direct power of $F_1(\mathfrak{V})$; thus by 15.62, $\mathfrak{V}=$var $F_1(\mathfrak{V})$. //

But there are less trivial examples; in fact this ascending chain of varieties is known to be infinite in many cases. We give one example in some detail:

16.36 **Example.** *Let* $\mathfrak{V}$ *be the variety defined by the law* $(x^2y^2)^2$. *Then* $\mathfrak{V}$ *consists of all groups, A say, possessing a normal subgroup N such that N and A/N are of exponent* 2. $\mathfrak{V}$ *is not generated by any one of its free groups of finite rank.*

Proof. Let N be the word subgroup $N=\{x^2\}(A)$; then N is fully invariant, hence normal, and A/N is of exponent two. Now the given law implies the law $(x^2)^2$, hence the generators of N are of order two. But then $(x^2y^2)^2=1$ ensures that the product of two generators of N also has order two; thus N has exponent two.

Conversely, if $N\lhd A$ and both N and A/N have exponent two then any two elements $a, b\in A$ have the properties $a^2\in N$, $b^2\in N$, and as N is of exponent two, $(a^2b^2)^2=1$. Thus $(x^2y^2)^2$ is a law in A.

Now consider $H_n=F_n(\mathfrak{V})=F_n/V(F_n)$. Its verbal subgroup $\{x^2\}(H_n)$ corresponds, by 13.32, to a verbal subgroup $U(F_n)$ such that $V(F_n)\subset U(F_n)\subset F_n$. Now $F_n/U(F_n)$ and $U(F_n)/V(F_n)$ are elementary abelian 2-groups generated by n and N elements respectively, where by Schreier's formula 11.22, $N=(n-1)\,2^n+1$. Hence

$$|F_n(\mathfrak{V})|=2^{(n-1)\,2^n+1+n}=2^{k(n)},\quad \text{say}.$$

Thus $F_n(\mathfrak{V})$ is nilpotent, of class c_n, say, where c_n is bounded by the order of $F_n(\mathfrak{V})$: $c_n<k(n)$ trivially. Thus var $F_n(\mathfrak{V})$ consists of nilpotent groups of class at most $k(n)$.

On the other hand, $\mathfrak{B}$ contains the wreath product C_2 wr C_2^m where C_2 is the cyclic group of order two, because (cf. Chapter 2, Section 2) the wreath product is an extension of a direct power of C_2 by C_2^m. The nilpotency class of this group can be computed easily to be exactly $m+1$ (LIEBECK [*1*]). Now take m so that $m+1>k(n)$, then var $F_n(\mathfrak{B})$ does not contain C_2 wr C_2^m; therefore for every n, var $F_n(\mathfrak{B})$ is a proper subvariety of $\mathfrak{B}$. //

In this particular example, the chain of subvarieties is, in fact, properly ascending in each step, that is var $F_n(\mathfrak{B}) \subset$ var $F_{n+1}(\mathfrak{B})$ for each n. In other cases the chain may be stationary in between, and yet be infinite: M. F. NEWMAN (unpublished) has, in a different context, computed the chain when $\mathfrak{B}$ is the variety, $\mathfrak{M}_4$ say, of all metabelian groups of exponent four; he found that the chain is properly ascending to var $F_3(\mathfrak{M}_4)$, then var $F_3(\mathfrak{M}_4) =$ var $F_4(\mathfrak{M}_4)$, after which the chain ascends properly in every step. And the same is true when $\mathfrak{M}_4$ is replaced by the subvariety of those groups whose derived group has exponent two.

Note that in the example 16.36 we have $\mathfrak{B} = \mathfrak{B}^{(2)}$ as $\mathfrak{B}$ is defined by a 2-variable law; thus the chain 16.23 has two distinct terms only. On the other hand we shall see later (Chapter 2, Section 5) that the variety of all metabelian groups used in example 16.24 is generated by its free group of rank two, so that here the chain 16.34 has two terms only while the chain 16.23 has four terms. Nevertheless the two concepts, the variety defined by the n-variable laws and the variety generated by the n-generator groups of $\mathfrak{B}$, have some bearing on each other. This is exhibited in the following statements.

16.41 *If* $\mathfrak{B}$ *has the property that* var $F_n(\mathfrak{B})$ *is properly contained in* var $F_{n+1}(\mathfrak{B})$, *let* w *be a law satisfied in* $F_n(\mathfrak{B})$ *but not in* $F_{n+1}(\mathfrak{B})$. *Then if* $W = \mathrm{cl}(w)$ *one has* $\mathfrak{W}^{(n)} \supset \mathfrak{W}$, *that is,* w *is not equivalent to any set of n-variable laws.*

Proof. $F_{n+1}(\mathfrak{B})$ does not satisfy w, but $F_n(\mathfrak{B})$ does. Hence $F_{n+1}(\mathfrak{B})$ does not belong to $\mathfrak{W}$, but all its n-generator subgroups do. Thus $F_{n+1}(\mathfrak{B}) \in \mathfrak{W}^{(n)}$, $F_{n+1}(\mathfrak{B}) \notin \mathfrak{W}$. Corollary 16.22 now completes the proof. //

16.42 **Example.** (For details see LEVI and VAN DER WAERDEN [*1*].)

Take $\mathfrak{B} = \mathfrak{B}_3$, the Burnside variety of exponent 3 defined by the law x^3. This implies $[x, y, y]$. In $F_2(\mathfrak{B}_3)$ the law $[x, y, z]$ holds, but this does not hold in $F_n(\mathfrak{B}_3)$ for $n \geqq 3$ as these groups are nilpotent of class 3 precisely. Thus $[x, y, z]$ is not equivalent to any set of 2-variable words.

16.43 *Let* $\mathfrak{B}$ *be a variety such that* $\mathfrak{B}^{(n-1)} \supset \mathfrak{B}^{(n)}$ *and let* A *be a group in* $\mathfrak{B}^{(n-1)}$ *but not in* $\mathfrak{B}^{(n)}$. *If* $\mathfrak{W} =$ var A, *then* var $F_{n-1}(\mathfrak{W})$ *is a proper subvariety of* var $F_n(\mathfrak{W})$.

Proof. As $A \notin \mathfrak{V}^{(n)}$, some n-generator subgroup of A does not belong to $\mathfrak{V}$; as every n-generator subgroup of A is a factor group of $F_n(\mathfrak{W})$, the latter does not belong to $\mathfrak{V}$. But $A \in \mathfrak{V}^{(n-1)}$, that is, A satisfies the $(n-1)$-variable laws of $\mathfrak{V}$, therefore so does $F_{n-1}(\mathfrak{W})$. Thus, by 16.1 $F_{n-1}(\mathfrak{W}) \in \mathfrak{V}$, and so var $F_{n-1}(\mathfrak{W})$ is a subvariety of $\mathfrak{V}$, and the latter does not contain $F_n(\mathfrak{W})$. This proves the statement. //

16.44 **Example.** We use the example 16.24: the Sylow 2-subgroup A of the symmetric group of degree 8 is generated by three elements and is not metabelian, but all its 2-generator subgroups are. Thus the 2-generator groups of var A are metabelian but not all the 3-generator groups are and so $F_2(\text{var } A)$ generates a proper subvariety of that generated by $F_3(\text{var } A)$.

Finally:

16.51 **Theorem.** *The varieties* var $F_n(\mathfrak{V})$ *and* $\mathfrak{V}^{(n)}$ *are respectively the least and the greatest variety whose free group of rank n is* $F_n/V(F_n) = F_n/V_n\xi$.

Equivalently:

16.52 **Theorem.** *If* $\mathfrak{U}$ *is any variety whose free group of rank n is* $F_n(\mathfrak{V})$ *then*

$$\text{var } F_n(\mathfrak{V}) \subseteq \mathfrak{U} \subseteq \mathfrak{V}^{(n)}.$$

Proof. As $F_n(\mathfrak{V}) = F_n(\mathfrak{U})$, var $F_n(\mathfrak{V}) = \text{var } F_n(\mathfrak{U}) \subseteq \mathfrak{U}$. Also, the n-variable laws of $\mathfrak{U}$ and $\mathfrak{V}$ are the same, hence $\mathfrak{U}$ satisfies the n-variable laws of $\mathfrak{V}$ which define $\mathfrak{V}^{(n)}$, so $\mathfrak{U} \subseteq \mathfrak{V}^{(n)}$. //

Note. Graham Higman, in [*1*], says the *n-generator groups of* $\mathfrak{V}$ *determine the variety* $\mathfrak{V}$ if

$$\text{var } F_n(\mathfrak{V}) = \mathfrak{V} = \mathfrak{V}^{(n)}.$$

Thus, assuming that $\mathfrak{V}$ is generated by one of its free groups of finite rank, and that it can be defined by some set of laws in a finite number of variables, one has

16.53 *If k is the least integer such that* var $F_k(\mathfrak{V}) = \mathfrak{V}$ *and l is the least integer such that* $\mathfrak{V} = \mathfrak{V}^{(l)}$, *then the n-generator groups determine* $\mathfrak{V}$ *if and only if* $n \geqq \max(k, l)$.

It may not be superfluous to add a caution. It follows from 14.31 and 15.82 that the verbal subgroup lattice of $F_\infty(\mathfrak{V})$ is anti-isomorphic to the lattice of subvarieties of $\mathfrak{V}$. It is clear from the discussion of this paragraph that in general the verbal subgroup lattice of a free group $F_n(\mathfrak{V})$ of finite rank will not similarly give a faithful picture of the subvariety lattice of $\mathfrak{V}$. We stress that even a free group $F_n(\mathfrak{V})$ that determines the variety $\mathfrak{V}$ in the sense explained above will not normally suffice to determine the subvarieties of $\mathfrak{V}$ from its verbal subgroups. The examples already considered illustrate this.

From 16.24, 16.36 and the discussion following 16.36 we know that the variety $\mathfrak{S}_2$ of all metabelian groups is determined by $F_4(\mathfrak{S}_2)$. It contains the variety of all metabelian groups of exponent four which in turn contains the properly infinite ascending chain of varieties discussed in example 16.36. The verbal subgroups of $F_4(\mathfrak{S}_2)$ corresponding to this chain all contain the verbal subgroup $\{x^4\}(F_4(\mathfrak{S}_2))$ of $F_4(\mathfrak{S}_2)$ which is of finite index in $F_4(\mathfrak{S}_2)$; hence this verbal subgroup chain is not properly descending.

Anticipating the concepts introduced in the next paragraph and the result 25.34 we point out that this group $F_4(\mathfrak{S}_2)$ not only determines the variety of all metabelian groups but also *discriminates* it. Hence not even this additional virtue ensures that the subvariety lattice may be determined from the verbal subgroups of this free group. On the other hand it is not always necessary to go as far as $F_\infty(\mathfrak{V})$ before one finds a free group whose verbal subgroup lattice is anti-isomorphic to the subvariety lattice of $\mathfrak{V}$; in fact the verbal subgroup lattice of the infinite cyclic group $F_1(\mathfrak{A})$ is clearly anti-isomorphic to the subvariety lattice of the variety $\mathfrak{A}$ of all abelian groups.

7. Discrimination and Residual Properties

We discuss in this paragraph an intrinsic property of groups and sets of groups which is most useful for the study of the variety generated by these groups. We recollect that X_n is the free group on $x_1, \dots, x_n$ as free generators, so that every finite set $\mathfrak{w}$ of words is a subset of X_n for some n.

The following definition is that of GILBERT BAUMSLAG, B. H. NEUMANN, HANNA NEUMANN and PETER M. NEUMANN [*1*]*; compare BAUMSLAG [*2*] for a slightly different version.

17.11 **Definition.** *A set $\mathfrak{D}$ of groups is discriminating if to every finite set $\mathfrak{w}$ of words with the property that to each $w \in \mathfrak{w}$ there exists a homomorphism δ_w of X_n into some group of $\mathfrak{D}$ such that $w\delta_w \neq 1$ in that group, there exists a group $D \in \mathfrak{D}$ and a homomorphism δ of X_n into D such that $w\delta \neq 1$ in D for all $w \in \mathfrak{w}$.*

Put differently, if each word w in $\mathfrak{w}$ takes a non-trivial value in at least one of the groups of $\mathfrak{D}$, then there also is a group D in $\mathfrak{D}$ in which the equations $w=1$ (all $w \in \mathfrak{w}$) can be simultaneously falsified, that is by one and the same substitution of elements $d_1, \dots, d_n \in D$ for $x_1, \dots, x_n$.

When $\mathfrak{D}$ consists of a single group, we get a discriminating group D. For its importance we define it explicitly:

---

* In future quoted as $B+3N$.

17.12 **Definition.** *A group D is discriminating if every finite set of equations* $w=1$ *that can be falsified in D can be simultaneously falsified in D.*

Although discrimination so defined is an intrinsic property of the groups, it is used here mostly related to varieties, as follows:

17.21 **Definition.** *A set* $\mathfrak{D}$ *of groups discriminates the variety* $\mathfrak{B}$ *if* $\mathfrak{D}\subseteq\mathfrak{B}$ *and to every finite set* $\mathfrak{w}$ *of words that are not laws of* $\mathfrak{B}$ *there exists a group* $D\in\mathfrak{D}$ *in which the equations* $w=1$, $w\in\mathfrak{w}$, *can be simultaneously falsified.*

It is immediately clear from the definitions that:

17.22 *A set* $\mathfrak{D}$ *is discriminating if and only if it discriminates the variety it generates*; *and it can discriminate no other variety.* //

The way a discriminating set is frequently used is contained in the next version of discrimination:

17.23 **Lemma.** *If* $\mathfrak{D}$ *discriminates* $\mathfrak{B}$, *then to every finite set* $\mathfrak{w}$ *of words there exists a group* $D\in\mathfrak{D}$ *and elements* $d_1, \ldots, d_n\in D$ *such that* $u(d_1, \ldots, d_n)\neq v(d_1, \ldots, d_n)$ *for all pairs of words* $u, v\in\mathfrak{w}$ *which can take different values in some group B of* $\mathfrak{B}$.

Note that in this lemma, $\mathfrak{w}$ may include the empty word 1.

Proof. Apply 17.21 to the words uv^{-1}: whenever the words u and v take different values in some group of $\mathfrak{B}$, uv^{-1} is not a law in $\mathfrak{B}$. //

It follows:

17.31 **Theorem.** *Every non-trivial word subgroup of a discriminating group is infinite.*

Proof. If the n-variable word w takes a non-trivial value in the discriminating group D say, w is not a law in $\mathfrak{B}=\operatorname{var} D$. Thus in $H=F_\infty(\mathfrak{B})$ freely generated by $\mathfrak{h}$, the elements $w(h_{(k-1)n+1}, \ldots, h_{kn})$ are distinct values of the words $w_k=w(x_{(k-1)n+1}, \ldots, x_{kn})$ for $k=1, 2, \ldots m$. By 17.23 there exist elements $d_1, d_2, \ldots, d_{mn}\in D$ such that the values $w_k(d)$, $d=(d_1, \ldots, d_{mn})\in D^{mn}$, are distinct for $k=1, \ldots, m$. Since this is true for every value of m, $w(D)$ is infinite. //

17.32 **Corollary.** *Every non-trivial discriminating group is infinite.* //

By the same argument:

17.33 **Corollary.** *A discriminating set of finite groups is an infinite set.* //

Discriminating sets are easily found. Obviously:

17.41 *The set of all free groups* $F_n(\mathfrak{B})$ *of finite rank discriminates* $\mathfrak{B}$ *and the free group* $F_\infty(\mathfrak{B})$ *is a discriminating group for* $\mathfrak{B}$. //

17.42 **Theorem.** *If $\mathfrak{X}$ is any set of groups, then* $\mathrm{D}\mathfrak{X}$ *is a discriminating set, and it discriminates the variety generated by* $\mathfrak{X}$.

Proof. As $\mathfrak{X} \subseteq \mathrm{D}\mathfrak{X} \subseteq \mathrm{cl}(\mathfrak{X})$, $\mathfrak{X}$ and $\mathrm{D}\mathfrak{X}$ generate the same variety. The words we have to consider may therefore be assumed to be words that are not laws in var $\mathfrak{X}$. Let a finite set $\mathfrak{w}$ be given, and

$$w_i(b_1^{(i)}, \ldots, b_n^{(i)}) \neq 1 \quad \text{in} \quad B_i \in \mathfrak{X}, \qquad i = 1, \ldots, m.$$

Put $B = \prod_{i=1}^{m} B_i \in \mathrm{D}\mathfrak{X}$, and choose in B the elements $\beta_1, \ldots, \beta_n$ by setting $\beta_j(i) = b_j^{(i)}$ for each $j = 1, \ldots, m$ and $i = 1, \ldots, n$. Then

$$\begin{aligned} w_i(\beta_1, \ldots, \beta_n)\,(i) &= w_i(\beta_1(i), \ldots, \beta_n(i)) \\ &= w_i(b_1^{(i)}, \ldots, b_n^{(i)}) \neq 1; \end{aligned}$$

thus $w_i(\beta_1, \ldots, \beta_n) \neq 1$ in B for all i. //

17.43 **Corollary.** *The finite powers A^n of a group $A \neq \{1\}$ form a discriminating set.* //

17.44 **Corollary.** *The direct power $A^{(I)}$ of a non-trivial group is discriminating.* //

Further:

17.5 *If $\mathfrak{D}$ discriminates the variety $\mathfrak{V}$ and if $\mathfrak{D} \subseteq \mathrm{QS}\mathfrak{D}_1$ where $\mathfrak{D}_1 \subseteq \mathfrak{V}$, then $\mathfrak{D}_1$ also discriminates $\mathfrak{V}$.*

Proof. To every finite set of words, there is a group D in $\mathfrak{D}$ and elements $d_1, \ldots, d_n \in D$ which falsify the words simultaneously. But D is a factor of some group $D_1 \in \mathfrak{D}_1$, and the counter images of $d_1, \ldots, d_n$ in that group D_1 will then do equally well to falsify the equations. //

We turn to an example of a finitely generated discriminating group:

17.6 **Example.** *The infinite cyclic group is discriminating.*

Proof. This is just the theorem that a set of linear equations can be simultaneously falsified. Write the infinite cycle as the additive group Z of integers. The words $w_1, \ldots, w_m$, as non-laws in the variety of abelian groups, may be assumed in the form (additive again):

$$w_i = \sum_{j=1}^{n} a_{ij} x_j, \; a_{ij} \text{ integers, not all zero for each } i.$$

We want integers n_j such that $\sum_j a_{ij} n_j \neq 0$ for all i. But clearly, putting $n_j = k^j$ $(j = 1, \ldots, n)$ where $k = 2 \max_{i,j} |a_{ij}| + 1$, will solve the problem. //

This 'small' discriminating group is a very special case of a more general class arising out of the close connection between the concept of discrimination and that of residual properties introduced by P. HALL (cf. GRUENBERG [*1*]). Before turning to these we first have to add a little to the notation for cartesian and direct products in Section 5:

Put $C = C\Pi A_\lambda$ containing $D = \Pi A_\lambda$. Then for each $\lambda \in \Lambda$ the mapping π_λ given by

$$\pi_\lambda:\ \varphi \in C(\text{or } D) \to \varphi(\lambda) \in A_\lambda$$

is called the *projection of C (or D) onto* A_λ. If H is a subgroup of C (or D), then the restriction of π_λ to H, $\pi_\lambda|_H\colon H \to A_\lambda$, is called the *projection of H into* A_λ. A subgroup H of C or D is called *subcartesian product of the set* A_λ, or *subdirect product of the set* A_λ, if $H\pi_\lambda = A_\lambda$ for all λ, i.e. the projection of the subgroup is the whole constituent A_λ for each λ. Note, for example, that by Theorem 15.4, the free groups $F_n(\text{var}\, A)$ are subgroups of cartesian powers of A but not in general subcartesian powers of A.

17.71 **Definition** (P. HALL). *A group A has the property $\mathscr{P}$ residually if to every element $a \neq 1 \in A$ there is a normal subgroup N_a of A not containing a such that A/N_a has property $\mathscr{P}$.*

We say also A is *residually* $\mathscr{P}$. Thus we have:

17.72 *The group A is residually $\mathscr{P}$ if and only if the normal subgroups whose factor groups have property $\mathscr{P}$ intersect in the unit element.*

17.73 *The group A is residually $\mathscr{P}$ if and only if it is a subcartesian product of groups having property $\mathscr{P}$.*

Proof. 17.71$\Leftrightarrow$17.72 is obvious, as to every $a \in A$, $a \neq 1$, there exists a normal subgroup of the required kind excluding a. Thus no element $a \neq 1$ can belong to all these normal subgroups.

17.72$\Rightarrow$17.73: Denote by N_λ the normal subgroup of A such that $A/N_\lambda = A_\lambda$ has property $\mathscr{P}$ .Define a mapping α of A into $C\Pi A_\lambda$ by:

$$\alpha\colon a \to \varphi_a \quad \text{where} \quad \varphi_a(\lambda) = a N_\lambda \in A_\lambda .$$

Then α is a homomorphism, and $\varphi_a = \varphi_b$ implies $aN_\lambda = bN_\lambda$ for all λ, hence $ab^{-1} \in N_\lambda$ for all λ, hence $ab^{-1} = 1$. Thus α is a monomorphism, and clearly the projections of $A\alpha$ are the whole groups A_λ for each λ.

17.73$\Rightarrow$17.71: Assume $A \leqq C\Pi A_\lambda$, where the A_λ have property $\mathscr{P}$, and $A\pi_\lambda = A_\lambda$. Put $A \cap \ker \pi_\lambda = N_\lambda$, then N_λ is normal in A_λ, and $\bigcap N_\lambda = \{1\}$ as $\bigcap \ker \pi_\lambda = \{1\}$. Also $A/N_\lambda \cong A \ker \pi_\lambda / \ker \pi_\lambda \cong A\pi_\lambda$ has property $\mathscr{P}$ as required. //

17.74 **Corollary.** *'Residually (residually $\mathscr{P}$)' is the same as 'residually $\mathscr{P}$'.*

Proof. A subcartesian product of subcartesian products is a subcartesian product. //

Moreover:

17.75 *If the property $\mathscr{P}$ is inherited by subgroups then we can replace the word 'subcartesian' in 17.73 by 'subgroup of cartesian'.*

Proof. If A is a subgroup of $C\Pi A_\lambda$, then it is a subcartesian product of the projections $A\pi_\lambda \subseteq A_\lambda$, and by assumption these also have the property $\mathscr{P}$. //

We now link up the two concepts discussed so far in this paragraph:

17.81 **Theorem.** *If $\mathscr{P}$ is a property inherited by subgroups then the free groups of the variety $\mathfrak{V}$ are residually $\mathscr{P}$ if and only if the finitely generated groups with the property $\mathscr{P}$ in $\mathfrak{V}$ generate $\mathfrak{V}$.*

17.82 **Theorem.** *If $\mathscr{P}$ is a property inherited by subgroups and finite direct products, then the free groups of the variety $\mathfrak{V}$ are residually $\mathscr{P}$ if and only if the finitely generated groups with the property $\mathscr{P}$ in $\mathfrak{V}$ discriminate $\mathfrak{V}$.*

Note. In both statements the term 'finitely generated' is put in only because we are interested in restricting the size of a generating or discriminating set. Clearly under the assumption on $\mathscr{P}$, the finitely generated groups with property $\mathscr{P}$ generate (or discriminate) $\mathfrak{V}$ if and only if all groups with the property $\mathscr{P}$ do.

Proof. Theorem 17.82 is weaker than 17.81 in one direction: if the groups with property $\mathscr{P}$ discriminate $\mathfrak{V}$, then they generate $\mathfrak{V}$ and so 17.81 applies. Nor is the other direction much more than 17.81: 17.81 shows that the set $\mathfrak{X}$ of groups with property $\mathscr{P}$ generates $\mathfrak{V}$; but then by 17.42 $\mathrm{D}\mathfrak{X}$ is discriminating and must discriminate $\mathfrak{V}$; and by assumption $\mathrm{D}\mathfrak{X} \subseteq \mathfrak{X}$.

It remains to prove 17.81: if the finitely generated groups with $\mathscr{P}$ generate $\mathfrak{V}$, the construction of Theorem 15.4 shows that every group $F_n(\mathfrak{V})$ is a subgroup of a cartesian product of these groups, hence by 17.75 it is residually $\mathscr{P}$. Conversely, if $F_n(\mathfrak{V})$ is residually $\mathscr{P}$, then $F_n(\mathfrak{V}) \leqq C\Pi A_\lambda$ where each A_λ has property $\mathscr{P}$ and is a homomorphic image of $F_n(\mathfrak{V})$, hence belongs to $\mathfrak{V}$ and is finitely generated. Clearly the closure of all these groups A_λ contains every group $F_n(\mathfrak{V})$, hence is equal to $\mathfrak{V}$. //

Properties inherited by subgroups and finite direct products include the majority of properties we shall be concerned with: solubility, nilpotency, periodicity, finiteness, being of prime power order, of finite exponent, et alia. We add one further useful result on these properties, close to 17.82 but going a little further as is indicated by the corollary:

17.83 **Theorem.** *If the property $\mathscr{P}$ is inherited by subgroups and finite idrect products, and if D is a discriminating group which is residually $\mathscr{P}$,* *then the set* $\mathfrak{D}$ *of factor groups* $D_i = D/N_i$ *of* D *that have property* $\mathscr{P}$ *is discriminating and discriminates, of course, the same variety* var D.

17.84 **Corollary.** *If* D *is residually* $\mathscr{P}$, *discriminating and can be generated by* n *elements, then* var D *possesses a discriminating set* $\mathfrak{D}$ *consisting of* n*-generator groups with the property* $\mathscr{P}$.

Proof. Note that under our assumptions, with $D_1 = D/N_1$ and $D_2 = D/N_2$ also $D^* = D/N_1 \cap N_2$ belongs to $\mathfrak{D}$; because $D^* = D/N_1 \cap N_2 \leqq D/N_1 \times D/N_2$. Thus, inductively, if D_i $(i=1, \ldots, m)$ is a finite set of factor groups D/N_i, then also $D/\bigcap N_i$ belongs to $\mathfrak{D}$.

Now let $\mathfrak{w}$ be any finite set of words that are not laws in every group D_i; then none of them is a law in D. As D is discriminating, there exists an n-tuplet $d \in D^n$ such that $w_i(d) \neq 1$ for all $w_i \in \mathfrak{w}$. As D is residually $\mathscr{P}$, there is to each value $w_i(d)$ a factor group $D_i = D/N_i$ with the property $\mathscr{P}$ in which $w_i(d) \neq 1$, that is $w_i(d) \notin N_i$. But then $w_i(d) \notin N = \bigcap N_j$ for $i = 1, \ldots, m$. And so $w_i(d) \neq 1$ in $D^* = D/N$ and $D^* \in \mathfrak{D}$, as required. //

Finally a similar argument will provide us with finitely generated discriminating groups:

17.9 **Theorem.** ($B+3N$.) *If the group* D *is residually a finite* p*-group for infinitely many primes* p, *then* D *is discriminating.*

Proof. Let $\mathfrak{w}$ be a set of words w_i $(i=1, \ldots, m)$ that are not laws in D. Then each of these words takes a non-trivial value in D. As D is residually a p-group for infinitely many p, we can choose distinct primes p_i corresponding to distinct words w_i, and to each one a factor group P_i of D of finite order a power of p_i such that w_i has a non-trivial value in P_i, $w_i(d_1^{(i)}, \ldots, d_n^{(i)}) \neq 1$ in P_i say. Then consider the elements $\varphi_1, \ldots, \varphi_n$ in the direct product $P_1 \times \cdots \times P_m$ given by $\varphi_j(i) = d_j^{(i)}$ for each j and $i = 1, \ldots, m$. Then all values $w_i(\varphi_1, \ldots, \varphi_n)$ are non-trivial in $P_1 \times \cdots \times P_n$. Thus all equations $w_i = 1$ are simultaneously falsified in this direct product. But if $P_i \cong D/N_i$, then as the P_i are of relatively prime orders, $D/\bigcap N_i \cong \Pi\, D/N_i$; thus the equations are simultaneously falsified in a factor group of D, hence in D. //

Note. Clearly, example 17.6 is just a special case of this. In fact we shall see (Chapter 3) that by means of 17.9 every torsion-free nilpotent or polynilpotent group is discriminating.

8. Verbal Products

This section will do no more than give an outline of the multiplication of groups associated with an arbitrary variety in the same way as direct multiplication is associated with the variety of abelian groups and free multiplication is associated with the variety of all groups. We shall barely use verbal products but want to mention them occasionally.

For further details we refer to the literature, in particular the papers by O. N. GOLOVIN, S. MORAN and RUTH R. STRUIK listed in the bibliography.

We summarize the basic properties of the *free product* of groups. Again we refer to the textbooks by A. G. KUROSH and MARSHALL HALL for details, or to B. H. NEUMANN [*4*].

18.11 **Definition.** *The group A is called the free product of its subgroups A_λ, $\lambda \in \Lambda$, if*

(i) *it is generated by these subgroups,*

(ii) *to given homomorphisms ϑ_λ: $A_\lambda \to B$ of the groups A_λ into a group B there exists a homomorphism ϑ: $A \to B$ whose restriction to A_λ coincides with ϑ_λ for each $\lambda \in \Lambda$.*

The A_λ are called *constituents* of A; we say A is *freely generated* by the A_λ and write $A = \Pi^*_\Lambda A_\lambda$, or $A = A_1 * A_2 * \cdots$ when there are only a few constituents. A subgroup of A is a *free factor* of A if it is a constituent in some representation of A as a free product.

The definition means, loosely, that A is maximal with respect to being generated by subgroups isomorphic to the A_λ; this is in close analogy to the maximality of an absolutely free group as described by 11.12. In fact:

18.12 *The free group F is the free product of as many infinite cyclic groups (that is: free groups of rank one) as its rank indicates.*

One shows easily:

18.13 *Every element $a \neq 1$ of $A = \Pi^*_\Lambda A_\lambda$ is uniquely representable in the form*

$$a = a_1 a_2 \ldots a_l, \qquad 1 \neq a_i \in A_{\lambda(i)}, \qquad \lambda(i) \neq \lambda(i+1).$$

The a_i are called *syllables* of the *normal form* for a. This representation indicates a procedure to construct the free product of a given family of abstract groups: the set of formal products of the form 18.13 is made into a group in the obvious way, and one obtains:

18.14 *To every family A_λ, $\lambda \in \Lambda$, of groups there exists a group, unique to within isomorphisms, which is the free product of subgroups isomorphic to the A_λ.*

The definition 18.11 gives at once:

18.15 (i) *Let $\mathrm{M} \subset \Lambda$ be a subset of the index set, then the subgroup* $\mathrm{gp}(A_\mu \mid \mu \in \mathrm{M})$ *of $\Pi^*_\Lambda A_\lambda$ is the free product $\Pi^*_\mathrm{M} A_\mu$.*

(ii) *The normal closure of $\Pi^*_\mathrm{M} A_\mu$ in $A = \Pi^*_\Lambda A_\lambda$ avoids the subgroup generated by the remaining constituents.*

This means that to each subset M of Λ there is a *projection* in the usual sense, that is a retractive endomorphism of $\Pi^*_\Lambda A_\lambda$ onto $\Pi^*_{\mathrm{M}} A_\mu$. We denote the projection onto the single constituent A_λ by δ^*_λ.

The free product is furthermore *associative* in the following strong sense:

18.16 *If, for each* λ, $A_\lambda = \Pi^* B_{\lambda,\mu}$, $\mu \in \mathrm{M}(\lambda)$, *then* $\Pi^*_\Lambda A_\lambda = \Pi^* B_{\lambda,\mu}$, $\lambda \in \Lambda$, $\mu \in \mathrm{M}(\lambda)$.

Again, it is an immediate consequence of the definition that there is an epimorphism mapping the free product of a given family of abstract groups on the direct product of the same family in a natural way.

18.17 *Let* φ^*: $\Pi^*_\Lambda A_\lambda \twoheadrightarrow \Pi_\Lambda(A_\lambda \varphi^*)$ *be such that* φ^* *restricted to* A_λ *is an isomorphism onto* $A_\lambda \varphi^*$ *for each* $\lambda \in \Lambda$. *Then the kernel of* φ^* *is the normal closure of* $\mathrm{gp}([A_\lambda, A_\mu] \mid \lambda, \mu \in \Lambda, \lambda \neq \mu)$ *in the free product.*

The kernel of this, and therefore of every, mapping of the free product onto the direct product of the corresponding constituents is called the *cartesian subgroup* of the free product. We denote it by $[A_\lambda]^*$. The properties of the mapping show:

18.18 *The cartesian subgroup avoids the constituents:* $[A_\lambda]^* \cap A_\mu = \{1\}$ *for all* $\mu \in \Lambda$.

We turn to verbal subgroups of a free product. To determine these we rewrite the representation 18.13 of the elements of the free product in the same way as we rewrote a word in the proof of 12.12. For convenience we assume the index set Λ ordered. Then

18.21 *If* $a \in \Pi^*_\Lambda A_\lambda$, *then* $a = a_{\lambda_1} a_{\lambda_2} \dots a_{\lambda_m} c$ *where* $a_{\lambda_i} \neq 1$ *for all* i, $\lambda_1 < \lambda_2 < \dots < \lambda_m$ *and* $c \in [A_\lambda]^*$. *The elements* a_{λ_i} *and* c *are uniquely determined by* a *and the chosen order of* Λ.

Proof. A representation 18.21 is obtained from 18.13 by rearranging the syllables; this produces commutators which may be collected on the right hand side using the identity $xy = yx[x, y]$. By means of the natural mapping of the free onto the direct product one sees that $c \in [A_\lambda]^*$.

Now we use the projection δ^*_λ of the free product onto A_λ; then $a\delta^*_{\lambda_i} = a_{\lambda_i}$ for each $i = 1, \dots, m$ which shows that the a_{λ_i} are uniquely determined by a; therefore also c is determined when the order of the a_{λ_i} is given. //

Using 18.21 and $V(A)\,\delta^*_\lambda = V(A\delta^*_\lambda) = V(A_\lambda)$ one obtains:

18.22 *If* $V(A)$ *is a verbal subgroup of* $A = \Pi^*_\Lambda A_\lambda$ *then* $V(A) \cap A_\lambda = V(A_\lambda)$ *for all* $\lambda \in \Lambda$. //

And, using 18.21 once more, it follows

18.23 **Theorem.** *If* $A = \Pi^*_\Lambda A_\lambda$, *then the verbal subgroup* $V(A)$ *is the product of the verbal subgroups* $V(A_\lambda)$ *of the constituents and the intersection* $V(A) \cap [A_\lambda]^*$ *of* $V(A)$ *with the cartesian subgroup.* //

We now define verbal products:

18.31 **Definition.** *If* $\mathfrak{V}$ *is a variety,* V *the corresponding set of words, then the verbal product associated with* $\mathfrak{V}$ *of the family of groups* A_λ *is, to within isomorphisms, the factor group* $\Pi^*_\Lambda A_\lambda / V(A) \cap [A_\lambda]^*$.

The verbal product is also known as *varietal product* or simply $\mathfrak{V}$*-product*. If $\mathfrak{V} = \mathfrak{O}$ is the variety of all groups, then V is the trivial group and the corresponding verbal product is the free product; if $\mathfrak{V} = \mathfrak{A}$ is the variety of all abelian groups, $V(A)$ is the commutator subgroup of the free product A and this contains the cartesian subgroup; hence the verbal product is the direct product. We keep the notation Π^* and Π for free and direct products respectively, but write $\mathfrak{V}\Pi_\Lambda A_\lambda$ for the $\mathfrak{V}$-product of the family of groups A_λ, $\lambda \in \Lambda$.

The $\mathfrak{V}$-product of the A_λ is 'between' the free product and the direct product in the sense that the natural epimorphism of the free product onto the direct product can be factored through the $\mathfrak{V}$-product.

18.32 $\Pi^*_\Lambda A_\lambda \xrightarrow{v} \mathfrak{V}\Pi_\Lambda (A_\lambda v) \xrightarrow{\varphi(V)} \Pi_\Lambda (A_\lambda \varphi^*), \qquad \varphi^* = v\varphi(V),$

the factors being natural epimorphisms in the sense that the restrictions to a group A_λ are isomorphisms onto the corresponding subgroup of the image.

In particular this shows that the projection δ^*_λ: $\Pi^*_\Lambda A_\lambda \twoheadrightarrow A_\lambda$ which can be factored through $\Pi_\Lambda A_\lambda$, can just as well be factored through $\mathfrak{V}\Pi_\Lambda A_\lambda$:

18.33 $\Pi^*_\Lambda A_\lambda \xrightarrow{v} \mathfrak{V}\Pi_\Lambda (A_\lambda v) \xrightarrow{\delta_\lambda(V)} A_\lambda \delta^*_\lambda, \qquad \delta^*_\lambda = v\delta_\lambda(V),$

giving to each λ a projection $\delta_\lambda(V)$ of the $\mathfrak{V}$-product onto the corresponding constituent.

We shall normally assume projections to be the identity on the projected constituents or constituent so that they are endomorphisms of the whole product. That is in this case:

$$(\Pi^*_\Lambda A_\lambda)\delta^*_\lambda = (\mathfrak{V}\Pi_\Lambda A_\lambda)\delta_\lambda(V) = A_\lambda .$$

From 18.32 we conclude that the kernel of the natural epimorphism $\varphi(V)$ of the $\mathfrak{V}$-product onto the direct product of the A_λ is the cartesian subgroup of $\mathfrak{B}\Pi_{\Lambda} A_{\lambda}$, that is the normal closure in the $\mathfrak{B}$-product of $\mathrm{gp}([A_{\lambda}, A_{\mu}] \mid \lambda \neq \mu, \lambda, \mu \in \Lambda)$. We use the notation $[A_{\lambda}]^{V}$; then

18.34 $\ker \varphi(V) = [A_{\lambda}]^{V} = [A_{\lambda}]^{*} \nu$ *where* $\varphi^{*} = \nu \varphi(V)$ *as given by 18.32.*

Moreover one has also in the $\mathfrak{B}$-product the representation corresponding to 18.21 for the non-trivial elements:

18.35 *If* $a \neq 1$ *is an element of* $\mathfrak{B}\Pi_{\Lambda} A_{\lambda}$, *then*

$$a = a_{\lambda_1} \dots a_{\lambda_m} c, \quad 1 \neq a_{\lambda_i} \in A_{\lambda_i}, \quad \lambda_1 < \lambda_2 < \dots < \lambda_m, \quad c \in [A_{\lambda}]^{V},$$

and the a_{λ_i} *and* c *are uniquely determined by* a *and the chosen order of* Λ.

Proof. The existence of such a representation may be established by applying the epimorphism ν to the representation 18.21 of a counter-image of a in the free product. The uniqueness follows as in the free product by means of the projections, $\delta_{\lambda}(V)$ in this case, onto the constituents. //

Now 18.15 can be extended to $\mathfrak{B}$-products:

18.36 (i) *Let* $\mathrm{M} \subset \Lambda$ *be a subset of the index set, then the subgroup* $\mathrm{gp}(A_{\mu} \mid \mu \in \mathrm{M})$ *of* $\mathfrak{B}\Pi_{\Lambda} A_{\lambda}$ *is the* $\mathfrak{B}$*-product* $\mathfrak{B}\Pi_{\mathrm{M}} A_{\mu}$.

(ii) *The normal closure of* $\mathfrak{B}\Pi_{\mathrm{M}} A_{\mu}$ *in* $\mathfrak{B}\Pi_{\Lambda} A_{\lambda}$ *avoids the subgroup generated by the remaining constituents.*

Thus to every subset M *of the index set* Λ, *the* $\mathfrak{B}$*-product* $\mathfrak{B}\Pi_{\Lambda} A_{\lambda}$ *possesses a retractive endomorphism projecting it onto the* $\mathfrak{B}$*-product* $\mathfrak{B}\Pi_{\mathrm{M}} A_{\mu}$.

Proof. Consider the projection π^{*} of $\Pi^{*}_{\Lambda} A_{\lambda}$ onto $\Pi^{*}_{\mathrm{M}} A_{\mu}$ followed by the natural epimorphism $\nu(\mathrm{M})$ of $\Pi^{*}_{\mathrm{M}} A_{\mu}$ onto $\mathfrak{B}\Pi_{\mathrm{M}}(A_{\mu}\nu(\mathrm{M}))$. The kernel $[A_{\lambda}]^{*} \cap V(\Pi^{*}_{\Lambda} A_{\lambda})$ of the natural mapping $\nu(\Lambda)$: $\Pi^{*}_{\Lambda} A_{\lambda} \twoheadrightarrow \mathfrak{B}\Pi_{\Lambda}(A_{\lambda}\nu(\Lambda))$ is contained in the kernel of the product $\pi^{*}\nu(\mathrm{M})$; hence the product $\pi^{*}\nu(\mathrm{M})$ can be factored through $\mathfrak{B}\Pi_{\Lambda}(A_{\lambda}\nu(\Lambda))$ so as to complete a commutative diagram:

$$\begin{array}{ccc} \Pi^{*}_{\Lambda} A_{\lambda} & \xrightarrow{\pi^{*}} & \Pi^{*}_{\mathrm{M}} A_{\mu} \\ \downarrow \nu(\Lambda) & & \downarrow \nu(\mathrm{M}) \\ \mathfrak{B}\Pi_{\Lambda}(A_{\lambda}\nu(\Lambda)) & \xrightarrow{\pi(V)} & \mathfrak{B}\Pi_{\mathrm{M}}(A_{\mu}\nu(\mathrm{M})). \end{array}$$

One can now check that the epimorphism $\pi(V)$ which completes the diagram maps the subgroup $\mathrm{gp}(A_{\mu}\nu(\Lambda) \mid \mu \in \mathrm{M})$ of $\mathfrak{B}\Pi_{\Lambda}(A_{\lambda}\nu(\Lambda))$ isomorphically onto $\mathfrak{B}\Pi_{\mathrm{M}}(A_{\mu}\nu(\mathrm{M}))$: using the representation 18.35 of the elements of a $\mathfrak{B}$-product, one first sees that the constituents $A_{\mu}\nu(\Lambda)$, $\mu \in \mathrm{M}$, are mapped isomorphically under $\pi(V)$ and that the intersection of $\ker \pi(V)$ with the subgroup generated by these constituents does in fact lie in the intersection of the cartesian with the subgroup generated by these constituents. By applying the mapping $\pi^{*}\nu(\mathrm{M})$ to a counter image in $\Pi^{*}_{\Lambda} A_{\lambda}$

of an element in this intersection, one finds that the element must have been the identity. This proves that the groups $A_\mu v(\Lambda)$, $\mu \in \mathrm{M}$, generate their $\mathfrak{V}$-product in $\mathfrak{V}\Pi_\Lambda(A_\lambda v(\Lambda))$ and that the normal closure of the remaining constituents intersects this subgroup trivially. From this (ii) follows. //

We only state the associativity:

18.37 *If* $A_\lambda = \mathfrak{V}\Pi B_{\lambda,\mu}$, $\mu \in \mathrm{M}(\lambda)$ *for each* λ, *then*

$$\mathfrak{V}\Pi_\Lambda A_\lambda = \mathfrak{V}\Pi B_{\lambda,\mu}, \quad \lambda \in \Lambda, \quad \mu \in \mathrm{M}(\lambda).$$

Its proof requires an examination of the connection between the various relevant cartesian subgroups. We refer to Golovin [*1*] or Moran [*1*] for details.

Finally we come to the maximality of the $\mathfrak{V}$-product relative to the variety $\mathfrak{V}$.

We assume that all the groups A_λ belong to $\mathfrak{V}$, that is $V(A_\lambda) = \{1\}$ for all λ. Hence 18.23 shows that $V(\Pi^*_\Lambda(A_\lambda)) \subseteq [A_\lambda]^*$. That is

18.41 *If* $A_\lambda \in \mathfrak{V}$ *for all* λ *then* $\ker v = V(\Pi^*_\Lambda A_\lambda)$ *where* v: $\Pi^*_\Lambda A_\lambda \twoheadrightarrow \mathfrak{V}\Pi_\Lambda(A_\lambda v)$; *hence* $\mathfrak{V}\Pi_\Lambda A_\lambda \in \mathfrak{V}$. //

It now follows easily:

18.42 **Theorem.** *If* $A_\lambda \in \mathfrak{V}$ *for all* λ *and* ϑ_λ: $A_\lambda \to B$ *are given homomorphisms of the* A_λ *into a group* B *of* $\mathfrak{V}$, *then there exists a homomorphism* ϑ: $\mathfrak{V}\Pi_\Lambda A_\lambda \to B$ *such that* ϑ *restricted to the constituent* A_λ *coincides with* ϑ_λ *for each* λ.

Proof. We take isomorphic copies $A_\lambda \alpha_\lambda^{-1}$ of the groups A_λ. By 18.11 there exists a homomorphism ϑ^* of $\Pi^*_\Lambda A_\lambda \alpha_\lambda^{-1}$ into B which restricted to the constituents $A_\lambda \alpha_\lambda^{-1}$ coincides with $\alpha_\lambda \vartheta_\lambda$ for each λ.

As $B \in \mathfrak{V}$, the kernel of this homomorphism contains $V(\Pi^*_\Lambda A_\lambda \alpha_\lambda^{-1})$, which by 18.41 is the kernel of a natural mapping of the free product onto the $\mathfrak{V}$-product in this case. Hence ϑ^* can be factored through the $\mathfrak{V}$-product

$$\Pi^*_\Lambda(A_\lambda \alpha_\lambda^{-1}) \xrightarrow{v} \mathfrak{V}\Pi_\Lambda A_\lambda \xrightarrow{\vartheta} B, \quad v\vartheta = \vartheta^*,$$

where we have chosen the natural mapping v so that it continues the isomorphisms α_λ: $A_\lambda \alpha_\lambda^{-1} \twoheadrightarrow A_\lambda$ for each λ. Then $\alpha_\lambda^{-1} \vartheta^* = \vartheta_\lambda$ by the choice of ϑ^*, but also $\alpha_\lambda^{-1}\vartheta^* = \alpha_\lambda^{-1} v\vartheta = \vartheta$ by the choice of v, so that ϑ restricted to A_λ does in fact coincide with the given mappings ϑ_λ. //

From 13.11 we have

18.43 **Corollary.** *The* $\mathfrak{V}$*-product of* $\mathfrak{V}$*-free cyclic groups* $\mathrm{gp}(h_\lambda)$, $\lambda \in \Lambda$ *is the* $\mathfrak{V}$*-free group of rank* $|\Lambda|$ *freely generated by the set* $\mathfrak{h} = \{h_\lambda \mid \lambda \in \Lambda\}$. //

Here, of course, a cyclic group is $\mathfrak{V}$-free if and only if its order is the exponent of $\mathfrak{V}$.

Chapter 2

Product Varieties

1. The Algebra of Varieties

We call the group C an extension of A by B if C possesses a normal subgroup isomorphic to A whose factor group is isomorphic to B.

21.11 **Definition.** *If* $\mathfrak{U}$ *and* $\mathfrak{B}$ *are varieties of groups, then the product* $\mathfrak{U}\mathfrak{B}$ *is the variety of all groups that are extensions of a group in* $\mathfrak{U}$ *by a group in* $\mathfrak{B}$.

That this class is in fact a variety is easily checked using the closure operations.

21.12 *If* U, V *are the fully invariant subgroups of* X_∞ *representing the laws of* $\mathfrak{U}$ *and* $\mathfrak{B}$ *respectively, then the laws of* $\mathfrak{U}\mathfrak{B}$ *are given by the verbal subgroup* $U(V)$ *of* V.

Proof. A word $w \in U(V)$ is a product of words of the form $u(v_1, \dots, v_n)$, $u \in U$, $v_i \in V$. Hence to show that w is a law in $\mathfrak{U}\mathfrak{B}$ it suffices to show that all words of the form $u(v_1, \dots, v_n)$ are laws in $\mathfrak{U}\mathfrak{B}$.

Let $C \in \mathfrak{U}\mathfrak{B}$ and $A \lhd C$ such that $A \in \mathfrak{U}$, $C/A \in \mathfrak{B}$. As the v_i are laws in C/A, the values in C of every v_i lie in A: $v_i(c^{(i)}) \in A$, where $c^{(i)} \in C^{m(i)}$. Therefore $u(v_1(c^{(1)}), \dots, v_n(c^{(n)})) = u(a)$ for some $a \in A^n$. But u is a law in A, hence $u(a) = 1$ in A as required.

Conversely, assume a group C satisfies all laws of the form $u(v_1, \dots, v_n)$. Put $A = V(C)$, the verbal subgroup corresponding to V. Then $A \lhd C$ and $C/A \in \mathfrak{B}$. Also, as V is closed, $V(C)$ consists of all the elements $v(c)$, $v \in V$, $c \in C^m$ for some m. Thus $u(a_1, \dots, a_n) = u(v_1(c^{(1)}), \dots, v_n(c^{(n)}))$, $c^{(i)} \in C^{m(i)}$, and so by assumption $u(a) = 1$ for all n-tuplets $a \in A^n$, that is u is a law in A. //

21.13 **Corollary.** *If neither* $\mathfrak{U}$ *nor* $\mathfrak{B}$ *is the variety* $\mathfrak{O}$ *of all groups, then a free group* $F(\mathfrak{U}\mathfrak{B})$ *of infinite rank is an extension of* $F(\mathfrak{U})$ *by* $F(\mathfrak{B})$ *where both are of the same infinite rank as* $F(\mathfrak{U}\mathfrak{B})$; *a free group* $F_n(\mathfrak{U}\mathfrak{B})$ *of finite rank is an extension of* $F_m(\mathfrak{U})$ *by* $F_n(\mathfrak{B})$ *where* $m = (n-1)|F_n(\mathfrak{B})| + 1$.

Proof. We have $F(\mathfrak{U}\mathfrak{B}) \cong F/U(V(F))$ by 21.12. Now $U(V(F)) \subseteq V(F) \subseteq F$ and $V(F)$ is, by 11.21, an absolutely free group. Hence $V(F)/U(V(F)) \cong F(\mathfrak{U})$ where $F(\mathfrak{U})$ has the same rank as $V(F)$. Moreover this subgroup of $F(\mathfrak{U}\mathfrak{B})$ has in $F(\mathfrak{U}\mathfrak{B})$ the factor group $F/V(F) \cong F(\mathfrak{B})$, the free group of $\mathfrak{B}$ of the same rank as $F(\mathfrak{U}\mathfrak{B})$.

If F is of infinite rank, $V(F)$ is of the same infinite rank whenever V is non-trivial. In F_n, $V(F_n)$ is of infinite rank when its index j in F_n is infinite, otherwise of rank $(n-1)j+1$, by 11.23 and 11.22; but $j=|F_n(\mathfrak{V})|$. //

21.14 **Corollary.** *The free groups $F_n(\mathfrak{U}\mathfrak{V})$ are finite for all $n\in I$ if and only if the free groups $F_n(\mathfrak{U})$ and $F_n(\mathfrak{V})$ are finite for all $n\in I$.* //

We denote the variety corresponding to $[U, V]$ by $[\mathfrak{U}, \mathfrak{V}]$; it consists of all those groups whose U-subgroups and V-subgroups centralize each other. As U and V are normal subgroups of X_∞, $[U, V]\subseteq U\cap V$, that is $[\mathfrak{U}, \mathfrak{V}]\supseteq \mathfrak{U}\vee\mathfrak{V}$.

To list the effect of multiplication on the inclusion relation as well as on the lattice operations and commutation, we remark first that right multiplication by $\mathfrak{V}\neq\mathfrak{O}$ corresponds to operating with word subgroups of V, itself a free group of rank $\aleph_0$. Thus to every operation with word subgroups of X_∞ one obtains the exact replica in V by replacing in every word the free generators $\mathfrak{x}$ of X_∞ by a system of free generators of V. It follows at once:

21.21 *$\mathfrak{U}_1\subseteq\mathfrak{U}_2$ implies $\mathfrak{U}_1\mathfrak{V}\subseteq\mathfrak{U}_2\mathfrak{V}$; if $\mathfrak{V}\neq\mathfrak{O}$ then, conversely, $\mathfrak{U}_1\mathfrak{V}\subseteq\mathfrak{U}_2\mathfrak{V}$ implies $\mathfrak{U}_1\subseteq\mathfrak{U}_2$; in particular $\mathfrak{U}_1\mathfrak{V}=\mathfrak{U}_2\mathfrak{V}$ implies $\mathfrak{U}_1=\mathfrak{U}_2$.*

Clearly:

21.22 *For every variety $\mathfrak{U}$;*

$$\mathfrak{U}\mathfrak{O}=\mathfrak{O}\mathfrak{U}=\mathfrak{O} \quad \textit{and} \quad \mathfrak{U}\mathfrak{E}=\mathfrak{E}\mathfrak{U}=\mathfrak{U}.$$

Our remark above gives further:

21.23
$$(\mathfrak{U}_1\vee\mathfrak{U}_2)\,\mathfrak{V}=\mathfrak{U}_1\mathfrak{V}\vee\mathfrak{U}_2\mathfrak{V}, \quad \textit{in fact} \quad (\vee\,\mathfrak{U}_\lambda)\,\mathfrak{V}=\vee(\mathfrak{U}_\lambda\mathfrak{V});$$
$$(\mathfrak{U}_1\wedge\mathfrak{U}_2)\,\mathfrak{V}=\mathfrak{U}_1\mathfrak{V}\wedge\mathfrak{U}_2\mathfrak{V}, \quad \textit{in fact} \quad (\wedge\,\mathfrak{U}_\lambda)\,\mathfrak{V}=\wedge(\mathfrak{U}_\lambda\mathfrak{V});$$
$$[\mathfrak{U}_1, \mathfrak{U}_2]\,\mathfrak{V}=[\mathfrak{U}_1\mathfrak{V}, \mathfrak{U}_2\mathfrak{V}].$$

Again from the definition of the product:

21.24
$$\mathfrak{V}_1\subseteq\mathfrak{V}_2 \quad \textit{implies} \quad \mathfrak{U}\mathfrak{V}_1\subseteq\mathfrak{U}\mathfrak{V}_2.$$

Here we cannot say more at this stage, in particular cancellation of a left-hand factor $\neq\mathfrak{O}$ will prove permissible only later (cf. 23.23).

Next:

21.25
$$\mathfrak{U}(\mathfrak{V}_1\vee\mathfrak{V}_2)\supseteq\mathfrak{U}\mathfrak{V}_1\vee\mathfrak{U}\mathfrak{V}_2,$$
$$\mathfrak{U}(\mathfrak{V}_1\wedge\mathfrak{V}_2)\subseteq\mathfrak{U}\mathfrak{V}_1\wedge\mathfrak{U}\mathfrak{V}_2,$$

but the inclusions may be proper; $\mathfrak{U}[\mathfrak{V}_1, \mathfrak{V}_2]$ and $[\mathfrak{U}\mathfrak{V}_1, \mathfrak{U}\mathfrak{V}_2]$ may be incomparable.

Proof. The inclusions are obvious. Examples to prove the remaining statements can be found in B. H. NEUMANN, HANNA NEUMANN and PETER M. NEUMANN [*1*]. We shall only give one of them by way of illustration; namely we exhibit a group $A \in \mathfrak{U}(\mathfrak{V}_1 \vee \mathfrak{V}_2)$ but not contained in $\mathfrak{U}\mathfrak{V}_1 \vee \mathfrak{U}\mathfrak{V}_2$. The other examples are similar.

Take $\mathfrak{U} = \mathfrak{A}_7$, $\mathfrak{V}_1 = \mathfrak{A}_2$, $\mathfrak{V}_2 = \mathfrak{A}_3$. Let A be the extension of the cycle of order seven, C_7, by its automorphism of order 6; that is

$$A = \mathrm{gp}(a, b; a^7 = b^6 = 1, a^b = a^3).$$

Since $C_6 \in \mathfrak{A}_2 \vee \mathfrak{A}_3$, $A \in \mathfrak{A}_7(\mathfrak{A}_2 \vee \mathfrak{A}_3)$.

The laws of $\mathfrak{A}_7\mathfrak{A}_2 \vee \mathfrak{A}_7\mathfrak{A}_3$ are the intersection of the laws of $\mathfrak{A}_7\mathfrak{A}_2$, and of $\mathfrak{A}_7\mathfrak{A}_3$. Hence, as x^{14} is a law in $\mathfrak{A}_7\mathfrak{A}_2$ and x^{21} is a law in $\mathfrak{A}_7\mathfrak{A}_3$, $[x^{14}, y^{21}]$ is a law in $\mathfrak{A}_7\mathfrak{A}_2 \vee \mathfrak{A}_7\mathfrak{A}_3$.

But in A, taking $x = ab^4$, $y = b$ one computes $x^{14} = a^3 b^2$, $y^{21} = b^3$, and $a^3 b^2 b^3 = a^3 b^{-1}$ but $b^3 a^3 b^2 = a^{-3} b^{-1}$, thus $[x^{14}, y^{21}] = 1$ is not satisfied by these two elements. //

21.26 *If Λ is an ordered set, and $\mathfrak{V}_\lambda \subseteq \mathfrak{V}_\mu$ when $\lambda < \mu$, then*
(i) $\mathfrak{U}(\wedge \mathfrak{V}_\lambda) = \wedge(\mathfrak{U}\mathfrak{V}_\lambda)$ *and* (ii) $\mathfrak{U}(\vee \mathfrak{V}_\lambda) = \vee(\mathfrak{U}\mathfrak{V}_\lambda)$.

Proof. We have, from the inclusions 21.24, at once the corresponding inclusions here. In the first case it remains to prove

$$\mathfrak{U}(\wedge \mathfrak{V}_\lambda) \supseteq \wedge(\mathfrak{U}\mathfrak{V}_\lambda),$$

or equivalently for the corresponding word subgroups:

$$U(\mathrm{gp}(V_\lambda)) \subseteq \mathrm{gp}(U(V_\lambda)).$$

Take any element on the left hand side; it is of the form $u(w_1, \ldots, w_n)$ where the w_i are products of elements of the groups V_λ. Only a finite number of these can occur and as the set of groups is ordered by inclusion, there is amongst them one, V_μ say, containing the others. But then $w_i \in V_\mu$ for $i = 1, \ldots, n$ and so $u(w_1, \ldots, w_n) \in U(V_\mu)$ belongs to the right hand side. //

Note that we have not used that the V_λ are fully invariant; therefore, using the isomorphism between X_∞ and F_∞:

21.27 *Any set of subgroups A_λ of F_∞, ordered by inclusion, satisfies* $U(\mathrm{gp}(A_\lambda)) = \mathrm{gp}(U(A_\lambda))$.

Further: $U(\bigcap A_\lambda) = \bigcap U(A_\lambda)$ provided only the set $\{A_\lambda\}$ is closed under finite intersections.

The latter result, due to M. J. DUNWOODY [*1*] is deeper. We shall not give the proof; nor do we give, at this point, the proof of our 21.26 (ii). It will be obtained as a by-product of results in the next section (cf. 22.45).

Next some properties of varieties that have only the trivial group in common. By way of preparation:

21.31 *Every non-trivial variety contains a non-trivial abelian variety.*

This is immediate from 13.52. Hence:

21.32 *Two non-trivial varieties intersect in the trivial variety if and only if they are of finite relatively prime exponents.* //

21.33 *If* $\mathfrak{U} \wedge \mathfrak{V} = \mathfrak{E}$, *then* $F(\mathfrak{U} \vee \mathfrak{V}) = F(\mathfrak{U}) \times F(\mathfrak{V})$ *where all three free groups have the same rank.*

Proof. We have $U(F)\,V(F) = F$ and the fully invariant subgroup corresponding to $\mathfrak{U} \vee \mathfrak{V}$ is $U(F) \cap V(F)$. Hence $F(\mathfrak{U} \vee \mathfrak{V}) = F/U(F) \cap V(F)$ contains the normal subgroups

$$U(F)/U(F) \cap V(F) \cong U(F)\,V(F)/V(F) = F/V(F) \cong F(\mathfrak{V})$$

and

$$V(F)/U(F) \cap V(F) \cong U(F)\,V(F)/U(F) = F/U(F) \cong F(\mathfrak{U}),$$

and these intersect trivially in $F(\mathfrak{U} \vee \mathfrak{V})$. //

Remark. This is not the only way in which a reduced free group can be a direct product. It follows from work by C. H. Houghton (unpublished) that every free group $F_k(\mathfrak{A}_m \mathfrak{A}_n)$ has a non-trivial centre which is a direct factor of the group whenever m and n are relatively prime. The finitely generated free groups of the variety generated by the icosahedral group are direct products (Sheila Oates [*1*]; cf. also p. 141). On the other hand we shall see in Chapter 4, Section 4 that large classes of reduced free groups are directly indecomposable. For the absolutely free group this is the well known Theorem of Baer and Levi (cf. Kurosh Vol. 2, p. 28).

We know $\mathfrak{U}\mathfrak{V}$ contains both $\mathfrak{U}$ and $\mathfrak{V}$, hence $\mathfrak{U}\mathfrak{V} \wedge \mathfrak{V}\mathfrak{U} \supseteq \mathfrak{U} \vee \mathfrak{V}$. Here:

21.34 *If* $\mathfrak{U} \wedge \mathfrak{V} = \mathfrak{E}$ *then* $\mathfrak{U}\mathfrak{V} \wedge \mathfrak{V}\mathfrak{U} = \mathfrak{U} \vee \mathfrak{V}$.

Proof.

$$\begin{aligned} \mathfrak{U} \vee \mathfrak{V} &= \mathfrak{E}(\mathfrak{U} \vee \mathfrak{V}) \\ &= (\mathfrak{U} \wedge \mathfrak{V})\,(\mathfrak{U} \vee \mathfrak{V}) \\ &= \mathfrak{U}(\mathfrak{U} \vee \mathfrak{V}) \wedge \mathfrak{V}(\mathfrak{U} \vee \mathfrak{V}) \quad \text{by 21.23} \\ &\supseteq \mathfrak{U}\mathfrak{V} \wedge \mathfrak{V}\mathfrak{U} \quad \text{by 21.24,} \end{aligned}$$

and so equality follows. //

21.35 *If* $\mathfrak{U}$ *and* $\mathfrak{V}$ *are proper subvarieties of* $\mathfrak{O}$, *then so is* $\mathfrak{U} \vee \mathfrak{V}$.

Proof. The case $\mathfrak{U} = \mathfrak{V}$ is obvious. Assume $\mathfrak{U} \neq \mathfrak{V}$; then U and V are non-trivial distinct fully invariant subgroups of X_∞. But $U \cap V$ represents the laws of $\mathfrak{U} \vee \mathfrak{V}$; it contains $[U, V]$, and this is non-trivial as two elements u and v of a free group commute only if they are powers of the same element. //

We add here an interesting fact, following the question raised by 21.31 a little further: What 'small' sub-varieties does a variety possess?

21.4 **Theorem** (SHEILA OATES, unpublished.) *If the non-abelian variety $\mathfrak{U}$ is generated by its finite groups, then it contains non-abelian metabelian groups.*

Proof. If $\mathfrak{U}$ is metabelian, we have finished. Otherwise consider the subvariety $\mathfrak{V}$ of all metabelian groups in $\mathfrak{U}$; then $\mathfrak{V} \subset \mathfrak{U}$ and we must show that $\mathfrak{V}$ is not abelian. As $\mathfrak{U}$ is generated by its finite groups, there exists a finite group in $\mathfrak{U}$ outside $\mathfrak{V}$. Take one of minimal order, A say. Then all its proper subgroups belong to $\mathfrak{V}$; hence if $\mathfrak{V}$ were abelian, then by a theorem of O. J. SCHMIDT that a finite group all whose proper subgroups are abelian is metabelian*, the group A would be metabelian, hence in $\mathfrak{V}$, which is a contradiction. //

So the question arises:

Problem 5. *Does there exist a non-abelian variety without a non-abelian metabelian subvariety?*

By Theorem 21.4, every finite group in such a variety must be abelian. Also, any properly metabelian group generates a variety containing finite properly metabelian groups. For if it is not abelian, one can pick out a 2-generator non-abelian subgroup, and this has by a result of B. H. NEUMANN (Lemma 7.2 of [*2*]) finite non-abelian factor groups. Thus we can re-formulate:

Problem 5. (alternative formulation). *Does there exist a non-abelian variety all whose finite groups are abelian?*

In this form the problem has some bearing on the existence of *verbal products with an amalgamated subgroup.* It is well known (due to O. SCHREIER; cf. MARSHALL HALL, Chapter 17) that in the variety $\mathfrak{O}$ every *amalgam* of two groups is embeddable in a group. It also is well known, and easy to confirm (cf. e.g. B. H. NEUMANN [*3*], Chapter ix), that in every abelian variety an amalgam of two groups can be embedded in a group of that variety. Expressed differently, the verbal product with one amalgamated subgroup exists in the varieties $\mathfrak{O}$, $\mathfrak{A}$ and $\mathfrak{A}_m$ for all m.

Problem 6. *Does the verbal product with one amalgamated subgroup exist, that is: can every amalgam of two $\mathfrak{U}$-groups be embedded in a $\mathfrak{U}$-group, in any variety other than $\mathfrak{O}$, $\mathfrak{A}$, $\mathfrak{A}_m$?*

* For an elementary proof, cf. L. RÉDEI, Algebra, I. Akademische Verlagsgesellschaft, Leipzig 1959, p. 721.

Work by JAMES WIEGOLD [*1*], [*2*] and GRAHAM HIGMAN [*4*] shows incidentally that in certain nilpotent varieties not every amalgam can be embedded, and some conditions for embeddability are obtained. It follows from a construction of B. H. NEUMANN (reported in [*3*], Chapter xi) that if $\mathfrak{U}$ contains finite non-abelian groups and possesses a verbal product with an amalgamated subgroup, then $\mathfrak{U}=\mathfrak{O}$. Hence a negative answer to Problem 5 implies a negative answer to Problem 6.

We return to the multiplication of varieties:

21.51 **Theorem.** *Multiplication of varieties is associative.*

Proof. From the definition of the product the inclusion $\mathfrak{U}(\mathfrak{V}\mathfrak{W})\subseteq(\mathfrak{U}\mathfrak{V})\,\mathfrak{W}$ is immediate. Now let $C\in(\mathfrak{U}\mathfrak{V})\,\mathfrak{W}$. Then there exists a normal subgroup $N\lhd C$, such that $N\in\mathfrak{U}\mathfrak{V}$, $C/N\in\mathfrak{W}$. In particular, N may be taken as the word subgroup $W(C)$, so that it is fully invariant in C. Now $V(N)$ is normal in N, and $V(N)\in\mathfrak{U}$. As fully invariant subgroup of a fully invariant subgroup it is fully invariant in C; thus certainly $V(N)\lhd C$. Also $C/V(N)\in\mathfrak{V}\mathfrak{W}$, as $W(C/V(N))=W(C)/V(N)$. Thus $C\in\mathfrak{U}(\mathfrak{V}\mathfrak{W})$. //

Remark. The associativity of this multiplication is peculiar to varieties. For other classes of groups, even some that are closely related to varieties, it may fail; cf. HANNA NEUMANN [*1*].

We can now write the polynilpotent variety $\mathfrak{P}$ introduced in 14.66 in the form

21.52 *The polynilpotent variety* $\mathfrak{P}$ *of class row* $(c_1, \ldots, c_l)$ *is* $\mathfrak{P}=\mathfrak{N}_{c_l}\ldots\mathfrak{N}_{c_2}\mathfrak{N}_{c_1}$; *in particular* $\mathfrak{S}_l=\mathfrak{A}^l$.

We call a variety *indecomposable* if it cannot be written as the product of two non-trivial factors. To obtain the factorization of any variety $\neq\mathfrak{O}$ into a finite number of indecomposable ones, we need a lemma by F. W. LEVI [*1*]. For the proof we recall some properties of *Nielsen systems* in free groups. Details can be found in textbooks [MARSHALL HALL, A. G. KUROSH].

In the free group $F_\infty=\mathrm{gp}(\mathfrak{f})$ we write each element $a\neq 1$ in the form

$$f_{i_1}^{\varepsilon_1}\ldots f_{i_l}^{\varepsilon_l} \quad\text{with}\quad \varepsilon_\lambda=\pm 1, \quad f_{i_\lambda}^{\varepsilon_\lambda}f_{i_{\lambda+1}}^{\varepsilon_{\lambda+1}}\neq 1 \quad\text{for}\quad \lambda\geqq 1.$$

Then $l=l(a)$ is called the *length* of the element a. Put $l(1)=0$. If $\mathfrak{a}\subseteq F_\infty$ is a subset $\neq\{1\}$ of F_∞, the *length* $l(\mathfrak{a})$ of $\mathfrak{a}$ is defined by

$$l(\mathfrak{a})=\min l(a), \qquad a\neq 1\in\mathfrak{a}.$$

If $A \subseteq F_\infty$ is a non-trivial subgroup, there exists a *Nielsen reduced* system of generators for A, that is a set $\mathfrak{a}$ of free generators for A such that

(i) $l(a_i^{\varepsilon_i} a_j^{\varepsilon_j}) \geqq \max(l(a_i), l(a_j))$ unless $a_i^{\varepsilon_i} a_j^{\varepsilon_j} = 1$;

(ii) if $a \in A$, $a \neq 1$, and $a = \prod_j a_{i(j)}^{\varepsilon_j}$ is the reduced representation of a in terms of $\mathfrak{a}$, then $l(a) \geqq \max l(a_{i(j)})$;

(iii) if in (ii) all $a_{i(j)}$ have the same length l, then $l(a) = l$ only if a is a generator or a product of two generators.

21.61 **Lemma** (Levi [*1*]). *If $F_\infty = A_0 \supset A_1 \supset A_2 \ldots$ is a chain of subgroups, each characteristic in its predecessor, then $l(A_k) > l(A_{k-1})$ for all $k \geqq 1$.*

Proof. Choose a Nielsen reduced generating set $\mathfrak{a}$ for A_{k-1} $(k \geqq 1)$, and let $a_1 \in \mathfrak{a}$ be a generator of minimal length; then $l(A_{k-1}) = l(a_1)$. If b is an element of shortest length in A_k, $b \neq 1$, then $l(A_k) = l(b)$. Also $b \in A_{k-1}$, so that $b = \prod a_{i(j)}^{\varepsilon_j}$, $a_{i(j)} \in \mathfrak{a}$. From (ii) $l(b) > l(a_1)$ unless all the generators occurring in b are of the same shortest length; in that case, from (iii), again either $l(b) > l(a_1)$, or b is a generator or a product of two generators. If b is a generator, $b \in \mathfrak{a}$, then A_k contains the whole of $\mathfrak{a}$, as A_k is characteristic in A_{k-1}, and so $A_k = A_{k-1}$ which is excluded. But if b is a product of two generators, let $b = a_i^{\varepsilon_i} a_j^{\varepsilon_j}$ $(i \neq j)$; then replacing a_i and a_j in $\mathfrak{a}$ by a_i and b gives a new set of generators and, as before, $A_{k-1} = A_k$ follows. Hence $b = a_i^2$ (or its inverse). But then $l(b) > l(a_i)$; for if a_i is of even length $2m$, say, $a_i = rs$, where each of r, s has length m. Then $b = rsrs$ and this has length $\leqq 2m$ only if $s\,r$ cancels, i.e. $r = s^{-1}, a_i = 1$, which is impossible. Hence a_i is of odd length $2m+1$, then again at most m letters can cancel in the product a_i^2 giving $l(b) \geqq l(a_i) + 1$.

Thus in any case $l(b) = l(A_k) > l(A_{k-1}) = l(a_i)$. //

21.62 **Corollary.** *If $F_\infty = A_0 \supset A_1 \supset \cdots$ is an infinite properly descending chain of subgroups, each characteristic in its predecessor, then $\bigcap A_i = \{1\}$.* //

21.63 **Corollary.** *If $F_\infty = A_0 \supset A_1 \cdots \supset A_k$ is a properly descending chain of subgroups, each characteristic in its predecessor, then $l(A_k) > k$.* //

Application to products of varieties gives:

21.71 *If $\mathfrak{B} \neq \mathfrak{E}$, then the powers $\mathfrak{B}^n$ generate $\mathfrak{O}$.*

Proof. The corresponding sets of laws form the chain $X_\infty \supset V \supset V(V) \supset V(V(V)) \supset \cdots$, where each term is fully invariant, hence characteristic, in the predecessor, and is properly contained in it. //

21.72 **Theorem.** *If $\mathfrak{B} \neq \mathfrak{O}$, $\mathfrak{E}$, then $\mathfrak{B}$ is a product of a finite number of indecomposable varieties.*

Proof. If $\mathfrak{B}$ is indecomposable, there is nothing to prove. Otherwise $\mathfrak{B} = \mathfrak{B}_1 \mathfrak{B}_2$. If either of these is decomposable, write it as a product.

This way one arrives at a decomposition of the form $\mathfrak{V}=\mathfrak{V}_1\dots\mathfrak{V}_k$; to it corresponds a chain of fully invariant subgroups

$$V=V_1(V_2(\dots(V_k)\dots))\subset\dots\subset V_{k-1}(V_k)\subset V_k\subset X_\infty:$$

By 21.63, $k<l(V)$; therefore after at most $l(V)$ steps all the factors must be indecomposable. //

2. Wreath Products and Discrimination *

We develop here the fundamental relation between wreath products and product varieties. Further properties of wreath products will be established as needed; for reference see PETER M. NEUMANN [2].

We shall only use standard wreath products here. Let A and B be non-trivial groups. We construct their wreath product as follows:

We take A^B, the cartesian power of A consisting of all functions φ: $B\to A$ multiplied componentwise. For each element $b\in B$ we define a mapping

$$\beta:\quad \varphi\to\varphi^b \quad\text{of}\quad A^B \quad\text{by}\quad \varphi^b(y)=\varphi(y\,b^{-1}) \quad\text{for all}\quad y\in B.$$

Then β is an automorphism of A^B and the set of all these automorphisms is a group isomorphic to B. Let P be the extension of A^B by this group of automorphisms; that is, we take pairs (b,φ), $b\in B$, $\varphi\in A^B$, with multiplication

$$(b,\varphi)\,(c,\psi)=(b\,c,\varphi^c\,\psi),$$

and identify $\mathrm{gp}((b,1)\,|\,b\in B)$ with B and $\mathrm{gp}((1,\varphi)\,|\,\varphi\in A^B)$ with A^B so that the elements of P become products $b\varphi$, where $\varphi^b=b^{-1}\varphi b$ tallies with the usual notation. P is called the complete (or unrestricted) *wreath product* of A by B and we write $P=A$ Wr B. The direct power $A^{(B)}$ is a subgroup of A^B which admits the automorphisms $\varphi\to\varphi^b$; thus A Wr B contains as a subgroup the direct power $A^{(B)}$ extended by B which we shall call the restricted wreath product of A by B, written A wr B.

We collect some simple properties of wreath products.

22.11 *If α: $A\twoheadrightarrow A^*$ is an epimorphism of A onto A^*, then there exists an epimorphism μ: A Wr $B\twoheadrightarrow A^*$ Wr B whose restriction to A wr B maps it onto A^* wr B, whose restriction to the coordinate subgroup A_b in A^B is the epimorphism naturally corresponding to α on A, and whose restriction to B is the identical mapping.*

* The ideas and methods presented here and in the rest of the chapter are developed in B. H. NEUMANN, HANNA NEUMANN and PETER M. NEUMANN [1], A. L. ŠMELKIN [1], [3] and $B+3N$; see also GILBERT BAUMSLAG [2]. We give individual references only occasionally, but point out that the original papers go further, in different directions, than we report here.

Proof. Define μ by $(b\varphi)\,\mu = b\varphi^*$ where $\varphi^*(y) = \varphi(y)\,\alpha$ for all $y \in B$. //

22.12 *If* $A_1 \leqq A$, *then* A_1 Wr $B \leqq A$ Wr B *and* A_1 wr $B \leqq A$ wr B.

Proof. Take the set of elements $b\varphi_1$ where $\varphi_1\colon B \to A_1$ runs through all the functions taking values in A_1. //

22.13 *If* $B_1 \leqq B$, *then* A Wr $B_1 \leqq A$ Wr B *and* A wr $B_1 \leqq A$ wr B.

Proof. Take all elements of the form $b_1\varphi_1$ where $b_1 \in B_1$ and $\sigma(\varphi_1) \subseteq B_1$. //

22.14 *If* $B_1 \leqq B$ *and* T *is a left transversal of* B_1 *in* B (*that is* $B = TB_1$), *then* A^T Wr $B_1 \leqq A$ Wr B *and* $A^{(T)}$ wr $B_1 \leqq A$ wr B.

Proof. Consider the set of all functions $b_1\varphi$ with $b_1 \in B_1$. We write for each $y \in B$,

$$\begin{aligned}\varphi(y) &= \varphi(tx), \qquad t \in T, \qquad x \in B_1\\ &= \Phi(x)\,(t),\end{aligned}$$

so that $\Phi(x)$ is for each fixed x a function defined on T, taking values in A:

$$\Phi(x)\colon \ T \to A,$$

and so

$$\Phi\colon \ B_1 \to A^T.$$

Now one checks: 1. $b_1\Phi = b_1'\Phi'$ only if $b_1 = b_1'$ and $\Phi = \Phi'$; this is true because $b_1\varphi = b_1'\varphi'$ only if $b_1 = b_1'$ and $\varphi = \varphi'$.

2. All $b_1\Phi$ with $b_1 \in B_1$ and $\Phi \in (A^T)^{B_1}$ occur.

3. $\Phi^{b_1} = b_1^{-1}\Phi b_1$ is the function given by $\Phi^{b_1}(x) = \Phi(xb_1^{-1})$ for every $x \in B_1$.

To see this, take the value of $\varphi^{b_1} = b_1^{-1}\varphi b_1$ at y:

$$\varphi^{b_1}(y) = \varphi(y\,b_1^{-1}) = \varphi(t\,x\,b_1^{-1}) = \Phi(x\,b_1^{-1})\,(t),$$

that is $\Phi^{b_1}(x) = \Phi(xb_1^{-1})$ as required.

Thus the set of elements $b_1\Phi$ is a subgroup isomorphic to A^T Wr B_1.

Finally, the functions φ of finite support give precisely the functions Φ of finite support on B_1 with values that are functions of finite support on T. That is $A^{(T)}$ wr $B_1 \leqq A$ wr B. //

22.21 **Theorem** (KALOUJNINE and KRASNER [*1*] *). *The complete wreath product* A Wr B *contains an isomorphic copy of every group that is an extension of* A *by* B.

---

* In fact this embedding occurs much earlier in the literature. For finite B — but this restriction is inessential — it is a special case of a result of FROBENIUS on monomial representations (cf. Section 6 of WIELANDT and HUPPERT [*1*] for a recent exposition of these ideas).

Proof. Let C contain a normal subgroup N isomorphic to A with factor group $C/N \cong B$. Let T be a transversal of N in C, and let τ be the natural $1-1$ map of B onto T corresponding to the isomorphism $B \cong C/N$. Take μ to be the natural homomorphism of C onto B with kernel N and let α be a fixed isomorphism of N onto A. Now we define a mapping γ: $C \to A \text{ Wr } B$ as follows: For $c \in C$, put

$$c\gamma = c\mu\varphi_c, \quad \text{where for all } y \in B$$

$$\varphi_c(y) = ((y(c\mu)^{-1})\tau c(y\tau)^{-1})\alpha;$$

the right-hand side can easily be checked to be meaningful. A straightforward computation confirms that γ is a monomorphism. //

22.22 **Corollary.** *The complete wreath product* $F_\infty(\mathfrak{U}) \text{ Wr } F_\infty(\mathfrak{V})$ *generates* $\mathfrak{U}\mathfrak{V}$.

Proof. Clearly the wreath product belongs to the variety $\mathfrak{U}\mathfrak{V}$; also from 21.13 and 22.21

$$F_\infty(\mathfrak{U}\mathfrak{V}) \leqq F_\infty(\mathfrak{U}) \text{ Wr } F_\infty(\mathfrak{V})$$

so that $\mathfrak{U}\mathfrak{V} = \text{var } F_\infty(\mathfrak{U}\mathfrak{V}) \subseteq \text{var } (F_\infty(\mathfrak{U}) \text{ Wr } F_\infty(\mathfrak{V})) \subseteq \mathfrak{U}\mathfrak{V}$. //

Here we can replace $F_\infty(\mathfrak{U})$ by any group that generates $\mathfrak{U}$.

22.23 *If A generates $\mathfrak{U}$, then A Wr $F_\infty(\mathfrak{V})$ generates $\mathfrak{U}\mathfrak{V}$.*

Proof. We use 22.14: Let $F_\infty(\mathfrak{V}) = H$ be freely generated by $h_1, h_2, \ldots$ and put $H_1 = \text{gp}(h_1, h_3, h_5, \ldots)$; then $H_1 \cong H$ and H_1 has a transversal T in H that is countably infinite. Now 22.14 gives:

$$A \text{ Wr } H \geqq A^T \text{ Wr } H_1,$$

and from 22.12 and 15.4

$$A^T \text{ Wr } H_1 \geqq F_\infty(\mathfrak{U}) \text{ Wr } H_1 \cong F_\infty(\mathfrak{U}) \text{ Wr } H.$$

Therefore $\mathfrak{U}\mathfrak{V} \supseteq \text{var } (A \text{ Wr } H) \supseteq \text{var } (F_\infty(\mathfrak{U}) \text{ Wr } H) = \mathfrak{U}\mathfrak{V}$, and the assertion follows. //

Note that $F_\infty(\mathfrak{V})$ cannot in general be replaced by an arbitrary group B generating $\mathfrak{V}$. Example 16.36 shows that the variety $\mathfrak{A}_2^2$ is not generated by C_2 Wr C_2; in fact it is not even generated by $F_\infty(\mathfrak{A}_2)$ Wr C_2, although C_2 generates $\mathfrak{A}_2$. But it is possible to replace $F_\infty(\mathfrak{V})$ by the direct power $B^{(I)}$ of a generating group B of $\mathfrak{V}$. It is this modification of the generating group for $\mathfrak{U}\mathfrak{V}$ that remains to be made before we can use these results in the next section to prove that the factorization of a variety into indecomposable varieties is unique. This last preparatory step will be obtained as a by-product of a rather more elaborate application of wreath products to discrimination. It is worth stressing that the arguments, cut down to a proof of no more than the limited result needed in the next section, are considerably simpler than would appear from the remainder of this section.

We first reduce the size of the generating groups obtained in 22.22 and 22.23:

22.31 *For any groups A and B, the wreath products A* Wr *B and A* wr *B generate the same variety.*

22.32 **Corollary.** *If A generates* $\mathfrak{U}$ *then A* wr $F_\infty(\mathfrak{B})$ *generates* $\mathfrak{U}\mathfrak{B}$.

We preface the proof of 22.31 with a computational remark that will be used again and again.

22.33 *Let* a_i, t_i *be arbitrary elements of some group,* $\varepsilon_i = \pm 1$ *for* $i=1, \ldots, m$. *Then*

$$\prod_{i=1}^{m} (t_i a_i)^{\varepsilon_i} = \prod_{i=1}^{m} t_i^{\varepsilon_i} \prod_{i=1}^{m} a_i^{\varepsilon_i u_i},$$

where $u_i = \prod_{j=\tau_i}^{m} t_j^{\varepsilon_j}$ *with* $\tau_i = i + \frac{1}{2}(\varepsilon_i + 1)$, *and* $u_m = 1$ *when* $\tau_m = m+1$.

This can be checked by induction over m; we omit the details. //

It follows:

22.34 *Let* $N \lhd C$, *T a transversal for C modulo N, so that* $C = TN$. *If w is a word in n variables,* $t_i \in T$, $a_i \in N$, *then*

$$w(t_1 a_1, \ldots, t_n a_n) = w(t_1, \ldots, t_n) \prod_{\mu=1}^{l} a_{i(\mu)}^{\varepsilon_{i(\mu)} u_{i(\mu)}(t_1, \ldots, t_n)}$$

where l is the length of w, each $a_{i(\mu)}$ *is one of the* a_i, *the exponent* $\varepsilon_{i(\mu)} = \pm 1$ *depends on w and* μ *only and each* $u_{i(\mu)}$ *is a word determined by w and* μ *only.* //

In fact the words $u_{i(\mu)}$ that occur here are the *Fox derivatives* of the word w (cf. Fox [*1*]).

Proof of 22.31. Clearly var (A wr B) $\subseteq$ var (A Wr B). To show equality we must show that the restricted wreath product satisfies no more laws than the unrestricted one.

Let w be a word that is not a law in A Wr B. If w involves n variables, there exist elements $b_1 \varphi_1, \ldots, b_n \varphi_n$ in A Wr B such that

$$w(b_1 \varphi_1, \ldots, b_n \varphi_n) \neq 1.$$

Now using 22.34

$$w(b_1 \varphi_1, \ldots, b_n \varphi_n) = w(b_1, \ldots, b_n) \Pi \, \varphi_{i(\mu)}^{\varepsilon_{i(\mu)} u_{i(\mu)}(b_1, \ldots, b_n)}.$$

If $w(b_1, \ldots, b_n) \neq 1$, then this is a non-trivial value of w also in A wr B and we have finished. We therefore may assume that

$$w(b_1, \ldots, b_n) = 1 \quad \text{and} \quad \Pi\, \varphi_{i(\mu)}^{\varepsilon_{i(\mu)}\, u_{i(\mu)}(b_1, \ldots, b_n)} \neq 1 .$$

If this element of A^B is not the identity function, then there exists $b \in B$ such that its value at b is not 1; from our definition of the standard wreath product this means

$$\Pi\, \varphi_{i(\mu)}^{\varepsilon_{i(\mu)}}(b\, u_{i(\mu)}^{-1}(b_1, \ldots, b_n)) = a \neq 1, \quad a \in A .$$

Now define functions $\psi_1, \ldots, \psi_n \in A^{(B)}$ by

$$\psi_{i(\mu)}(b\, u_{i(\mu)}^{-1}(b_1, \ldots, b_n)) = \varphi_{i(\mu)}(b\, u_{i(\mu)}^{-1}(b_1, \ldots, b_n)) .$$

These equations for $i(\mu) = i$ define ψ_i at $b u_{i(\mu)}^{-1}(b_1, \ldots, b_n)$; at all other arguments $y \in B$ we put $\psi_i(y) = 1$. Then the ψ_i have finite support so that the elements $b_i \psi_i$ belong to A wr B, and

$$w(b_1 \psi_1, \ldots, b_n \psi_n) = w(b_1, \ldots, b_n)\, \Pi\, \psi_{i(\mu)}^{\varepsilon_{i(\mu)}\, u_{i(\mu)}(b_1, \ldots, b_n)} \neq 1 ,$$

because $w(b_1, \ldots, b_n) = 1$; but the other factor is a function which at b takes the value

$$\Pi\, \psi_{i(\mu)}^{\varepsilon_{i(\mu)}}(b\, u_{i(\mu)}^{-1}(b_1, \ldots, b_n)) = \Pi\, \varphi_{i(\mu)}^{\varepsilon_{i(\mu)}}(b\, u_{i(\mu)}^{-1}(b_1, \ldots, b_n)) = a \neq 1 .$$

Thus w is not a law in A wr B. //

With the aid of Corollary 22.32 we now obtain a rather stronger result of which we shall need two different specializations:

22.41 **Lemma.** *Let $\mathfrak{C}$ be a set of groups such that to any finite set of non-laws of the variety $\mathfrak{U} = \operatorname{var} \mathfrak{C}$ there is a single group in $\mathfrak{C}$ in which all these words are not laws; let the set $\mathfrak{D}$ discriminate the variety $\mathfrak{B}$. Then the set $\mathfrak{C}$ wr $\mathfrak{D} = \{C \text{ wr } D \mid C \in \mathfrak{C}, D \in \mathfrak{D}\}$ discriminates the product variety $\mathfrak{U}\mathfrak{B}$.*

Proof. Let $\mathfrak{w}_1$ be an arbitrary finite set of words that are not laws in $\mathfrak{U}\mathfrak{B}$. We write $\mathfrak{w}_1 = \mathfrak{v} \cup \mathfrak{w}$ where $\mathfrak{v}$ consists of all those words of $\mathfrak{w}_1$ that are laws in $\mathfrak{B}$, and $\mathfrak{w}$ of all the rest. We have to find a wreath product C wr D, $C \in \mathfrak{C}$, $D \in \mathfrak{D}$ and a homomorphism of the free group X_k (for some sufficiently large rank k) into C wr D which maps every word $w \in \mathfrak{w}_1$ non-trivially. We first take the free group $G = F_\infty(\mathfrak{U})$ in place of C and show that we can find a group $D \in \mathfrak{D}$ and a homomorphism τ_1 of X_k into G wr D such that all images $w\tau_1$, $w \in \mathfrak{w}_1$, are non-trivial. Then we use the assumption on $\mathfrak{C}$ and the property 22.11 of wreath products to replace G by a group in $\mathfrak{C}$.

From 22.32 we know that G wr H generates $\mathfrak{U}\mathfrak{B}$ where $H = F_\infty(\mathfrak{B})$. Thus every word of $\mathfrak{w}_1$ takes a non-trivial value in G wr H. We take n such that every word in $\mathfrak{w}_1$ is a word in n variables. As those of $\mathfrak{w}$ are not laws in $\mathfrak{V}$, there exist elements $h_{w,1}, \ldots, h_{w,n} \in H$ such that

$$(1) \qquad w(h_{w,1}, \ldots, h_{w,n}) \neq 1 \quad \text{in} \quad H \quad (w \in \mathfrak{w}).$$

For the words $v \in \mathfrak{v}$, we take elements $h_{v,1}\varphi_{v,1}, \ldots, h_{v,n}\varphi_{v,n}$ such that

$$v(h_{v,1}\varphi_{v,1}, \ldots, h_{v,n}\varphi_{v,n}) = v(h_{v,1}, \ldots, h_{v,n})\,\Phi_v \neq 1.$$

But each $v \in \mathfrak{v}$ is a law in $\mathfrak{V}$, so the first term here is 1 and we have, using 22.34,

$$(2) \qquad \Phi_v = \prod_{\mu=1}^{l(v)} \varphi_{v,i(v,\mu)}^{\varepsilon_{v,\mu} u_{v,\mu}(h_{v,1}, \ldots, h_{v,n})} \neq 1.$$

Thus to each v there is a value $h_v \in H$ such that at h_v, Φ_v takes a non-trivial value:

$$(3) \qquad \Phi_v(h_v) = \prod_{\mu=1}^{l(v)} \varphi_{v,i(v,\mu)}^{\varepsilon_{v,\mu}}\left(h_v u_{v,\mu}^{-1}(h_{v,1}, \ldots, h_{v,n})\right) = g_v$$

$$\text{where} \quad g_v \neq 1 \quad \text{in} \quad G = F_\infty(\mathfrak{U}).$$

For use in the last step of the proof we 'spread out' the elements g_v in the free group $F_\infty(\mathfrak{U}) = G$:

If

$$(4) \qquad g_v = t_v(\mathfrak{g}), \qquad \mathfrak{g} \in \mathfrak{g}^N$$

for some integer N, is a representation of g_v in terms of the free generators of G, then the sets of free generators occurring in the elements g_v for different v may be assumed disjoint.

Proof of (4). The generators occurring in g_v are at most those that occur in the values of the functions $\varphi_{v,1}, \ldots, \varphi_{v,n}$. As these are of finite support, the set of generators occurring in the computation of g_v is finite. But the subgroups of G generated by $g_1, \ldots, g_N$ and $g_{1+l}, \ldots, g_{N+l}$ are isomorphic. Thus, replacing – if necessary – the functions $\varphi_{v,1}, \ldots, \varphi_{v,n}$ by those obtained by replacing the set of free generators occurring in their values by a different set, gives exact images of the equations (2) and (3), only written in terms of these different generators. The final values g_v will then still be non-trivial and satisfy (4). //

We want a group $D \in \mathfrak{D}$, elements $d_1, \ldots, d_n \in D$ and functions $\psi_1, \ldots, \psi_n$ from D to G such that

$$(5) \qquad w(d_1\psi_1, \ldots, d_n\psi_n) = w(d_1, \ldots, d_n)\,\Psi_w \neq 1,$$

which is satisfied as soon as

$$(5') \qquad w(d_1, \ldots, d_n) \neq 1 \quad \text{for each} \quad w \in \mathfrak{w};$$

and so that moreover for each $v \in \mathfrak{v}$:

(6) $$v(d_1\psi_1, \ldots, d_n\psi_n) = \Pi\, \psi_{i(v,\mu)}^{\varepsilon_{v,\mu} u_{v,\mu}(d_1, \ldots, d_n)} = \Psi_v \neq 1 .$$

We do this by 'imitating' the relations (1) and (3) as follows:

First we introduce further independent variables x_v, one for each $v \in \mathfrak{v}$ (thus we use altogether $n + |\mathfrak{v}|$ variables and the rank k of X_k will be taken as $k = n + |\mathfrak{v}|$). Then apply 17.23 to the set of words consisting of all $x_v u_{v,\mu}^{-1}$ ($v \in \mathfrak{v}$, $\mu = 1, \ldots, l(v)$), all $w \in \mathfrak{w}$ and the empty word 1. This is still a finite set, and as $\mathfrak{D}$ discriminates $\mathfrak{V}$, there exists therefore a group $D \in \mathfrak{D}$ and elements $d_v (v \in \mathfrak{v})$ and $d_1, \ldots, d_n$ in D such that

(7) $w(d_1, \ldots, d_n) \neq 1$ for all $w \in \mathfrak{w}$, as $w \in \mathfrak{w}$ is not a law in $\mathfrak{V}$.

Thus (5′), and therefore (5), is satisfied.

Also

(8) $$d_v u_{v,\mu}^{-1}(d_1, \ldots, d_n) \neq d_{v'} u_{v',\mu'}^{-1}(d_1, \ldots, d_n)$$

whenever for $v, v' \in \mathfrak{v}$ (possibly $v = v'$) $x_v u_{v,\mu}^{-1}$ and $x_{v'} u_{v',\mu'}^{-1}$ are capable of different values in $H = F_\infty(\mathfrak{V})$, which is certainly the case when $v \neq v'$, as $x_v, x_{v'}, x_1, \ldots, x_n$ are independent variables.

Now we can define the functions $\psi_1, \ldots, \psi_n$ as follows:

For each i, $1 \leq i \leq n$, and each $d \in D$ we put

(9) $$\psi_i(d) = \varphi_{v,\, i(v,\mu)}(h_v u_{v,\mu}^{-1}(h_{v,1}, \ldots, h_{v,n}))$$

whenever, for some $v \in \mathfrak{v}$ and $1 \leq \mu \leq l(v)$, $i = i(v, \mu)$ and $d = d_v u_{v,\mu}^{-1}(d_1, \ldots, d_n)$, and $\psi_i(d) = 1$ in all other cases.

This certainly makes the ψ_i of finite support; what we have to check is that they are in fact functions, that is that they are unambiguously defined on D.

Now as $v \neq v'$ implies

$$d_v u_{v,\mu}^{-1}(d_1, \ldots, d_n) \neq d_{v'} u_{v',\mu'}^{-1}(d_1, \ldots, d_n),$$

an element d can have two representations of the form used in (9) only if

$$d_v u_{v,\mu}^{-1}(d_1, \ldots, d_n) = d_v u_{v,\mu'}^{-1}(d_1, \ldots, d_n);$$

but then (8) sees to it that $u_{v,\mu}^{-1} = u_{v,\mu'}^{-1}$ is a law in $\mathfrak{V}$, that is in particular

$$h_v u_{v,\mu}^{-1}(h_{v,1}, \ldots, h_{v,n}) = h_v u_{v,\mu'}^{-1}(h_{v,1}, \ldots, h_{v,n}),$$

and so if also $i(v, \mu) = i(v, \mu') = i$, (9) determines the value of ψ_i at d uniquely.

We now check that for this choice of values in D and functions ψ_i, (6) is satisfied. But

$$v(d_1\psi_1, \dots, d_n\psi_n) = \prod_{\mu=1}^{l(v)} \psi_{i(v,\mu)}^{\varepsilon_{v,\mu} u_{v,\mu}(d_1, \dots, d_n)} = \Psi_v$$

takes at d_v, by (9), the value:

$$\prod_{\mu=1}^{l(v)} \psi_{i(v,\mu)}^{\varepsilon_{v,\mu}}(d_v u_{v,\mu}^{-1}(d_1, \dots, d_n) = \prod_{\mu=1}^{l(v)} \varphi_{v,i(v,\mu)}^{\varepsilon_{v,\mu}}(h_v u_{v,\mu}^{-1}(h_{v,1}, \dots, h_{v,n}))$$

$$= g_v \neq 1, \quad \text{by (3)}.$$

Thus we have completed the first step: taking τ_1 as the homomorphism

(10) $$\tau_1 \colon X_k \to G \operatorname{wr} D$$

defined by

$$x_v \tau_1 = d_v, \quad x_i \tau_1 = d_i \psi_i \quad (i = 1, \dots, n),$$

we have

$$w\tau_1 = w(d_1, \dots, d_n)\Psi_w \neq 1 \quad \text{as} \quad w(d_1, \dots, d_n) \neq 1 \quad \text{in} \quad H$$

and

$$v\tau_1 = \Psi_v \neq 1 \quad \text{in} \quad G^{(D)} \quad \text{as} \quad \Psi_v(d_v) = g_v \neq 1 \quad \text{in} \quad G.$$

Finally we replace G by a group in $\mathfrak{C}$:

By (3) and (4), $g_v = t_v(g) \neq 1$, so that the words t_v are not laws in $\mathfrak{U}$. Thus there exists a group $C \in \mathfrak{C}$ in which all these words take non-trivial values:

$t_v(c(v)) \neq 1$ for each $v \in \mathfrak{v}$ and suitable N-tuplets $c(v) = (c_1(v), \dots, c_N(v))$ of elements in C. As $\mathfrak{g}$ is a set of free generators, and the subsets occurring in the distinct words $t_v(g)$ are disjoint, we can define a mapping

$$\gamma \colon G \to C \quad \text{by setting} \quad g_{i_\mu}\gamma = c_\mu(v) \quad \text{if} \quad g_v = t_v(g_{i_1}, \dots, g_{i_N})$$

and mapping the remaining generators in $\mathfrak{g}$ in some arbitrarily chosen way. The corresponding homomorphism τ_2 of $G \operatorname{wr} D$ onto $G\gamma \operatorname{wr} D \leqq C \operatorname{wr} D$ according to 22.11 and 22.12 maps $w(d_1, \dots, d_n)$ identically for each $w \in \mathfrak{w}$, and maps $v(d_1\psi_1, \dots, d_n\psi_n) = \Psi_v$ onto $\Psi_v\tau_2$, where

$$\Psi_v \tau_2(d_v) = g_v \gamma = t_v(c_1(v), \dots, c_N(v)) \neq 1.$$

Thus the product $\tau_1\tau_2$ of τ_1 as defined in (10) and τ_2 is a homomorphism of X_k into $C \operatorname{wr} D$ with the property $w\tau_1\tau_2 \neq 1$ in $C \operatorname{wr} D$ for all $w \in \mathfrak{w}_1$, as required. //

In applications we use mainly the following two specializations of Lemma 22.41:

By adding to the assumptions on $\mathfrak{C}$ we obtain

22.42 **Theorem** (BAUMSLAG [2]). *If the set $\mathfrak{C}$ discriminates $\mathfrak{U}$ and the set $\mathfrak{D}$ discriminates $\mathfrak{V}$, then the set $\mathfrak{C}\ \mathrm{wr}\ \mathfrak{D}=\{C\ \mathrm{wr}\ D \mid C\in\mathfrak{C}, D\in\mathfrak{D}\}$ discriminates $\mathfrak{U}\mathfrak{V}$ and therefore also generates $\mathfrak{U}\mathfrak{V}$.* //

By taking $\mathfrak{C}$ to consist of a single group we obtain:

22.43 **Theorem** ($B+3N$). *If the group A generates $\mathfrak{U}$ and the set $\mathfrak{D}$ discriminates $\mathfrak{V}$, then the set $A\ \mathrm{wr}\ \mathfrak{D}=\{A\ \mathrm{wr}\ D \mid D\in\mathfrak{D}\}$ discriminates $\mathfrak{U}\mathfrak{V}$, and therefore also generates $\mathfrak{U}\mathfrak{V}$.* //

22.44 **Corollary.** *If the group A generates $\mathfrak{U}$ and the group D discriminates $\mathfrak{V}$, then the group $A\ \mathrm{wr}\ D$ discriminates $\mathfrak{U}\mathfrak{V}$, and therefore also generates $\mathfrak{U}\mathfrak{V}$.* //

Theorem 22.43 leads to a simple proof of 21.26 (ii).

22.45 *If the set $\{\mathfrak{V}_\lambda\}$ of varieties is ordered by inclusion as given in 21.26, then*

$$\mathfrak{U}(\bigvee \mathfrak{V}_\lambda)=\bigvee(\mathfrak{U}\mathfrak{V}_\lambda).$$

Proof. The right-hand side is trivially contained in the left-hand side. To prove the reverse inclusion take $A=F_\infty(\mathfrak{U})$, $\mathfrak{D}=\{F_\infty(\mathfrak{V}_\lambda) \mid \lambda\in\Lambda\}$. The assumptions on the set $\mathfrak{V}_\lambda$ imply that $\mathfrak{D}$ discriminates $\bigvee\mathfrak{V}_\lambda$, therefore 22.43 shows that the set A wr $\mathfrak{D}$ discriminates $\mathfrak{U}(\bigvee\mathfrak{V}_\lambda)$ and therefore certainly generates it. But A wr $\mathfrak{D}$ is a subset of $\bigvee\mathfrak{U}\mathfrak{V}_\lambda$, and $\mathfrak{U}(\bigvee\mathfrak{V}_\lambda)\subseteq\bigvee(\mathfrak{U}\mathfrak{V}_\lambda)$ follows. //

Finally we look once more at the proof of 22.41 in the situation of this last corollary, taking moreover $H=F_\infty(\mathfrak{V})$ as the discriminating group D. This gives us the following additional information needed later:

22.46 **Theorem** ($B+3N$). *Let $\mathfrak{U}=\mathrm{var}\ A$, $H=F_\infty(\mathfrak{V})$ freely generated by the set $\mathfrak{h}$, $K=F_\infty(\mathfrak{U}\mathfrak{V})$ freely generated by $\mathfrak{k}$; to any given finite set $\mathfrak{s}$ of non-trivial elements of K there exists a homomorphism $\kappa\colon K\to A\ \mathrm{wr}\ H$ such that*

(i) *$s\kappa\neq 1$ for every $s\in\mathfrak{s}$,*

(ii) *if $k\in\mathfrak{k}$ then $k\kappa=h\varphi\in A\ \mathrm{wr}\ H$ where $h\in\mathfrak{h}$,*

(iii) *if $t\in K$ and $t\kappa\in A^{(H)}$, then $t\in V(K)$, that is, κ maps no more than the subgroup $V(K)$ of K into the base group $A^{(H)}$ of A wr H.*

Proof. Let $s=w_s(k)$, $k\in\mathfrak{k}^n$, be a representation of s as word in the free generators $\mathfrak{k}$ for each $s\in\mathfrak{s}$, and denote the set of words $w_s(s\in\mathfrak{s})$ by $\mathfrak{w}_1$; the w_s are clearly not laws in $\mathfrak{V}$. The group D to be chosen in 22.41 is now simply $H=F_\infty(\mathfrak{V})$ without choice. It is immediately clear that the elements d_i and d_v needed in the construction of the homomorphism τ_1 in the proof of 22.41 can be taken as some of the free generators of H so as to satisfy (7) and (8). Then (10) shows that the images $x\tau_1$ are of the form $x\tau_1=h\varphi$ with $h\in\mathfrak{h}$. Define images of the remaining free generators of the group X_∞ arbitrarily as elements of $\mathfrak{h}$, then one gets a homomorphism $\tau_1\colon X_\infty \to G \text{ wr } H$ such that $x\tau_1 = h\varphi$ with $h \in \mathfrak{h}$ for each $x \in \mathfrak{x}$ and of course $w_s\tau_1 \neq 1$ for all $s \in \mathfrak{s}$.

As $G \text{ wr } H \in \mathfrak{U}\mathfrak{V}$, the kernel of τ_1 contains the verbal subgroup $U(V)$ which defines K. Hence τ_1 can be factored through K, that is $\tau_1 = \rho_1\rho_2$ where ρ_1 is the natural mapping of X_∞ onto K defined by mapping $\mathfrak{x}$ onto $\mathfrak{k}$ in a $1-1$ manner; ρ_2 is then given by $k\rho_2 = (x\rho_1)\rho_2 = x\tau_1$, for $k \in \mathfrak{k}$. Now ρ_2 is a homomorphism of K into $G \text{ wr } H$ such that $s\rho_2 = w_s\tau_1 \neq 1$ for each $s \in \mathfrak{s}$. Moreover, as for each $k \in \mathfrak{k}$, $k\rho_2 = h\varphi$ with $h \in \mathfrak{h}$, an element $t \in K$, $t = w(k)$, is mapped onto $t\rho_2 = w(k\rho_2) = w(h)\,\varphi_t$, and so $t\rho_2 \in G^{(H)}$ if and only if $w(h) = 1$, that is $w \in V$, that is if and only if $w(k) = t \in V(K)$.

The epimorphism $\tau_2\colon G \text{ wr } H \twoheadrightarrow A \text{ wr } H$ used in the second step of the proof of 22.41 maps H identically and maps $G^{(H)}$ onto $A^{(H)}$; therefore the product $\rho_2\tau_2 = \kappa$, which maps K into $A \text{ wr } H$, has the required properties. //

The full force of these results will come into play only later.

Theorem 22.46 can be strengthened using only very minor modifications of these arguments. The details, and the substance – though not this formulation – of the following theorem can be found in BAUMSLAG [*2*].

22.47 **Theorem.** *Let F be an absolutely free group, R a normal subgroup, $H = F/R$ and $K = F/U(R)$. Let $\mathfrak{h}$ and $\mathfrak{k}$ be generating sets of H and K respectively obtained in the natural way from the same set $\mathfrak{f}$ of free generators of F. Then to every set $\mathfrak{s}$ of non-trivial elements of K there is a homomorphism $\kappa\colon K \to A \text{ wr } H$, where $\operatorname{var} A = \mathfrak{U}$, such that*

(i) *$s\kappa \neq 1$ for $s \in \mathfrak{s}$,*

(ii) *if $k \in \mathfrak{k}$ and $h \in \mathfrak{h}$ are corresponding generators, then $k\kappa = h\varphi$, $\varphi \in A^{(H)}$,*

(iii) *only elements of $R/U(R)$ are mapped into the base group $A^{(H)}$.*

We do not give the proof but point out that as a consequence the arguments in Section 6 of this chapter establish *residual properties of* $F/U(R)$ that are inherited from F/R and $R/U(R)$ in the same way in which certain residual properties of $F(\mathfrak{U}\mathfrak{V})$ will there be shown to be inherited from $F(\mathfrak{U})$ and $F(\mathfrak{V})$ (see also the footnote to 26.31, p. 15).

Finally, A. L. ŠMEL'KIN has modified 22.47 further, by using the *verbal wreath product* (whose base group is a verbal product rather than the direct product), to obtain an actual embedding of $F/U(R)$ in a verbal wreath product:

22.48 **Theorem** (ŠMEL'KIN [*3*]). *Let F be absolutely free, R normal in F, $H = F/R$, $K = F/U(R)$. Let $\mathfrak{h}$ and $\mathfrak{k}$ be generating sets of H and K respectively obtained in the natural way from the same set $\mathfrak{f}$ of free generators of F.*

Let $G=F(\mathfrak{U})$ be of the same rank as F, freely generated by $\mathfrak{g}$. Then there is an embedding $\kappa\colon K \rightarrowtail G \operatorname{wr}_{\mathfrak{U}} H$ such that for each generator $k \in \mathfrak{k}$ the embedding gives $k\kappa = h g_1$ where k and h are corresponding generators of K and H and the element g_1 is that element of the base group which corresponds to $g \in \mathfrak{g}$ in a fixed constituent $G_1 \cong G$.

3. The Uniqueness of Factorization

We now apply the earlier results to prove that the factorization of a variety into indecomposable varieties obtained in 21.72 is in fact unique.

23.11 **Lemma.** *Let A, B, C be non-trivial groups and $b \neq 1$ in B. Then the normal closure in $A \operatorname{Wr}(B \times C)$, or in $A \operatorname{wr}(B \times C)$, of $\operatorname{gp}(b, C)$ possesses a factor isomorphic to $A \operatorname{Wr} C$, or to $A \operatorname{wr} C$ respectively.*

Proof. The proof will be given for the unrestricted wreath product. To make it fit the restricted case, just replace every cartesian power of A that occurs by the direct power and add to the definition of every function that occurs that it be of finite support.

We write the elements of $B \times C$ as pairs (x, y), $x \in B$, $y \in C$. Consider the following subgroup of $A^{B \times C}$: $A^* = \operatorname{gp}(\varphi \mid \varphi(1, y) = \varphi^{-1}(b, y)$ for all $y \in C$ and $\varphi(x, y) = 1$ whenever $x \neq 1, b)$.

This subgroup A^* admits C, in fact even its generating set is transformed into itself by every element $(1, c)$ of $B \times C$: As $\varphi^{(1,c)}$ is given by $\varphi^{(1,c)}(x, y) = \varphi(x, yc^{-1})$ and the conditions defining the generators φ of A^* are conditions involving only the first component of the argument (x, y), the assertion is immediate. Thus $\operatorname{gp}(A^*, C) = CA^*$.

Further, A^* is contained in the normal closure of b in the whole wreath product. Again this is true provided it is true for the generators of A^*. To each function φ as defined above we take a function ψ given by $\psi(1, y) = \varphi(1, y)$ for all $y \in C$, $\psi(x, y) = 1$ whenever $x \neq 1$.

Then
$$(\psi^{-b}\psi)(x, y) = \psi^{-1}(x b^{-1}, y)\, \psi(x, y),$$
hence for all y:
$$(\psi^{-b}\psi)(1, y) = \psi(1, y) = \varphi(1, y)$$
$$(\psi^{-b}\psi)(b, y) = \psi^{-1}(1, y) = \varphi^{-1}(1, y) = \varphi(b, y),$$
and
$$(\psi^{-b}\psi)(x, y) = \psi^{-1}(x b^{-1}, y)\, \psi(x, y) = 1 \quad \text{for} \quad x \neq 1, b.$$

Thus $\varphi = \psi^{-b}\psi = b^{-1} b^{\psi}$ belongs to the normal closure of b, and so CA^* is a subgroup of the normal closure of $\operatorname{gp}(b, C)$.

Next we show that there is an epimorphism of CA^* onto A Wr C. Let

$$\vartheta\colon (1,c)\Phi \to c\Psi, \quad \Phi\in A^*\subseteq A^{B\times C}, \quad \Psi\in A^C \quad \text{where} \quad \Psi(y)=\Phi(1,y)$$
$$\text{for all } y\in C.$$

To check that ϑ is homomorphic, let

$$\vartheta\colon (1,c')\Phi' \to c'\Psi' \quad \text{with} \quad \Psi'(y)=\Phi'(1,y) \quad \text{for all } y.$$

Now $(1,c')\,\Phi'\cdot(1,c)\,\Phi=(1,c'c)\,\Phi'^{(1,c)}\cdot\Phi$ and its image under ϑ is $c'c\Psi^*$ where

$$\Psi^*(y)=(\Phi'^{(1,c)}\Phi)\,(1,y)$$
$$=\Phi'(1,yc^{-1})\,\Phi(1,y)=\Psi'(yc^{-1})\,\Psi(y).$$

But in A Wr C, $c'\Psi'c\Psi=c'c\Psi'^{c}\Psi$ where

$$(\Psi'^{c}\Psi)\,(y)=\Psi'(yc^{-1})\,\Psi(y),$$

hence

$$c'c\Psi^*=c'\Psi'c\Psi \quad \text{and} \quad \vartheta \text{ is homomorphic.}$$

It remains to show that ϑ is onto; let $c\Psi\in A$ Wr C be given; then this is the image under ϑ of $(1,c)\,\varphi$ where φ is that generator of A^* given by $\varphi(1,y)=\varphi^{-1}(b,y)=\Psi(y)$ for all y. //

23.12 **Lemma.** *If* $\mathfrak{U}=\operatorname{var} A$ *and* $\mathfrak{B}=\operatorname{var} B$, *then* $\mathfrak{U}\mathfrak{B}=\operatorname{var}(A \text{ wr } B^{(I)})$.

Proof. By 17.44 $B^{(I)}$ discriminates $\mathfrak{B}$; hence the lemma is immediate from 22.44. //

Of course A Wr $B^{(I)}$ then also generates $\mathfrak{U}\mathfrak{B}$. Combining this with 23.11 we obtain:

23.13 **Lemma.** *If* $\mathfrak{U}=\operatorname{var} A$, *and if for some set* $\mathfrak{w}$ *of words* $\mathfrak{w}(B)=C$ *is non-trivial, then the verbal subgroup* $\mathfrak{w}(A \text{ Wr } B^{(I)})$, *as also* $\mathfrak{w}(A \text{ wr } B^{(I)})$, *possesses a factor that generates* $\mathfrak{U}\mathfrak{W}$ *where* $\mathfrak{W}=\operatorname{var} C$.

Proof. Again the proof is given for the unrestricted case; as Lemmas 23.11 and 23.12 hold equally in both cases, the proof remains the same in the restricted case.

Clearly $\mathfrak{w}(A \text{ Wr } B^{(I)})\supseteq\mathfrak{w}(B^{(I)})=\mathfrak{w}(B)^{(I)}$, and as a verbal subgroup is normal, it contains the normal closure of $\mathfrak{w}(B)^{(I)}=C^{(I)}$. On the other hand by 22.13, A Wr $B^{(I)}\geqq A$ Wr $C^{(I)}$. Write the latter as A Wr $(C\times C^{(I')})$ where $I'=\{2,3,\ldots\}$. Then 23.11 shows that the normal closure of $\operatorname{gp}(c, C^{(I')})$ (where $c\neq 1$ is an element of the first factor C) even in this smaller wreath product possesses a factor isomorphic to A Wr $C^{(I')}$ which, by 23.12, generates $\mathfrak{U}\mathfrak{W}$. //

Now we can deduce:

23.21 **Lemma.** *If* $\mathfrak{U}_1, \mathfrak{U}_2, \mathfrak{V}_1, \mathfrak{V}_2$ *are all different from* $\mathfrak{O}$ *and if* $\mathfrak{U}_1\mathfrak{U}_2 \subseteq \mathfrak{V}_1\mathfrak{V}_2$, *then* $\mathfrak{U}_2 \nsubseteq \mathfrak{V}_2$ *implies that there exists a non-trivial variety* $\mathfrak{W}$ *such that* $\mathfrak{U}_1\mathfrak{W} \subseteq \mathfrak{V}_1$. *If* $\mathfrak{U}_1\mathfrak{U}_2 = \mathfrak{V}_1\mathfrak{V}_2$, *then* $\mathfrak{U}_1\mathfrak{W} = \mathfrak{V}_1$.

Proof. Let $\mathfrak{U}_1 = \operatorname{var} A_1$ and $\mathfrak{U}_2 = \operatorname{var} A_2$; then $P = A_1 \operatorname{Wr} A_2^{(I)}$ generates $\mathfrak{U}_1\mathfrak{U}_2$ by 23.12. As $\mathfrak{U}_2$ is not contained in $\mathfrak{V}_2$, we have $V_2(A_2) = C \neq \{1\}$. Hence 23.13 shows that $V_2(P)$ possesses a factor that generates $\mathfrak{U}_1\mathfrak{W}$ where $\mathfrak{W} = \operatorname{var} C$ is non-trivial. But $\mathfrak{U}_1\mathfrak{U}_2 \subseteq \mathfrak{V}_1\mathfrak{V}_2$, so that $P \in \mathfrak{V}_1\mathfrak{V}_2$. Therefore $V_2(P) \in \mathfrak{V}_1$, and so $\mathfrak{U}_1\mathfrak{W} \subseteq \mathfrak{V}_1$ as asserted.

Now assume $\mathfrak{U}_1\mathfrak{U}_2 = \mathfrak{V}_1\mathfrak{V}_2$. The inclusion $\mathfrak{U}_1\mathfrak{W} \subseteq \mathfrak{V}_1$ gives, by 21.21, $\mathfrak{U}_1\mathfrak{W}\mathfrak{V}_2 \subseteq \mathfrak{V}_1\mathfrak{V}_2$.

On the other hand A_2 is an extension of $V_2(A_2) = C \in \mathfrak{W}$ by a $\mathfrak{V}_2$-group; that is $A_2 \in \mathfrak{W}\mathfrak{V}_2$, and so $\operatorname{var} A_2 = \mathfrak{U}_2 \subseteq \mathfrak{W}\mathfrak{V}_2$. Hence $\mathfrak{U}_1\mathfrak{U}_2 = \mathfrak{V}_1\mathfrak{V}_2 \subseteq \mathfrak{U}_1\mathfrak{W}\mathfrak{V}_2$, and $\mathfrak{V}_1\mathfrak{V}_2 = \mathfrak{U}_1\mathfrak{W}\mathfrak{V}_2$ follows. But then 21.21 gives $\mathfrak{V}_1 = \mathfrak{U}_1\mathfrak{W}$. //

23.22 **Lemma.** *If* $\mathfrak{V} = \mathfrak{U}\mathfrak{W}$, *and* $\mathfrak{V} \neq \mathfrak{O}, \mathfrak{W} \neq \mathfrak{E}$, *then* $\mathfrak{U}$ *is properly contained in* $\mathfrak{V}$, $\mathfrak{U} \subset \mathfrak{V}$.

Proof. $\mathfrak{V} = \mathfrak{U} = \mathfrak{U}\mathfrak{W}$ implies $\mathfrak{U} = \mathfrak{U}\mathfrak{W}^n$ for all positive integers n. Hence $\mathfrak{W}^n \subseteq \mathfrak{U}$ for all n, and so by 21.71, $\mathfrak{O} \subseteq \mathfrak{U}$, that is $\mathfrak{O} = \mathfrak{U}$ contradicting $\mathfrak{U}\mathfrak{W} = \mathfrak{V} \neq \mathfrak{O}$. //

We now obtain the cancellation law for left-hand factors $\neq \mathfrak{O}$, both in inclusions and in equalities, that we had to postpone in Section 1:

23.23 **Theorem.** *If* $\mathfrak{U}\mathfrak{V}_1 \subseteq \mathfrak{U}\mathfrak{V}_2$ *and* $\mathfrak{U} \neq \mathfrak{O}$, *then* $\mathfrak{V}_1 \subseteq \mathfrak{V}_2$; *if* $\mathfrak{U}\mathfrak{V}_1 = \mathfrak{U}\mathfrak{V}_2$ *with* $\mathfrak{U} \neq \mathfrak{O}$, *then* $\mathfrak{V}_1 = \mathfrak{V}_2$.

Proof. Assume $\mathfrak{V}_1 \nsubseteq \mathfrak{V}_2$, then 23.21 gives $\mathfrak{U}\mathfrak{W} \subseteq \mathfrak{U}$ for some non-trivial $\mathfrak{W}$; but $\mathfrak{U} \subset \mathfrak{U}\mathfrak{W}$ by 23.22. If now $\mathfrak{U}\mathfrak{V}_1 = \mathfrak{U}\mathfrak{V}_2$ and $\mathfrak{V}_1 \subset \mathfrak{V}_2$, then $\mathfrak{V}_2 \nsubseteq \mathfrak{V}_1$ and again 23.21 gives $\mathfrak{U}\mathfrak{W} = \mathfrak{U}$ for some non-trivial $\mathfrak{W}$, again contradicting 23.22. //

The uniqueness of factorization is now an easy consequence of 23.21:

23.31 **Lemma.** *If* $\mathfrak{U}_1, \mathfrak{V}_1, \mathfrak{U}_2, \mathfrak{V}_2$ *are different from* $\mathfrak{O}$ *and* $\mathfrak{E}$, *and if* $\mathfrak{U}_1$ *and* $\mathfrak{V}_1$ *are indecomposable, then* $\mathfrak{U}_1\mathfrak{U}_2 = \mathfrak{V}_1\mathfrak{V}_2$ *implies* $\mathfrak{U}_1 = \mathfrak{V}_1$ *and* $\mathfrak{U}_2 = \mathfrak{V}_2$.

Proof. Assume $\mathfrak{U}_2 \neq \mathfrak{V}_2$, then either $\mathfrak{U}_2 \nsubseteq \mathfrak{V}_2$ or $\mathfrak{V}_2 \nsubseteq \mathfrak{U}_2$. We may assume the former; then 23.21 shows that $\mathfrak{U}_1\mathfrak{W} = \mathfrak{V}_1$ for some non-trivial $\mathfrak{W}$. As $\mathfrak{V}_1$ is indecomposable, $\mathfrak{U}_1 = \mathfrak{E}$ which contradicts the assumption. //

An obvious induction now gives

23.32 **Theorem** (B. H. NEUMANN, HANNA NEUMANN and PETER M. NEUMANN [*1*], ŠMEL'KIN [*1*]). *If* $\mathfrak{U}_1, \ldots, \mathfrak{U}_k$ *and* $\mathfrak{V}_1, \ldots, \mathfrak{V}_l$ *are indecom-*

posable and different from $\mathfrak{E}$ *and* $\mathfrak{O}$, *then* $\mathfrak{U}_1 \mathfrak{U}_2 \ldots \mathfrak{U}_k = \mathfrak{V}_1 \mathfrak{V}_2 \ldots \mathfrak{V}_l$ *implies* $k=l$ *and* $\mathfrak{U}_i = \mathfrak{V}_i$ *for* $i=1, \ldots, k$. //

Together with 21.72 this means

23.4 **Theorem.** *The semigroup of varieties other than* $\mathfrak{O}$ *is freely generated by the indecomposable varieties.* //

A proof of 23.32 operating directly with the verbal subgroups of F_∞ was recently found by M. J. DUNWOODY (unpublished). It relies on the following striking lemma: *If* R *and* S *are normal subgroups of* F_∞, *then* $U(R) \subseteq V(S)$ *implies that either* $U \subseteq V$ *or* $R \subseteq S$.

4. Some Classes of Indecomposable Varieties

We describe here a number of situations which make factorization of a variety impossible. The list is not likely to cover anything like all the possible reasons for indecomposability, but it shows even as it is that the number of indecomposable varieties is 'large'.

We start with a simple remark:

24.11 *If* var $B \subseteq$ var A *and* $\mathfrak{w}$ *is any set of words, then* var $\mathfrak{w}(B) \subseteq$ var $\mathfrak{w}(A)$.

Proof. Put $\mathfrak{U} =$ var $\mathfrak{w}(A)$, and let $\mathfrak{W}$ be the variety defined by $\mathfrak{w}$. Then $A \in \mathfrak{U}\mathfrak{W}$, hence $B \in \mathfrak{U}\mathfrak{W}$ and so $\mathfrak{w}(B) \in \mathfrak{U}$, that is var $\mathfrak{w}(B) \subseteq \mathfrak{U} =$ var $\mathfrak{w}(A)$. //

One deduces:

24.12 *If* var $A = \mathfrak{U}\mathfrak{V}$, *then* var $V(A) = \mathfrak{U}$. //

Hence, or directly:

24.13 **Theorem.** *The variety generated by a fully invariantly simple group is indecomposable.* //

The next class covers, roughly speaking, those varieties whose groups possess a non-trivial centre. First some auxiliary remarks:

24.21 *If* R *and* S *are normal subgroups of a free group* F *and* $[R, S] = R$, *then* $R = \{1\}$.

Proof. $[R, S] = R$ implies $[R, S, \ldots, S] = R$ for any number of repetitions of S. But with $n-1$ repetitions ($n \geqq 2$), the left hand side is contained in $F_{(n)}$, the n-th term of the lower central series of F.

Now $\bigcap_n F_{(n)} = \{1\}$ (cf. e.g. KUROSH, Vol. II, p. 38), hence $R = \{1\}$. //

24.22 (BAUMSLAG [*1*]) *If* C *is an infinite subset of the group* B, *then the centralizer of* C *in* Awr B *lies in* B.

Proof. Let $b\varphi$ belong to the centralizer of C; then for $c\in C$, $b^c\varphi^c=b\varphi$, that is $b^c=b$ and $\varphi^c=\varphi$. If φ is non-trivial, let $b'\in\sigma(\varphi)$ be an element of the support of φ. As $\varphi(b')=\varphi^c(b')=\varphi(b'c^{-1})$, $b'c^{-1}\in\sigma(\varphi)$ follows for every $c\in C$. But φ is of finite support, and C is infinite, hence $\sigma(\varphi)$ must be empty, and $b=b\varphi\in B$. //

Hence:

24.23 *If B is infinite, A wr B has trivial centre.* //

24.31 **Lemma** (Peter M. Neumann [*1*]). *Let $\mathfrak{U}$ and $\mathfrak{B}$ be arbitrary varieties other than $\mathfrak{O}$, and let the variety $\mathfrak{W}$ have the properties*

(i) $$\mathfrak{W}\nsubseteq\mathfrak{U},\quad \mathfrak{W}\nsubseteq\mathfrak{B},$$

(ii) $$\mathfrak{W}\subseteq[\mathfrak{U},\mathfrak{B}],$$

then $\mathfrak{W}=\mathfrak{X}\mathfrak{Y}$ implies $\mathfrak{Y}\subseteq\mathfrak{U}\wedge\mathfrak{B}$.

Proof. Put $A=F_\infty(\mathfrak{X})$, $B=F_\infty(\mathfrak{Y})$, then by 22.32 the restricted wreath product $P=A$ wr B generates $\mathfrak{W}=\mathfrak{X}\mathfrak{Y}$. Consider $U(B)$; if it is non-trivial, then it is infinite by 17.31 and 17.41. Also $U(B)\subseteq U(P)$, and (ii) shows that $U(P)$, and therefore $U(B)$, is centralized by $V(P)$. By 24.22, $V(P)\subseteq B$ follows, and so $V(P)\cap A^{(B)}=\{1\}$. But then these two normal subgroups of P centralize each other. On the other hand it follows straight from the definition of the wreath product that $A^{(B)}$ is not centralized by any non-trivial element outside $A^{(B)}$; thus $V(P)=\{1\}$, $P\in\mathfrak{B}$ and so $\mathfrak{W}=$ var $P\subseteq\mathfrak{B}$ contradicting (i). Thus $U(B)$ must be trivial, which means $B\in\mathfrak{U}$ and so $\mathfrak{Y}=$var $B\subseteq\mathfrak{U}$. By symmetry, $\mathfrak{Y}\subseteq\mathfrak{B}$, and so $\mathfrak{Y}\subseteq\mathfrak{U}\wedge\mathfrak{B}$. //

24.32 **Corollary.** *If under the same assumptions as before $\mathfrak{U}\wedge\mathfrak{B}=\mathfrak{E}$, then $\mathfrak{W}$ is indecomposable.* //

Hence:

24.33 **Theorem.** *If $\mathfrak{U}\wedge\mathfrak{B}=\mathfrak{E}$ and $\mathfrak{U}\neq\mathfrak{O}\neq\mathfrak{B}$, then every subvariety of $[\mathfrak{U},\mathfrak{B}]$ that is not contained in $\mathfrak{U}$ or $\mathfrak{B}$ is indecomposable. In particular $[\mathfrak{U},\mathfrak{B}]$ and $\mathfrak{U}\vee\mathfrak{B}$ are indecomposable under these assumptions.*

Proof. Only the last part remains to be confirmed. Clearly $\mathfrak{U}\vee\mathfrak{B}$ is not contained in $\mathfrak{U}$ or $\mathfrak{B}$; if $[\mathfrak{U},\mathfrak{B}]$ were a subvariety of $\mathfrak{U}$, say, then $[\mathfrak{U},\mathfrak{B}]=\mathfrak{U}$, hence 24.21 gives $U=\{1\}$ contradicting $\mathfrak{U}\neq\mathfrak{O}$. //

Hence

24.34 **Theorem.** *Every nilpotent variety is indecomposable.*

Proof. If $\mathfrak{U}$ is nilpotent, of class c exactly, then $\mathfrak{U}\nsubseteq\mathfrak{N}_{c-1}$, but $\mathfrak{U}\subseteq\mathfrak{N}_c=[\mathfrak{N}_{c-1},\mathfrak{E}]$. Hence 24.32 applies. //

Note that this follows also directly from 24.23: $F_\infty(\mathfrak{X})$ wr $F_\infty(\mathfrak{Y})$ belongs to $\mathfrak{X}\mathfrak{Y}$, but has trivial centre, hence cannot be nilpotent.

Problem 7. *Prove or disprove that if neither of* $\mathfrak{U}$ *and* $\mathfrak{B}$ *is contained in the other, then* $\mathfrak{U} \vee \mathfrak{B}$ *and* $[\mathfrak{U}, \mathfrak{B}]$ *are decomposable if and only if* $\mathfrak{U}$ *and* $\mathfrak{B}$ *have a common non-trivial right-hand factor.*

Before we go on to other classes we remark that the decomposability or otherwise of $\mathfrak{U} \wedge \mathfrak{B}$ is of little interest: the intersection $\mathfrak{U} \wedge \mathfrak{B}$ can easily be decomposable even if $\mathfrak{U}$ and $\mathfrak{B}$ are not. One need only take $\mathfrak{U} = \mathfrak{A}_2^2 \vee \mathfrak{A}_3$ and $\mathfrak{B} = \mathfrak{A}_2^2 \vee \mathfrak{A}_5$. These are indecomposable by 24.33, but $\mathfrak{U} \wedge \mathfrak{B} = \mathfrak{A}_2^2$.

We now turn to varieties of finite exponent. Clearly, if $\mathfrak{U}$ has exponent m and $\mathfrak{B}$ has exponent n, then $\mathfrak{U}\mathfrak{B}$ has exponent mn. Hence:

24.41 **Theorem.** *Every variety of prime exponent is indecomposable.* //

However we also have information on the case of composite exponents. We require the following lemma:

24.42 **Lemma** (GILBERT BAUMSLAG and PETER M. NEUMANN, unpublished). *Given a prime* p *and an integer* $n > 1$, *there exists a metabelian group of exponent* p^n *in which*

$$(x^{p^{n-1}} y^{p^{n-1}})^{p^{n-1}}$$

is not a law.

Proof. Let C_1 and C be cyclic groups of order p^n generated by c_1 and c respectively; then $P = C_1 \operatorname{wr} C$ is metabelian of exponent p^{2n}. Consider the subgroup N of P consisting of all functions ψ such that $[\psi, c^{p^{n-1}}] = 1$. Then N is normal in P, for it is trivially normal in C_1^C which is abelian, and moreover

$$[\psi^c, c^{p^{n-1}}] = [\psi, c^{p^{n-1}}]^c = 1,$$

so that $\psi^c \in N$. Put $A = P/N$, then A is the required group: it is clearly (at most) metabelian. To show that it is of exponent p^n we have to verify that the p^n-th power of an arbitrary element $c^k \varphi$ of P belongs to N. We may assume $k \geqq 0$, in fact $k > 0$, as C_1^C is of exponent p^n. But then $c^{p^{n-1}}$ is a power of c^k and so it suffices to prove that c^k centralizes $(c^k \varphi)^{p^n}$. Now

$$\begin{aligned}(c^k \varphi)^{p^n} &= \varphi^{c^{-k}} \varphi^{c^{-2k}} \ldots \varphi^{c^{-p^n k}} \\ &= \varphi^{c^{-k}} \varphi^{c^{-2k}} \ldots \varphi^{c^{-(p^n-1)k}} \varphi,\end{aligned}$$

and

$$(c^k \varphi)^{p^n c^k} = ((c^k \varphi)^{c^k})^{p^n} = (\varphi c^k)^{p^n} = \varphi \varphi^{c^{-k}} \varphi^{c^{-2k}} \ldots \varphi^{c^{-(p^n-1)k}};$$

as the base group is abelian, this shows

$$(c^k \varphi)^{p^n} = (c^k \varphi)^{p^n c^k}$$

as required.

Finally, we take $x=c^{-1}$, $y=c\varphi_1$, where φ_1 is the particular function given by $\varphi_1(1)=c_1$, $\varphi_1(c^\alpha)=1$ for $o<\alpha<p^n$. Then

$$x^{p^{n-1}}=c^{-p^{n-1}}$$

and

$$y^{p^{n-1}}=c^{p^{n-1}}\varphi_1^{c^{p^{n-1}-1}}\varphi_1^{c^{p^{n-1}-2}}\cdots\varphi_1^c\varphi_1$$

$$=c^{p^{n-1}}\Phi_1$$

where

$$\Phi_1(c^\beta)=c_1 \quad \text{for} \quad \beta=0,1,\dots,p^{n-1}-1$$

and

$$\Phi_1(c^\beta)=1 \quad \text{for} \quad \beta\geqq p^{n-1};$$

in particular, Φ_1 has order exactly p^n, also modulo N. But $x^{p^{n-1}}y^{p^{n-1}}=\Phi_1$ hence

$$(x^{p^{n-1}}y^{p^{n-1}})^{p^{n-1}}\neq 1. \quad //$$

We use this to prove

24.43 **Theorem** (GILBERT BAUMSLAG, unpublished). *Let $\mathfrak{B}$ be any variety of exponent n that contains all metabelian groups of exponent n, that is $\mathfrak{B}_n\wedge\mathfrak{S}_2\subseteq\mathfrak{B}\subseteq\mathfrak{B}_n$, then $\mathfrak{B}$ is indecomposable.*

Proof. By 24.41 we may assume that n is composite. Assume then a non-trivial factorization $\mathfrak{B}=\mathfrak{B}_1\mathfrak{B}_2$, where $\mathfrak{B}_1$ and $\mathfrak{B}_2$ are of exponent r and s respectively, with $rs=n$. First let r and s be relatively prime. As $\mathfrak{B}$ contains all metabelian groups of exponent n, it contains in particular the wreath product of a cycle C_s of order s by a cycle C_r of order r. But C_s wr C_r is certainly not an extension of a group of exponent r by one of exponent s, because the normal closure in C_s wr C_r of any element of order dividing r and hence prime to s contains elements of order dividing s. Thus this case is impossible.

Now assume that the greatest common factor of r and s is $d>1$; then there exists a prime p and integers α, $\beta>0$ such that p^α is the highest power of p in s, and $p^{\alpha+\beta}=p^\gamma$ is the highest power of p dividing n. Then the p-groups in $\mathfrak{B}$ are of exponent p^γ and are extensions of groups of exponent dividing p^α by groups of exponent dividing p^β, that is they all satisfy the law $(x^{p^\beta}y^{p^\beta})^{p^\alpha}$.

But by assumption, $\mathfrak{B}$ contains all metabelian groups of exponent n, hence it contains also all those of exponent p^γ, and in particular by Lemma 24.42 one not satisfying the law $(x^{p^{\gamma-1}}y^{p^{\gamma-1}})^{p^{\gamma-1}}$. This is again a contradiction as $\beta\leqq\gamma-1$, $\alpha\leqq\gamma-1$. Thus $\mathfrak{B}$ is not factorizable. //

Finally we show that it is exceptional for a product variety to be generated by a single finite group. This then means that 'usually' a finite group generates an indecomposable variety. The argument we give here *

* Due to PETER M. NEUMANN (unpublished). For special cases of the conclusion 24.61 see also HIGMAN [*2*] and PETER M. NEUMANN [*1*].

only tells part of the story; we present it because it is based on an elementary computation of a lower bound for the order of a finite relatively free group in terms of its rank. We add a summary of further information at the end of the paragraph.

24.51 **Lemma.** *If G_n is a finite relatively free group of rank n, and if G_n is not nilpotent of class $c-1$, then $|G_n|\geqq 2^N$ where $N=\sum_{r=1}^{m}\binom{n}{r}$ and $m=\min(c, n)$.*

Proof. Let $g_1, \ldots, g_n$ be a set of free generators. To every sequence j_r of integers, $j_r=(i(1), i(2), \ldots, i(r))$ where $1\leqq r\leqq m$ and $1\leqq i(1)<i(2)<\cdots<i(r)\leqq n$, put $c(j_1)=g_{i(1)}$ and $c(j_r)=[g_{i(1)}, \ldots, g_{i(r)}]$ for $r>1$.

This sees to it that each commutator $c(j_r)$, $r\geqq 1$, is completely determined by the set of free generators occurring in it. We order these commutators by fixing an arbitrary order between those of equal weight, and putting $c(j_r)<c(j_s)$ if $r<s$. Then we show: $c(j_r)\notin \mathrm{gp}(c(j_s)\,|\,c(j_s)>c(j_r))$. Assume this is false; then

$$c(j_r)=\prod_\sigma c(j_\sigma) \quad \text{where} \quad c(j_\sigma)>c(j_r) \quad \text{for all } \sigma.$$

As relation between the generators of the free group G_n this is a law in G_n. It gives a valid relation therefore if we substitute 1 for all those generators that do not occur in $c(j_r)$. But then every term $c(j_\sigma)$ on the right hand side will become trivial, because each one contains at least one free generator not occurring in $c(j_r)$. Thus $c(j_r)=1$ also is a law in G_n, but $r\leqq m\leqq c$, and G_n was assumed not to be nilpotent of class $c-1$. Thus our assumption was false.

But then the index of $\mathrm{gp}(c(j_s)\,|\,c(j_s)>c(j_r))$ in $\mathrm{gp}(c(j_s)\,|\,c(j_s)\geqq c(j_r))$ is at least 2; therefore taking these commutators one by one shows that they generate a subgroup of order at least 2^N in G_n where N is the number of these commutators. Clearly $N=\sum_{1}^{m}\binom{n}{r}$ as there are $\binom{n}{r}$ commutators $c(j_r)$ for each fixed r. //

24.52 **Corollary** (PETER M. NEUMANN). *If $\mathfrak{V}$ is not abelian, then*

$$|F_n(\mathfrak{V})|\geqq 2^{\frac{1}{2}n(n-1)};$$

if $\mathfrak{V}$ is not nilpotent of class $c-1$ then

$$|F_n(\mathfrak{V})|\geqq 2^{\binom{n}{c}} \quad \textit{for} \quad n\geqq c\geqq 2;$$

if $\mathfrak{V}$ is not nilpotent, then $|F_n(\mathfrak{V})|\geqq 2^{2^n}$.

This is immediate from 24.51. //

Now we can prove:

24.53 **Theorem.** *If $\mathfrak{U}$ and $\mathfrak{V}$ are non-trivial locally finite varieties and if either $\mathfrak{U}$ is not nilpotent or $\mathfrak{V}$ is not abelian, then for an arbitrary finite* *group A*:

$$|F_n(\mathfrak{U}\mathfrak{V})| > |F_n(\operatorname{var} A)|$$

for sufficiently large n.

Proof. We know from 15.71 that when $A \neq \{1\}$:

$$|F_n(\operatorname{var} A)| \leqq |A|^{|A|^n} \quad \text{for} \quad n > 1.$$

On the other hand, from 21.13 we have $|F_n(\mathfrak{U}\mathfrak{V})| = |F_m(\mathfrak{U})|\,|F_n(\mathfrak{V})|$ where $m = (n-1)\,|F_n(\mathfrak{V})| + 1$ and $n > 1$. Hence if $\mathfrak{U}$ is not nilpotent, 24.52 gives

$$|F_n(\mathfrak{U}\mathfrak{V})| \geqq 2^{2^m}\,|F_n(\mathfrak{V})|;$$

but obviously $|F_n(\mathfrak{V})| \geqq 2^n$, so that $m > 2^n$, and in this case certainly

$$|F_n(\mathfrak{U}\mathfrak{V})| > 2^{2^{2^n}}.$$

If alternatively, $\mathfrak{V}$ is not abelian, then 24.52 gives $|F_n(\mathfrak{V})| \geqq 2^{\frac{1}{2}n(n-1)}$, and this time we use that $|F_m(\mathfrak{U})| \geqq 2^m$ and obtain

$$|F_n(\mathfrak{U}\mathfrak{V})| > 2^{2^{\frac{1}{2}n(n-1)}}.$$

In either case the order of this free group is $> 2^{2^f}$ where $n^2 = O(f)$, which proves the theorem. //

We formulate the corollary with an eye on the main theme of the next paragraph:

24.61 **Corollary.** *If the finitely generated free groups of both* $\mathfrak{U}$ *and* $\mathfrak{V}$ *are finite and either* $\mathfrak{U}$ *is not nilpotent or* $\mathfrak{V}$ *is not abelian, then* $\mathfrak{U}\mathfrak{V}$ *can not be generated by* $F_k(\mathfrak{U}\mathfrak{V})$ *for any finite k.* //

Using 24.34 this shows incidentally:

24.62 **Corollary** (Šmel'kin [*3*]). *A product of at least three non-trivial factors cannot be generated by a finite group.* //

There is a further obviously necessary condition for $\mathfrak{U}\mathfrak{V}$ to be generated by a finite group:

24.63 *If* $\mathfrak{U}\mathfrak{V} = \operatorname{var} A$ *where A is finite, then the exponents of* $\mathfrak{U}$ *and* $\mathfrak{V}$ *are relatively prime.*

Proof. As a finite group of var *A* is a factor of a finite direct power of *A* by 15.73, the finite nilpotent groups of var *A* have class at most equal to the maximum of the classes of subgroups of *A*. But if the exponents of $\mathfrak{U}$ and $\mathfrak{V}$ have a common prime factor *p*, then $\mathfrak{A}_p \subseteq \mathfrak{U}$, $\mathfrak{A}_p \subseteq \mathfrak{V}$ and so $\mathfrak{A}_p^2 \subseteq \mathfrak{U}\mathfrak{V}$. But $\mathfrak{A}_p^2$ contains wreath products of arbitrarily high nilpotency class (compare Example 16.36 where the special case $p = 2$ was considered) which is a contradiction. //

In fact Šmel'kin shows that the conditions given in 24.61 and 24.63 are necessary and sufficient:

24.64 **Theorem** (Šmel'kin [*3*]). *A product variety* $\mathfrak{U}\mathfrak{V}$ *is generated by a finite group if and only if the exponents of* $\mathfrak{U}$ *and* $\mathfrak{V}$ *are relatively prime,* $\mathfrak{U}$ *is nilpotent and* $\mathfrak{V}$ *is abelian.*

Šmel'kin proves 24.61 using a *verbal wreath product* – that is a wreath product using the $\mathfrak{U}$-product in place of the direct product as base group – to generate the product variety $\mathfrak{U}\mathfrak{V}$. He proves the converse by showing that under the given conditions $\mathfrak{U}\mathfrak{V}$ is a Cross variety. We refer to Chapter 5 for the concepts and methods leading to a proof which is outlined in Section 3 of that chapter.

The following details complete the picture:

24.65 *The product* $\mathfrak{A}_m\mathfrak{A}_n$ *where m and n are relatively prime is generated by its free group of rank two.*

This was shown by Graham Higman [*2*] in the case when *m* is prime and extended by C. H. Houghton to the general case (unpublished).

Using verbal wreath products as well as properties of critical groups (cf. Chapter 5), R. G. Burns [*1*] shows:

24.66 *If* $\mathfrak{N}$ *is the variety of all groups of exponent m and nilpotent of class c* ($c>1$), *and if n is relatively prime to m, then* $\mathfrak{N}\mathfrak{A}_n$ *is generated by its c-generator groups but not by its* ($c-1$)*-generator groups.*

Compare also 53.63 and the remarks leading up to it.

5. Product Varieties Generated by a Finitely Generated Group

The question when a product variety may be generated by a finitely generated group arose naturally, in the case of locally finite varieties, out of the context of the preceding section; as reported there, the complete answer is known when both factors are locally finite. We turn to the general problem.

Two easy remarks outline the situation.

25.11 *If* $\mathfrak{U}$ *is generated by its m-generator groups, and* $\mathfrak{V}$ *is discriminated by an n-generator group, then* $\mathfrak{U}\mathfrak{V}$ *is generated – even discriminated – by an* ($m+n$)*-generator group.*

This is an immediate consequence of 22.44 and the observation that *A* wr *B* is generated by subgroups isomorphic to *A* and *B*. //

25.12 *If* $\mathfrak{U}\neq\mathfrak{O}$ *and* $\mathfrak{U}\mathfrak{V}$ *is generated by its n-generator groups, then so is* $\mathfrak{V}$.

Proof. The group $F_n(\mathfrak{U}\mathfrak{B})$ is an extension of some free group $F(\mathfrak{U})$ by $F_n(\mathfrak{B})$; hence

$$\mathfrak{U}\mathfrak{B} = \operatorname{var} F_n(\mathfrak{U}\mathfrak{B}) \subseteq \operatorname{var} F(\mathfrak{U}) \operatorname{var} F_n(\mathfrak{B}) \subseteq \mathfrak{U}\mathfrak{B}.$$

If $\operatorname{var} F_n(\mathfrak{B}) \subset \mathfrak{B}$, then 21.21 shows the last inclusion to be proper. But this is impossible. Hence

$$\operatorname{var} F_n(\mathfrak{B}) = \mathfrak{B}. \quad //$$

The main aim of this paragraph is to show that the assumption on $\mathfrak{U}$ in 25.11 is in fact superfluous whenever $\mathfrak{B}$ is non-trivial. Moreover we shall find that the least value for the rank of a free group generating $\mathfrak{U}\mathfrak{B}$ that is compatible with 25.12 does in fact occur in a large number of cases (cf. 25.31).

25.21 **Theorem** ($B+3N$). *If* $\mathfrak{B} \neq \mathfrak{E}$ *is discriminated by a finitely generated group, then so is* $\mathfrak{U}\mathfrak{B}$ *for arbitrary* $\mathfrak{U}$.

Proof. Let D be an n-generator group discriminating $\mathfrak{B}$; D is infinite by 17.32.

Also, 22.43 shows that $F_\infty(\mathfrak{U})$ wr D discriminates $\mathfrak{U}\mathfrak{B}$. Hence if we embed this group in a finitely generated group that still belongs to $\mathfrak{U}\mathfrak{B}$, then the latter will also discriminate the variety.

The construction which achieves this is in fact that of a 'twisted wreath product' (cf. B. H. Neumann [7]) of $F_\infty(\mathfrak{U})$ and the direct square $D \times D$. However, we construct the group here explicitly as the split extension of $P = F_\infty(\mathfrak{U})$ wr D by an automorphism group isomorphic to D. To this end we denote an isomorphic copy of D by C. As C is infinite, but countable, we can use its elements to index a set of free generators of $G = F_\infty(\mathfrak{U})$: $G = \operatorname{gp}(g_c \mid c \in C)$. Then, for each $c_0 \in C$, the permutation $g_c \to g_{c c_0}$ determines an automorphism γ_0 of G. These automorphisms clearly form a group isomorphic to C. By the property 22.11 of wreath products each such automorphism γ of G can be extended in the natural way to an automorphism of $P = G$ wr D whose restriction to D is the identity on D. Thus we obtain a group of automorphisms of P isomorphic to C. We denote by Q the split extension of P by the group C so that C acts on P according to this automorphism group just described. Then, in particular, C acts on $D \subseteq P$ trivially so that C and the subgroup D of P generate their direct product in Q. Therefore Q can also be looked upon as an extension of the base group $G^{(D)}$ of P by the direct product $C \times D$ in which C acts on $G^{(D)}$ by permuting the free generators of the constituents, and D acts on $G^{(D)}$ by 'wreathing' the constituents. As $C \cong D$, $C \times D \in \mathfrak{B}$, and so $Q \in \mathfrak{U}\mathfrak{B}$.

It remains to show that Q is finitely generated. The wreath product P, being a restricted wreath product, is generated by a coordinate subgroup,

G_1 say, and D; hence Q is generated by G_1, C and D. Now $G_1 \cong G$ and $G = \mathrm{gp}(g_c \mid c \in C)$ with $(g_1)^c = g_{1c} = g_c$ by definition of the action of C on $\mathfrak{g}$. As C acts correspondingly on each constituent of $G^{(D)}$, it produces in particular all generators of G_1 from the single generator of G_1 whose subscript is the unit element of C. As C itself has n generators, $\mathrm{gp}(G_1, C)$ has $n+1$ generators, and so $Q = \mathrm{gp}(G_1, C, D)$ has $2n+1$ generators. //

Note that the proof shows that any infinite finitely generated group of $\mathfrak{B}$ could have been used in place of C; in particular, if $\mathfrak{B}$ has exponent zero, an infinite cycle can be used. Hence we obtain

25.22 **Corollary** of the proof. *If $\mathfrak{B} \neq \mathfrak{E}$ is discriminated by an n-generator group, then $\mathfrak{U}\mathfrak{B}$, for arbitrary $\mathfrak{U}$, is discriminated by a $(2n+1)$-generator group. If the variety $\mathfrak{B}$ is of exponent zero then $\mathfrak{U}\mathfrak{B}$ is discriminated by an $(n+2)$-generator group.* //

The fact that this can, with a special effort, be reduced to $n+1$ (the proof is given in Hanna Neumann [*4*]) is not worth reporting in detail. Instead we prove:

25.31 **Theorem** $(B+3N)$. *If $\mathfrak{B} \neq \mathfrak{E}$ is of exponent zero and if it can be discriminated by an n-generator group that is residually periodic, then if $n \geqq 2$ the variety $\mathfrak{U}\mathfrak{B}$ is discriminated by an n-generator group for arbitrary $\mathfrak{U}$.*

We need the following lemma:

25.32 **Lemma.** *If $\mathfrak{B}$ has exponent zero and $D \in \mathfrak{B}$ is generated by n elements and periodic, then $F_m(\mathfrak{U})$ wr D is a factor of $F_n(\mathfrak{U}\mathfrak{B})$ for every m.*

Proof. Let $D = \mathrm{gp}(d_1, \ldots, d_n)$: we choose a prime $p > m$ which does not divide the order of d_1. Then it is sufficient (by 22.12) to prove that $F_p(\mathfrak{U})$ wr D is a factor of $F_n(\mathfrak{U}\mathfrak{B})$, or again, that it is a factor of some n-generator group in $\mathfrak{U}\mathfrak{B}$.

We put $F_p(\mathfrak{U}) = G$ and form a wreath product $P = G^p$ wr D. To describe a particular automorphism of G^p – hence of P, by 22.11 – we denote a set of free generators of G by $g_1, \ldots, g_p$ and distinguish between the generators of the p copies of G in $G^p = G(1) \times \cdots \times G(p)$ by writing $G(j) = \mathrm{gp}(g_{1,j}, \ldots, g_{p,j})$. Then the automorphism γ of G^p is given by:

$$g_{i,j}\gamma = g_{i,j+1} \qquad \text{for all } i \text{ and } 1 \leqq j \leqq p-1,$$

$$g_{i,p}\gamma = g_{i+1,1} \qquad \text{for } 1 \leqq i \leqq p-1,$$

$$g_{p,p}\gamma = g_{1,1}.$$

One checks that γ is of order p^2. Its extension to $P = G^p$ wr D is the identity on D. Hence, if Q is the split extension of P by this automorphism, then, as before, Q may also be considered as an extension of $(G^p)^{(D)}$ by a direct product $C \times D$ where $C = \mathrm{gp}(c)$ is a cycle of order p^2 that acts on each constituent G^p of the base group $(G^p)^{(D)}$ of P according to γ, and D does the wreathing. As $\mathfrak{V}$ is assumed of exponent zero, every cyclic group is in $\mathfrak{V}$, hence $C \times D \in \mathfrak{V}$ and so $Q \in \mathfrak{U}\mathfrak{V}$.

Now let $\varphi \in (G^p)^{(D)}$ be the function $\varphi(1) = g_{1,1}$, $\varphi(d) = 1$ for all $d \neq 1, \in D$. We consider the following n-generator subgroup of Q: $S = \mathrm{gp}(d_1 c, d_2 \varphi, d_3, \dots, d_n)$.

Note that we use here that $n \geqq 2$. Also, as the order p^2 of c is prime to the order of d_1 by the choice of p, S contains both d_1 and c; it therefore contains also $(d_2 \varphi)^c = d_2 \psi$ where

$$\psi(1) = g_{1,2}, \quad \psi(d) = 1 \quad \text{when} \quad d \neq 1, \in D.$$

Thus finally it contains the $p-1$ commutators

$$\psi_i = [c^{ip}, d_2 \psi] = [c^{ip}, \psi], \qquad i = 1, \dots, p-1.$$

As conjugation by c induces γ on the values of ψ, an easy calculation shows:

$$\psi_i(1) = g_{i+1,2}^{-1} g_{1,2}, \quad \psi_i(d) = 1 \quad \text{when} \quad d \neq 1, \in D.$$

Now the $g_{i,2}$ are free generators of the constituent $G(2)$ of G^p; hence also the elements $g_{1,2}, g_{2,2}^{-1} g_{1,2}, \dots, g_{p,2}^{-1} g_{1,2}$ are free generators, and so the functions $\psi, \psi_1, \dots, \psi_{p-1}$ are free generators of the constituent $G(2)$ of the coordinate subgroup corresponding to $1 \in D$. Now consider the subgroup $R \subseteq S$:

$$R = \mathrm{gp}(d_1, d_2 \varphi, d_3, \dots, d_n, \psi, \psi_1, \dots, \psi_{p-1}) \subseteq S \subseteq Q.$$

It is contained in $(G(1) \times G(2))$ wr D, and the epimorphism of Q induced by the epimorphism $G^p \twoheadrightarrow G(2)$ maps it onto a group isomorphic to G wr D. Thus G wr D is a factor group of a subgroup of the n-generator group S in $\mathfrak{U}\mathfrak{V}$. //

Proof of Theorem 25.31. Let D be the given residually periodic n-generator group that discriminates $\mathfrak{V}$, $\mathfrak{D}$ the set of all its periodic factor groups. By 17.83, $\mathfrak{D}$ discriminates $\mathfrak{V}$, and it consists of n-generator groups. Also the set of free groups $F_m(\mathfrak{U})$ ($m = 1, 2, \dots$) discriminates $\mathfrak{U}$, therefore by 22.42 the set $\{F_m(\mathfrak{U}) \text{ wr } \mathfrak{D}\}$ discriminates $\mathfrak{U}\mathfrak{V}$. But as every one of these groups is a factor of $F_n(\mathfrak{U}\mathfrak{V})$, it follows from 17.5 that $F_n(\mathfrak{U}\mathfrak{V})$ also discriminates $\mathfrak{U}\mathfrak{V}$. //

25.33 **Corollary.** *If $\mathfrak{U} \neq \mathfrak{O}$, then $\mathfrak{U}\mathfrak{A}$ is discriminated, hence generated, by its two-generator groups.*

This is immediate as $\mathfrak{A}$ is, by 17.6, discriminated even by its one-generator free group, hence certainly by its free group of rank two. //

We note particularly the special case:

25.34 **Corollary.** *The variety* $\mathfrak{A}^l = \mathfrak{S}_l$ *of all soluble groups of length* l *is discriminated, hence generated, by its free group of rank two.* //

See also 35.13 and 35.14 for further significant corollaries of Theorem 25.31.

Throughout this paragraph we had to make some assumption on $\mathfrak{B}$, requiring it to be of exponent zero, or at least to be discriminated by a single finitely generated group which must then be infinite. We add one result of a different nature:

25.41 *The variety* $\mathfrak{A}\mathfrak{A}_m$ *is generated by its two-generator groups.*

Proof. Clearly $\mathfrak{A} = \bigvee \mathfrak{A}_p$ where p runs through any infinite set of primes. By 21.23, $\mathfrak{A}\mathfrak{A}_m = (\bigvee_p \mathfrak{A}_p)\, \mathfrak{A}_m = \bigvee_p (\mathfrak{A}_p \mathfrak{A}_m)$, and by 24.65 (needed only in the special case where the exponent of the first factor is a prime; this is proved in GRAHAM HIGMAN'S paper [2]) every variety $\mathfrak{A}_p \mathfrak{A}_m$ is generated by its two-generator groups; so therefore is the variety they generate. //

Note that by contrast with the other results of this paragraph, $\mathfrak{A}\mathfrak{A}_m$ cannot be discriminated by a finitely generated group. In fact we have:

25.42 $(B+3N)$. *If* $\mathfrak{B}$ *is locally finite, then* $\mathfrak{A}\mathfrak{B}$ *cannot be discriminated by a finitely generated group.*

Proof. Let B be a finitely generated group of the variety $\mathfrak{A}\mathfrak{B}$: then $B/V(B)$ is finite, of order k, say. In particular $b^k \in V(B)$ for every $b \in B$. Now $[x^k, y]$ is not a law in $\mathfrak{A}\mathfrak{B}$, because the wreath product $C \operatorname{wr} F_\infty(\mathfrak{B})$ (C an infinite cycle) which generates $\mathfrak{A}\mathfrak{B}$ has trivial centre. Hence all the words

$$[x^k, x_1 x_2^{-1}],\ [x^k, x_1 x_3^{-1}],\ \ldots,\ [x^k, x_1 x_{k+1}^{-1}],\ \ldots,\ [x^k, x_k x_{k+1}^{-1}]$$

are distinct non-laws in $\mathfrak{A}\mathfrak{B}$. As $B/V(B)$ has only k distinct elements, any substitution of elements of B for the variables must result in at least one product $x_i x_j^{-1}$ taking a value in $V(B)$. As x^k has its values in $V(B)$, and $V(B)$ is abelian, the corresponding commutator takes value 1; therefore this finite set of non-laws cannot be simultaneously falsified in B and therefore B is not discriminating. //

Some further questions arise out of the results of this section. If a variety $\mathfrak{B}$ is generated by a free group $F_k(\mathfrak{B})$ of finite rank then, by Theorem 15.4, $F_n(\mathfrak{B})$ is a subgroup of a cartesian power of $F_k(\mathfrak{B})$; or, put differently, $F_n(\mathfrak{V})$ is residually a subgroup of a k-generator group for every $n \in I$. Two questions arise: is $F_n(\mathfrak{V})$ residually a k-generator group? It will follow from results on nilpotent varieties (cf. 36.35) that the answer is positive in the metabelian case $\mathfrak{A}^2$: the free metabelian groups are subcartesian powers of the two-generator group $F_2(\mathfrak{A}^2)$, that is they are residually two-generator metabelian groups. No more seems to be known:

Problem 8.* *Assuming $\mathfrak{U}\mathfrak{V}$ is generated by $F_k(\mathfrak{U}\mathfrak{V})$, give conditions for $F_n(\mathfrak{U}\mathfrak{V})$ to be residually a k-generator group.*

In particular

Problem 9.* *Prove that $F_n(\mathfrak{S}_l)$ for $n \geqq 2$ is residually a two-generator group for every $l \geqq 2$.*

The other, more significant, question is whether a cartesian power of $F_k(\mathfrak{V})$ is really needed to embed $F_n(\mathfrak{V})$ or whether a direct power is perhaps sufficient. It is a distinctive feature of many product varieties of exponent zero that a direct product is certainly not sufficient. This is, as we shall see, in marked contrast to the behaviour of free nilpotent groups and some other similar types. Of course:

25.5 *If a finitely generated group is embeddable in a direct product then it is embeddable in a finite direct product.*

Proof. The union of the supports of the generators of the given group is finite and only the factors of the direct product that contribute to the support of the generators are relevant. //

Hence the distinction is between $F_n(\mathfrak{V})$ being a subgroup of no less than an infinite cartesian power of $F_k(\mathfrak{V})$ or of a finite direct power of $F_k(\mathfrak{V})$.

We need some preparatory results.

25.61 (Peter M. Neumann [2].) *An element of the wreath product A wr B that has infinite order modulo the base group $A^{(B)}$ is conjugate in A Wr B to an element of B.*

Proof. An element of infinite order modulo $A^{(B)}$ has the form $b\varphi$, $b \in B$, $\varphi \in A^{(B)}$, where b is an element of infinite order of B. We determine a function $\psi \in A^B$ such that $\psi^{-1} b\varphi\psi = b$, that is $b\psi^{-b}\varphi\psi = b$, or $\varphi\psi = \psi^b$. We want therefore a function ψ that satisfies the equations $\varphi(y)\psi(y) = \psi(yb^{-1})$ for all $y \in B$. These equations connect only values of ψ at arguments belonging to one and the same coset of B modulo the cyclic group generated by b. Hence we may define ψ on each of these cosets independently of its values on the other cosets.

---

* Gilbert Baumslag writes that a sufficient condition for Problem 8 is that $\mathfrak{V} = \mathfrak{A}$. This disposes of Problem 9.

We start by giving ψ the value 1 on the elements of every coset that intersects the support $\sigma(\varphi)$ trivially. Next consider a coset that contains elements of $\sigma(\varphi)$. Choose a fixed coset representative t and let μ and ν be respectively the least and the greatest integer such that tb^μ and tb^ν belong to $\sigma(\varphi)$ (which is finite). As the conditions to be satisfied by ψ on the coset $\{tb^n\}$ are $\varphi(tb^n)\psi(tb^n)=\psi(tb^{n-1})$ for all integers n and as $\varphi(tb^n)=1$ for $n\leqq\mu-1$, we may put $\psi(tb^n)=1$ for $n\leqq\mu-1$. Then the equations are satisfied for these values of n, and the remaining equations determine the values of ψ at tb^n for $n\geqq\mu$ inductively. //

Note that, as $\varphi(tb^n)=1$ for $n>\nu$, ψ will be constant for $n\geqq\nu$. But this constant will normally be non-trivial so that ψ may in fact have to be taken in the unrestricted wreath product. Application of 24.22 gives:

25.62 *The centralizer of an element that has infinite order modulo the base group $A^{(B)}$ of A* wr *B has trivial intersection with the base group.* //

Now we apply Theorem 22.46 to obtain:

25.63 **Theorem** ($B+3N$; see also ŠMEL'KIN [3]). *The centralizer of an element of $K=F(\mathfrak{U}\mathfrak{V})$ that has infinite order modulo $V(K)$ intersects $V(K)$ trivially.*

Proof. We may assume $F(\mathfrak{U}\mathfrak{V})$ to be of countably infinite rank: the reduction of the case of uncountable rank to that of countable rank is trivial, and in the case of finite rank n consider $K_n=F_n(\mathfrak{U}\mathfrak{V})$ embedded in the natural way in $K_\infty=F_\infty(\mathfrak{U}\mathfrak{V})$ and use that $V(K_n)=V(K_\infty)\cap K_n$ by 13.42.

Now let $k\in K_\infty$ have infinite order modulo $V(K_\infty)$ and take $k'\neq 1$ in $V(K_\infty)$. Consider A wr H where A generates $\mathfrak{U}$ and $H=F_\infty(\mathfrak{V})$. Take a homomorphism κ: $K_\infty\to A$ wr H according to 22.46 such that $k'\kappa\neq 1$. As κ maps precisely $V(K_\infty)$ into $A^{(H)}$, $k\kappa$ has infinite order modulo $A^{(H)}$, while $k'\kappa\in A^{(H)}$. By 25.62 $[k\kappa, k'\kappa]\neq 1$, that is $[k, k']\kappa\neq 1$ and so certainly $[k, k']\neq 1$ in K_∞. //

We can now prove:

25.71 **Theorem** ($B+3N$). *If the variety $\mathfrak{V}$ has the property that the kernel of every homomorphism $F_n(\mathfrak{V})\to F_{n-1}(\mathfrak{V})$ $(n\geqq 2)$ contains an element of infinite order, and if $\mathfrak{U}\neq\mathfrak{E}$ is either nilpotent or has finite exponent, then $F_m(\mathfrak{U}\mathfrak{V})$ $(m>2)$ is not embeddable in a finite direct power of $F_{m-1}(\mathfrak{U}\mathfrak{V})$.*

Proof. Put $F_m(\mathfrak{U}\mathfrak{V})=K_m$, $F_{m-1}(\mathfrak{U}\mathfrak{V})=K_{m-1}$, and assume an embedding

$$K_m\leqq P=\prod_{i=1}^{s}K_{m-1}(i),\quad K_{m-1}(i)\cong K_{m-1}.$$

Let π_i be the projection of K_m into $K_{m-1}(i)$ and put $N_i = \ker \pi_i$ for $i = 1, \ldots, s$. Then $\bigcap_i N_i = \{1\}$. The contradiction will be obtained by constructing a non-trivial element in this intersection.

Let $\mu_i: K_{m-1}(i) \twoheadrightarrow F_{m-1}(\mathfrak{B})$ be the natural epimorphism of $K_{m-1}(i) \cong F_{m-1}(\mathfrak{U}\mathfrak{B})$ onto $F_{m-1}(\mathfrak{B})$. Then $\ker \mu_i = V(K_{m-1}(i))$ and $V(K_m) \subseteq \ker(\pi_i \mu_i)$ for each i since the image of K_m under $\pi_i \mu_i$ belongs to $\mathfrak{B}$. Therefore $\pi_i \mu_i$ induces a homomorphism of $K_m / V(K_m) \cong F_m(\mathfrak{B})$ into $F_{m-1}(\mathfrak{B})$. Its kernel contains by assumption an element of infinite order, that is, for each i, $\ker(\pi_i \mu_i)$ contains an element k_i of infinite order modulo $V(K_m)$, and we know moreover that $k_i \pi_i \in V(K_{m-1}(i))$ for $i = 1, \ldots, s$.

Now consider the two cases separately. Firstly, when $\mathfrak{U}$ is nilpotent, $V(K_m)$ being a free group of $\mathfrak{U}$ is nilpotent, of class c, say. Take $c_0 \neq 1$ in the lowest term $(V(K_m))_{(c)}$ of the lower central series of $V(K_m)$, and put for $j = 1, \ldots, s$

$$c_j = [c_0, k_1, \ldots, k_j] = [c_{j-1}, k_j].$$

By Theorem 25.63 the centralizer of each of the elements $k_1, \ldots, k_s$ intersects $V(K_m)$ trivially; hence inductively $c_j \neq 1$ for $j = 1, \ldots, s$. We show that c_s does in fact lie in each kernel $N_i = \ker \pi_i$.

Note first that $(V(K_m))_{(c)}$, as verbal subgroup of K_m, is normal in K_m and so $c_j \in (V(K_m))_{(c)}$ for each j.

Thus in particular

$$c_{i-1} \pi_i \in (V(K_m))_{(c)} \pi_i \subseteq (V(K_{m-1}(i)))_{(c)}.$$

Also, as remarked above,

$$k_i \pi_i \in V(K_{m-1}(i));$$

hence, as the lowest term is central,

$$c_i \pi_i = [c_{i-1} \pi_i, k_i \pi_i] = 1 \quad \text{for each } i.$$

But then for $i = 1, \ldots, s$

$$c_s \pi_i = [c_i, k_{i+1}, \ldots, k_s] \pi_i = [1, k_{i+1} \pi_i, \ldots, k_s \pi_i] = 1$$

as required.

Secondly, when $\mathfrak{U}$ is of finite exponent, e say, take $c_0 \neq 1$ arbitrarily in $V(K_m)$ and put for $j = 1, \ldots, s$

$$c_j = [c_0, k_1^e, \ldots, k_j^e].$$

Then $c_j \neq 1$ for $j = 1, \ldots, s$ as before since the powers k_i^e also have infinite order modulo $V(K_m)$. And this time $c_s \pi_i = 1$ for all i because

$$c_s \pi_i = [c_0 \pi_i, (k_1 \pi_i)^e, \ldots, (k_i \pi_i)^e, \ldots, (k_s \pi_i)^e]$$

and $k_i\pi_i \in V(K_{m-1}(i))$ which has exponent e. Hence again $c_s \in \bigcap_i N_i$ and $c_s \neq 1$ which is a contradiction. //

The conditions on $\mathfrak{U}$ can still be modified in various ways (cf. $B+3N$); that $\mathfrak{V}$ is of exponent zero is very likely indispensable (cf. 32.33), but the general question, non-trivial only when $\mathfrak{U}\mathfrak{V}$ is generated by a finitely generated group, remains open:

Problem 10. *If $\mathfrak{U} \neq \mathfrak{O}$, $\mathfrak{E}$ and $\mathfrak{V}$ is of exponent zero, prove that $F_n(\mathfrak{U}\mathfrak{V})$ cannot be embedded in a finite direct power of $F_{n-1}(\mathfrak{U}\mathfrak{V})$ for any n.*

We draw attention to some interesting special cases arising out of Theorem 25.71 by means of the observation that the conditions on $\mathfrak{V}$ are satisfied certainly if $F_n(\mathfrak{V})$ is torsion-free and cannot be embedded in $F_{n-1}(\mathfrak{V})$. It follows from standard properties of nilpotent groups (summarised in Section 1 of Chapter 3; cf. in particular 31.25 and 31.62) that this is the situation in the case of free nilpotent groups $F_n(\mathfrak{N}_c)$. Hence

25.72 **Corollary.** *If $l>1$, the free polynilpotent group $F_n(\mathfrak{N}_{c_l}\cdots\mathfrak{N}_{c_2}\mathfrak{N}_{c_1})$ cannot be embedded in a finite direct power of $F_{n-1}(\mathfrak{N}_{c_l}\cdots\mathfrak{N}_{c_2}\mathfrak{N}_{c_1})$ for any n.*

Proof. By induction over l: as $\mathfrak{N}_{c_1}$ satisfies the conditions imposed on $\mathfrak{V}$, the statement is true for $\mathfrak{N}_{c_2}\mathfrak{N}_{c_1}$ by 25.71. Then $F_n(\mathfrak{N}_{c_2}\mathfrak{N}_{c_1})$ can certainly not be embedded in a single copy of $F_{n-1}(\mathfrak{N}_{c_2}\mathfrak{N}_{c_1})$ and as the free groups of $\mathfrak{N}_{c_2}\mathfrak{N}_{c_1}$ are torsion-free as extensions of one torsion-free group by another, the induction carries on. //

It will be confirmed in Chapter 3 that this corollary is significant in that the polynilpotent varieties are generated by a free group of finite rank. Meanwhile we state explicitly the further specialization supplementing the result 25.34 on the varieties $\mathfrak{A}^l = \mathfrak{S}_l$:

25.73 **Corollary.** *If $l>1$, $F_n(\mathfrak{S}_l)$ cannot be embedded in a finite direct power of $F_{n-1}(\mathfrak{S}_l)$ for any n. Hence $F_n(\mathfrak{S}_l)$ cannot be embedded in a finite direct power of $F_2(\mathfrak{S}_l)$.* //

Finally we note a further partial answer to Problem 10:

25.74 *If $\mathfrak{U} \neq \mathfrak{O}$ and $F_n(\mathfrak{U}\mathfrak{V})$ can be embedded in a finite direct power of $F_{n-1}(\mathfrak{U}\mathfrak{V})$, then $F_n(\mathfrak{V})$ can be embedded in a finite direct power of the same number of copies of $F_{n-1}(\mathfrak{V})$.*

The proof consists, roughly speaking, in reducing the given embedding modulo the verbal subgroup corresponding to V. This requires the use of the following non-trivial property of free groups (cf. 43.41): If R is a normal subgroup of the absolutely free group F and $U(R)=U(F)$, then $R=F$. We omit the details, which can be found in $B+3N$.

6. Residual Properties of the Free Groups of Product Varieties

As is to be expected, the residual behaviour of wreath products will enter into the discussion. It is easy to see that the residual properties of the factors will not in general be inherited by the wreath product. To describe the special situation when they do persist, we first single out certain properties, the *star properties* (GRUENBERG [2], but called root properties there).

26.11 **Definition.** *The property* $\mathfrak{P}^*$ *is called a star property if and only if*

(i) *it is inherited by subgroups,*

(ii) *it is inherited by finite direct products,*

(iii) *if* $A \lhd C$, A *is residually* $\mathfrak{P}^*$ *and* C/A *has property* $\mathfrak{P}^*$, *then* C *is residually* $\mathfrak{P}^*$.

The conditions (i) and (ii) ensure that the remarks 17.81 – 17.84 apply to star properties. We note:

26.12 *Finiteness, being of p-power order, solubility are star properties; nilpotency is not.*

Proof. The symmetric group S_3 is an example to confirm the last statement.

To prove the others only the condition (iii) needs an argument. We want to find, in each of the cases for $\mathfrak{P}^*$, a system of normal subgroups of C whose factor groups have the property $\mathfrak{P}^*$ and whose intersection is trivial.

Let $c \neq 1, \in C$. If $c \notin A$, put $N_c = A$; then N_c is normal and its factor group has $\mathfrak{P}^*$ by assumption. If $c \in A$ then, by the assumption on A, there is a normal subgroup M of A such that M excludes c and A/M has property $\mathfrak{P}^*$. In the first two cases, the index of M in C is finite, or finite and a p-power. Thus M has a finite number of distinct conjugates M^x in C; these are normal in A, therefore $N_c = \bigcap_{x \in C} M^x$ is normal in C and of finite, or finite p-power index in C; and, of course, it still avoids c. In the last case we know that A/M is soluble; hence for some integer k, $A^{(k)} \subseteq M$. Now $A^{(k)}$ is a verbal subgroup of a normal subgroup of C, hence normal in C. As $C/A^{(k)}$ is an extension of $A/A^{(k)}$ by C/A, it is soluble. As $c \notin A^{(k)}$, we may put $N_c = A^{(k)}$. In all cases the intersection of all normal subgroups N_c, $c \in C$ is trivial. //

Next a remark on wreath products:

26.21 *If* A *and* B *are non-trivial and* C *is a non-trivial normal subgroup of* B, *then the normal closure of* C *in* $P = A \operatorname{wr} B$ *intersects each factor* A_b *of* $A^{(B)}$ *precisely in its derived group* A_b' *and the natural epimorph*

$\alpha\colon A \twoheadrightarrow A/A'$ and $\beta\colon B \twoheadrightarrow B/C$ have a common continuation $\gamma\colon A \operatorname{wr} B \twoheadrightarrow A\alpha \operatorname{wr} B\beta$.

Proof. Let $c \neq 1, \in B$, and let φ_a and $\varphi_{a'}$ be defined by

$$\varphi_a(1) = a\,,\qquad \varphi_a(y) = 1\,,\qquad 1 \neq y \in B\,,$$
$$\varphi_{a'}(1) = a',\qquad \varphi_{a'}(y) = 1\,,\qquad 1 \neq y \in B\,.$$

Then the commutator $[c, \varphi_a]$ takes at 1 the value a, at c it takes the value a^{-1} and everywhere else it has value 1. Hence one finds that $[c, \varphi_a, \varphi_{a'}]$ takes at 1 the value $[a, a']$ and has value 1 elsewhere. As $[c, \varphi_a, \varphi_{a'}]$ belongs to the normal closure of c in P for every pair a, a', it follows that the derived group A_1' belongs to this normal closure and hence also its conjugates A_b' for all $b \in B$.

Hence any homomorphism β of B, when extended to the whole of P, will map the base group onto an abelian group. The rest of the statement 26.21 now follows if we can show that the epimorphisms α and β have a common continuation γ.

Put $P_1 = A\alpha \operatorname{wr} B\beta$; then P_1 consists of elements of the form $(b\beta)\psi$ where $\psi\colon B\beta \to A\alpha$ is a function of finite support. We define γ by setting, for each element $b\varphi$ of P,

$$(b\varphi)\gamma = (b\beta)\psi \quad\text{with}\quad \psi(y\beta) = \prod_{c \in C} \varphi(yc)\alpha\,.$$

The product on the right is meaningful and unique, as φ has finite support and $A\alpha$ is abelian. Also, γ is clearly onto P_1, so we merely have to show that it is homomorphic. Assume therefore that

$$(b_1\varphi_1)\gamma = (b_1\beta)\psi_1 \quad\text{with}\quad \psi_1(y\beta) = \prod_{c \in C} \varphi_1(yc)\alpha;$$

then

$$(b\varphi b_1\varphi_1)\gamma = (b b_1 \varphi^{b_1}\varphi_1)\gamma = (b b_1)\beta\,\Psi$$

where

$$\Psi(y\beta) = \prod_{c \in C} ((\varphi^{b_1}\varphi_1)(yc))\alpha = \prod_{c \in C} (\varphi(ycb_1^{-1})\varphi_1(yc))\alpha$$
$$= \prod_{c \in C} \varphi(ycb_1^{-1})\alpha \prod_{c \in C} \varphi_1(yc)\alpha.$$

Also

$$(b\varphi)\gamma(b_1\varphi_1)\gamma = b\beta\, b_1\beta\, \psi^{b_1\beta}\psi_1 = (b b_1)\beta\,\Psi'$$

where

$$\Psi'(y\beta) = \psi(y\beta\, b_1^{-1}\beta)\psi_1(y\beta) = \psi((y b_1^{-1})\beta)\psi_1(y\beta)$$
$$= \prod_{c \in C} \varphi(y b_1^{-1} c)\alpha \prod_{c \in C} \varphi_1(yc)\alpha$$
$$= \prod_{c' \in C} \varphi(y c' b_1^{-1})\alpha \prod_{c \in C} \varphi_1(yc)\alpha\,,$$

the latter as $C \lhd B$. As the factors permute, $\Psi(y\beta) = \Psi'(y\beta)$ as required. //

We deduce:

26.22 **Lemma** (GRUENBERG [*2*]). *If A and B are residually $\mathscr{P}^*$, where $\mathscr{P}^*$ is a star property, then $P=A \operatorname{wr} B$ is residually $\mathscr{P}^*$ if and only if either B has property $\mathscr{P}^*$ or A is abelian.*

Proof. Assume that P is residually $\mathscr{P}^*$ and that A is not abelian; we have to show that B has the property $\mathscr{P}^*$.

As A is not abelian, there exists an element $a \neq 1$ in A'. Let φ_a be defined by $\varphi_a(1)=a$, $\varphi_a(y)=1$ for $y \neq 1$; then let N be a normal subgroup of P such that $\varphi_a \notin N$ and P/N has property $\mathscr{P}^*$.

Then 26.21 shows that N intersects B trivially, hence P/N contains a subgroup isomorphic to B, and as P/N has the property $\mathscr{P}^*$, so has B.

To prove the converse we assume first that B has property $\mathscr{P}^*$. As A is residually $\mathscr{P}^*$, so is $A^{(B)}$; hence by 26.11 (iii) also P is residually $\mathscr{P}^*$.

Next assume that A is abelian, and let $x \neq 1$ in P. If $x \notin A^{(B)}$, put $N_x=A^{(B)}$, then P/N_x is residually $\mathscr{P}^*$ by the assumption on B. If $x \in A^{(B)}$, $x=\varphi$ say, where the support of φ is $\sigma(\varphi)=\{b_1, \ldots, b_r\}$, then there exists a normal subgroup $C \lhd B$ such that B/C has property $\mathscr{P}^*$ and in B/C the elements $b_1 C, \ldots, b_r C$ are distinct. To see this, take to each quotient $b_i b_j^{-1} \neq 1$ a normal subgroup C_{ij} of B such that C_{ij} avoids $b_i b_j^{-1}$ and B/C_{ij} has property $\mathscr{P}^*$. Then put $C=\bigcap C_{ij}$; as B/C is isomorphic to a subgroup of the direct product $\Pi B/C_{ij}$, the conditions 26.11 (i) and (ii) ensure that B/C has property $\mathscr{P}^*$, and moreover $b_i C \neq b_j C$ in B/C. With this choice of C we now use the epimorphism γ of 26.21; then $P\gamma= A \operatorname{wr} B\beta$ where $B\beta$ has property $\mathscr{P}^*$. But here we know already that $P\gamma$ is residually $\mathscr{P}^*$; moreover $\varphi\gamma=\psi \neq 1$ because by the proof of 26.21, $\psi(b_i\beta)=\varphi(b_i) \neq 1$ since there is just one b_i in each coset $b_i C$. Hence we may put $N_\varphi=\ker \gamma$, then P/N_φ is residually $\mathscr{P}^*$. Thus P is residually $\mathscr{P}^*$ using 17.74. //

We can now prove

26.31 **Theorem** (BAUMSLAG [*2*], DUNWOODY [*1*]). *If the free groups of $\mathfrak{U}$ and of $\mathfrak{V}$ are residually $\mathscr{P}^*$ where $\mathscr{P}^*$ is a star property, then the free groups of $\mathfrak{U}\mathfrak{V}$ are residually $\mathscr{P}^*$.*

*Proof**. Let $\mathfrak{C}$ be the set of groups $F_n(\mathfrak{U})$ for all $n \in I$; by 17.41, $\mathfrak{C}$ discriminates $\mathfrak{U}$. Let $\mathfrak{D}$ be the set of finitely generated groups with the property $\mathscr{P}^*$ in $\mathfrak{V}$; by 17.82, $\mathfrak{D}$ discriminates $\mathfrak{V}$. Hence Theorem 22.42 shows that the set $\mathfrak{C} \operatorname{wr} \mathfrak{D}$ discriminates $\mathfrak{U}\mathfrak{V}$. By Lemma 26.22, every

---

* This proof arises naturally out of the tools used in this chapter. DUNWOODY's proof is simpler; it is based on his result on the verbal subgroups of an intersection of groups (cf. 21.27) and gives the residual properties of $F/U(R)$ mentioned in connection with Theorem 22.47.

member of this set is residually $\mathscr{P}^*$; it also is finitely generated. Thus we have found a set of finitely generated groups with the property $\mathscr{P}^*$ that discriminates $\mathfrak{U}\mathfrak{V}$. Using 17.82 again we conclude that the free groups of $\mathfrak{U}\mathfrak{V}$ are residually $\mathscr{P}^*$. //

26.32 **Corollary.** *The free soluble groups* $F(\mathfrak{S}_l)$ *are residually finite p-groups for every prime p.*

Proof. Free abelian groups are easily seen to be residually finite p-groups for every prime p. Now 26.31 permits an induction over l. //

Anticipating the result 32.22 of the next chapter one deduces more generally, by induction on the length of the class row:

26.33 **Corollary** (GRUENBERG [*2*]). *The free polynilpotent groups* $F(\mathfrak{N}_{c_l}\ldots\mathfrak{N}_{c_2}\mathfrak{N}_{c_1})$ *are residually finite p-groups for every prime p.*

Chapter 3

Nilpotent Varieties

1. Summary of Properties of Nilpotent Groups

We collect here, for easy reference, those properties of nilpotent groups that we use repeatedly. Unless proofs or references to other sources are given, the reader is referred to Chapters 10 and 11 of MARSHALL HALL's textbook for details.

As before we denote the *lower central series* of the group A by

$$A = A_{(1)}, [A_{(i-1)}, A] = A_{(i)} \quad \text{for} \quad i > 1 .$$

The *upper central series* is

$$\{1\} = Z_0(A), \quad Z_i(A) \lhd A \quad \text{such that} \quad Z_i(A)/Z_{i-1}(A)$$

is the centre of $A/Z_{i-1}(A)$.

The factor groups $A_{(i-1)}/A_{(i)}$ and $Z_i(A)/Z_{i-1}(A)$ are called the *lower central factors* and *upper central factors* of A respectively.

A is nilpotent of class c if and only if $A_{(c+1)} = \{1\}$, or equivalently $Z_c(A) = A$.

31.11 *If* $A = \mathrm{gp}(a_1, \ldots, a_n)$ *is finitely generated, so is every lower central factor.*

Proof. Inductively: if $b_1, \ldots, b_m$ generate $A_{(k-1)}$ modulo $A_{(k)}$ then the commutators $[b_i, a_j]$ generate $A_{(k)}$ modulo $A_{(k+1)}$. //

31.12 *A finitely generated nilpotent group is supersoluble**.

31.13 *In a finitely generated nilpotent group every subgroup is finitely generated; equivalently, a finitely generated nilpotent group satisfies the maximum condition for subgroups.*

In all subsequent statements the group A is nilpotent of class c.

31.21 *If* $B_0 = B \subseteq A$ *is a subgroup,* $B_1 = N(B)$ *its normalizer in* A, *generally* $B_i = N(B_{i-1})$, *then* $B_c = A$.

This follows from $Z_k(A) \subseteq B_k$, which is proved by induction. //

One deduces

31.22 *A maximal subgroup of* A *is normal in* A *and of prime index.*

* A group is *supersoluble* if it possesses a finite normal (chief) series with cyclic factors.

Hence:

31.23 *The Frattini subgroup $\Phi(A)$, that is, the intersection of all the maximal subgroups of A, contains the derived group A'.*

But also:

31.24 *The Frattini subgroups of a group consists of all elements that can be omitted from every generating set in which they occur ('non-generators').*

This leads to:

31.25 *If A is generated modulo A' by $a_1, \dots, a_r$, then A is generated by $a_1, \dots, a_r$.*

31.26 (P. HALL) *If $N \lhd A$, $N \neq \{1\}$, then $N \cap Z_1(A) \neq \{1\}$.*

Proof (BAUMSLAG and BLACKBURN [*1*]). There exists an integer k such that $N \cap Z_k(A) \neq \{1\}$; for example $k=c$ will do. Let k' be the least such integer and let $a \in N \cap Z_{k'}(A)$, $a \neq 1$. Then $[a, A] \subseteq N \cap Z_{k'-1}(A) = \{1\}$, hence $a \in Z_1(A)$ and $k'=1$ follows. //

Next some facts on periodic elements:

31.31 *If $A = \mathrm{gp}(a, b)$, $a^m \in A'$, $b^n \in A'$ for some positive integers m and n, then A is finite and $|A'|$ divides a power of d, where $d=(m, n)$ is the greatest common divisor of m and n.*

Proof (BLACKBURN). Use induction on c. The case $c=1$ is trivial. When $c=2$ one has $1=[a^m, b]=a^{-m}(a[a, b])^m=[a, b]^m$ as $[a, b]$ is central; similarly $[a, b]^n=1$, hence $[a, b]^d=1$.

Now take $c>2$. By the induction assumption $A_{(2)}/A_{(c)}$ is finite of order dividing a power of d, hence $A_{(c-1)}$ is generated modulo $A_{(c)}$ by elements $b_1, \dots, b_n$ (say) each having order dividing d^{β_i} for some positive integer β_i. The commutators $[b_i, a]$ and $[b_i, b]$ which generate $A_{(c)}$ are central, hence as before $1=[b_i^{d^{\beta_i}}, a]=[b_i, a]^{d^{\beta_i}}$ and $1=[b_i^{d^{\beta_i}}, b]=[b_i, b]^{d^{\beta_i}}$. As $A_{(c)}$ is abelian, the result follows. //

31.32 **Corollary.** *The periodic elements of A form a subgroup, hence a characteristic subgroup.*

Together with 31.26:

31.33 *If A contains non-trivial periodic elements, so does the centre of A.*

31.34 *A finite group is nilpotent if and only if it is a direct product of groups of prime power order.*

On torsion-free nilpotent groups we have:

31.41 *If A is torsion-free then $A/Z_1(A)$ is torsion free.*

Proof. If not, then by 31.33 there are periodic elements in $Z_2(A)/Z_1(A)$. Let $b \in Z_2(A)$, $b^m \in Z_1(A)$, $m>0$. Then for $a \in A$, $1=[b^m, a]=[b, a]^m$, as $[b, a] \in Z_1(A)$. But $Z_1(A)$ is torsion-free so that $[b, a]=1$, that is $b \in Z_1(A)$. //

By contrast:

31.42 *If A is torsion-free then $A/A_{(c)}$ need not be.*

Example (L. G. Kovács). Take $B=F_2(\mathfrak{N}_2)$, generated by a, b. Then $B'=\text{gp}[a, b]$ is infinite cyclic and central. Let $C=\text{gp}(c)$ and take A to be the generalized direct product of B and C amalgamating $\text{gp}(c^2)$ with $\text{gp}([a, b])$: $A=(B \times C;\, [a, b]=c^2)$. Then $Z_1(A)=C \supset A'=\text{gp}(c^2)$ so that A' has index two in $Z_1(A)$. This means that A/A' has elements of order two, but A is torsion free. //

Finally a summary of the definition and properties of *basic commutators*; for the details we refer mainly to P. Hall [4], or to Chapter 11 of Marshall Hall's book ★.

31.51 **Definition.** (i) *The letters $x_1, \ldots, x_n$ are basic commutators of weight one, ordered by setting $x_i<x_j$ if $i<j$.*

(ii) *If basic commutators c_i of weight* wt $c_i<k$ *are defined and ordered, define basic commutators of weight k by the rules: $[c_i, c_j]$ is a basic commutator of weight k if*

1. wt c_i+wt $c_j=k$,
2. $c_i>c_j$,
3. *if $c_i=[c_s, c_t]$, then $c_j \geqq c_t$.*

Then continue the order by setting $c>c_i$ whenever wt $c>$wt c_i *and fixing any order amongst those of weight k and finally numbering them in order.*

Then a *collecting process* shows:

31.52 *If $A=\text{gp}(a_1, \ldots, a_n)$ is nilpotent of class c, and $\alpha: X_n \twoheadrightarrow A$ is the natural epimorphism given by $x_i\alpha=a_i$, then every element $\neq 1$ of A is a product $a=(c_{i(1)}^{m_1} \cdots c_{i(l)}^{m_l})\,\alpha$ where the $c_{i(\lambda)}$ are basic commutators of weight $\leqq c$, $i(1)<\cdots<i(l)$, and the m_λ are integers $\neq 0$.*

31.53 *If in 31.52 $A=F_n(\mathfrak{N}_c)$, then the exponents m_λ take independently all integral values and the representation is unique.*

From this one deduces:

31.61 *The k-th lower central factor $A_{(k)}/A_{(k+1)}$ of the free nilpotent group $A=F_n(\mathfrak{N}_c)$ is a free abelian group, freely generated modulo $A_{(k+1)}$ by the distinct basic commutators of weight k.*

★ Although in the latter the exposition of the collecting process is lacunary.

Hence the rank of these factors can be computed (Witt's formula, WITT [*1*]).

31.62 *The free groups* $F_n(\mathfrak{N}_c)$ *are torsion-free.*

31.63 (WITT [*1*]) *If* $A=F_n(\mathfrak{N}_c)$, *then* $Z_1(A)=A_{(c)}$ *and generally* $Z_k(A)=A_{(c-k+1)}$ *for* $k=1, \ldots, c$.

31.64 *The lower central series of an absolutely free group F contracts to the unit element:*

$$\bigcap_n F_{(n)}=\{1\};$$

that is, F is residually nilpotent.

2. Residual Properties

We start with a lemma:

32.1 **Lemma.** (K. A. HIRSCH). *A polycyclic* group is residually finite.*

Proof. (This proof, due to P. HALL, is reported in GRUENBERG [*2*].) We need only show that a cyclic extension of a residually finite polycyclic group is residually finite; then induction completes the proof.

Let therefore C be an extension of the residually finite polycyclic group A by the cyclic group $B=\text{gp}(b)$, and let $c\neq 1$ be an element of C. If $c\notin A$, there is clearly a normal subgroup in C/A avoiding cA which is of finite index in C/A. The corresponding normal subgroup of C containing A avoids c and has finite index in C. Next take the case $c\in A$. By assumption there is a normal subgroup N of A avoiding c and of finite index in A. Therefore there exists an integer m such that the verbal subgroup $x^m(A)$ lies in N. As A is polycyclic this is still of finite index in A and it is normal in C. If B is finite, we have finished, we may put $N_c=x^m(A)$. So we assume now that B is infinite. As A and $x^m(A)$ are normal in C, conjugation by b induces an automorphism on $A/x^m(A)$. As this group is finite, this automorphism has finite order, n say. Then b^n centralizes A modulo $x^m(A)$. Now take $N_c=\text{gp}(x^m(A), b^n)$; then the index of N_c in C is finite, namely at most $n|A:x^m(A)|$. Also $N_c\lhd C$, because the elements of C are of the form ab^α, $a\in A$, and a transforms N_c in itself as it commutes with b^n modulo $x^m(A)$. Finally N_c avoids c, as b is of infinite order modulo A. //

We can now prove:

32.21 **Theorem** (GRUENBERG [*2*]). *A finitely generated torsion-free nilpotent group is residually a finite p-group for every prime p.*

---

* A group is *polycyclic* if it possesses a subnormal (cf. MARSHALL HALL, p. 124) series with cyclic factors.

Proof. We use induction over the class. When $c=1$, the group is free abelian, that is a direct product of infinite cycles. Each one is residually a finite p-group for any given prime p; for let d^m, $m \neq 0$, be an element of the cycle, then take p^r so large that it does not divide m. Then $d^m \notin \text{gp}(d^{p^r})$. But then the direct product also is residually a finite p-group.

Now let $c>1$ and A torsion-free of class c. Put $Z=Z_1(A)$; by 31.13, Z is a finitely generated torsion-free abelian group and, by 31.41, A/Z is torsion-free and nilpotent of class $c-1$. Therefore Z and, by the induction hypothesis, A/Z are residually finite p-groups for every prime p. Consider $1 \neq a \in A$; if $a \notin Z$ there exists a normal subgroup N^* of A/Z that avoids aZ and has finite p-power index in A/Z. In this case take N_a to be the counter image of N^* in A. If however $a \in Z$, then there is a subgroup M of Z, normal in A and such that $a \notin M$ and Z/M is of finite p-power order. By 31.13 there is a subgroup N of A that avoids a, is normal in A, contains M and is maximal with respect to these properties. Put $A/N=B$; then B is finitely generated, nilpotent, hence polycyclic. Also aN is non-trivial in B and every non-trivial normal subgroup of B contains aN. But, by 32.1, B is residually finite, so that B is, in fact, finite. By 31.34, B is a direct product of prime power groups; if now more than one prime occurred, B would have proper normal subgroups avoiding aN, which contradicts our earlier observation. Hence $|B|=q^\beta$ for some prime q. It remains to show that $p=q$. Now $B=A/N$, this contains the non-trivial subgroup $ZN/N \cong Z/Z \cap N$ which, as factor group of Z/M, has order a power of p. Thus $q=p$ and putting $N_a=N$ completes the proof. //

32.22 **Corollary.** *All the free groups $F(\mathfrak{N}_c)$ are residually finite p-groups for every prime p.*

Proof. If F has finite rank, 31.62 gives the result at once. But generally a $\mathfrak{V}$-free group is residually $\mathscr{P}$ if and only if the $\mathfrak{V}$-free groups of finite rank are residually $\mathscr{P}$: one only has to observe that the kernels of the retractive endomorphisms mapping the free group $F(\mathfrak{V})$ onto its free subgroups of finite rank generated by finite subsets of the free generating set of $F(\mathfrak{V})$ intersect in the trivial group, and then apply 17.74. //

This corollary confirms the corresponding result for free polynilpotent groups (26.33); moreover going back to 17.9 it shows:

32.23 *Every free polynilpotent group $F_n(\mathfrak{N}_{c_l} \dots \mathfrak{N}_{c_2}\mathfrak{N}_{c_1})$ is discriminating. Thus in particular every free nilpotent group $F_n(\mathfrak{N}_c)$ and every free soluble group $F_n(\mathfrak{S}_l)$ is discriminating.* //

We consider at this point the question whether a given finitely generated group is a subcartesian or a subdirect power of another one. We shall apply the results mainly in Section 5 of this chapter, but the arguments we use belong in the present context.

32.31 **Lemma** $(B+3N)$. *If A and B are finitely generated polycyclic groups and if A is embeddable in a cartesian power of B then A is embeddable in a finite direct power of B.*

Proof. Any polycyclic group has a subnormal series with cyclic factors of infinite or of prime power order. It follows at once that the orders of the periodic elements are bounded, namely by the product of the orders of the finite factors of such a subnormal series.

Now assume that for some index set Λ, $A \leqq B^{\Lambda}$. For each $\lambda \in \Lambda$ let π_λ be the projection of A into B_λ and $N_\lambda = \ker \pi_\lambda$. Then $\bigcap_{\lambda \in \Lambda} N_\lambda = \{1\}$. We want to show that there is a finite subset $\mathsf{M} \subset \Lambda$ such that $\bigcap_{\mu \in \mathsf{M}} N_\mu = \{1\}$, for then $A \leqq B^{\mathsf{M}}$ follows.

Let $A_0 = \{1\} \lhd A_1 \lhd \cdots \lhd A_m = A$ be a subnormal series of A with cyclic factors. We show inductively that to each i there is a finite subset $\mathsf{M}(i) \subset \Lambda$ such that $\bigcap_{\mu \in \mathsf{M}(i)} N_\mu$ avoids A_i.

Let $\mathsf{M}(0)$ be the empty set so that, with the usual convention $\bigcap_{\mu \in \mathsf{M}(0)} N_\mu = A$; certainly $A \cap A_0 = \{1\}$, as $A_0 = \{1\}$. Assume a finite subset $\mathsf{M}(i) \subseteq \Lambda$ has been found so that

$$A_i \cap \bigcap_{\mu \in \mathsf{M}(i)} N_\mu = \{1\}.$$

Consider

$$A_{i+1} \cap \bigcap_{\mu \in \mathsf{M}(i)} N_\mu = K_{i+1}, \quad \text{say.}$$

If $K_{i+1} = \{1\}$, we may take $\mathsf{M}(i+1) = \mathsf{M}(i)$. Otherwise note that $K_{i+1} \cap A_i = \{1\}$, so that the natural mapping of A_{i+1} onto A_{i+1}/A_i is a monomorphism on K_{i+1}. Thus K_{i+1} is either cyclic of prime power order or an infinite cycle. In the first case K_{i+1} is finite; to each non-trivial element a of K_{i+1} there is an element $\lambda(a) \in \Lambda$ such that the kernel $N_{\lambda(a)}$ avoids a. If we put $\mathsf{M}(i+1) = \mathsf{M}(i) \cup \{\lambda(a) \mid a \in K_{i+1}\}$, then $\mathsf{M}(i+1)$ is finite and

$$A_{i+1} \cap \bigcap_{\mu \in \mathsf{M}(i+1)} N_\mu = \{1\}.$$

Finally, if K_{i+1} is an infinite cycle, let β be the least common multiple of the orders of the periodic elements of B. Then if K_{i+1} is generated by a, take $\lambda(a) \in \Lambda$ such that $N_{\lambda(a)}$ avoids a^β. Then $N_{\lambda(a)}$ contains no power of a other than 1; for if it contains $a^\alpha \neq 1$, then α does not divide β and so $A\pi_{\lambda(a)} \cong A/N_{\lambda(a)} \leqq B$ would contain an element of order not dividing β contrary to the choice of β. Thus $N_{\lambda(a)} \cap K_{i+1} = \{1\}$ and we may take $\mathsf{M}(i+1) = \mathsf{M}(i) \cup \{\lambda(a)\}$ and again have

$$A_{i+1} \cap \bigcap_{\mu \in \mathsf{M}(i+1)} N_\mu = \{1\}. \quad //$$

Hence from 31.12 and 15.4:

32.32 **Corollary.** *If A and B are finitely generated nilpotent groups and $A \in \operatorname{var} B$, then A is a factor of a finite direct power of B.* //

Moreover we can deduce the following addition to 25.41 which was mentioned already in the context of Problem 10:

32.33 **Corollary.** *$F_n(\mathfrak{A}\mathfrak{A}_m)$ is a subgroup of a finite direct power of $F_2(\mathfrak{A}\mathfrak{A}_m)$ for every $n \geqq 2$.*

Proof. By 21.13, $F_k(\mathfrak{A}\mathfrak{A}_m)$ is, for every k, an extension of a free abelian group of finite rank by a finite abelian group, hence certainly polycyclic. //

Remark. The proof of 32.31 shows that the lemma holds for a slightly wider class of groups, including polycyclic-by-finite groups. It is pointed out in $B+3N$ that this enables one to use the lemma in a very different way exemplified by the following argument. Let B be nilpotent-by-finite (that is certainly polycyclic-by-finite by 31.12); let $N \lhd B$ be nilpotent such that $B/N = C$ is finite and set $\mathfrak{N} = \operatorname{var} N$, $\mathfrak{C} = \operatorname{var} C$. Then $\mathfrak{N}$ is nilpotent and finitely generated groups of $\mathfrak{C}$ are finite (15.72); also $B \in \mathfrak{N}\mathfrak{C}$, hence $\operatorname{var} B \subseteq \mathfrak{N}\mathfrak{C}$ so that finitely generated groups of var B are again nilpotent-by-finite. In particular take B supersoluble, then B is nilpotent-by-finite (cf. Scott, 7.2.21, p. 159), so therefore is any finitely generated group A in var B. But then A is polycyclic-by-finite and the lemma in its more general form shows that A is a factor of a finite direct power of B; hence A is even supersoluble:

32.34 *If B is supersoluble, then so is every finitely generated group in* var B. //

Here 'supersoluble' cannot be weakened to 'polycyclic' as is shown by the following example:

32.35 **Example** (B. H. Neumann). Let B be the metabelian group generated by a, b, c with $[a, b] = 1$, $a^c = ab$, $b^c = a^2 b$. It is polycyclic, but it generates the whole metabelian variety $\mathfrak{A}^2$. To see this, take in the cartesian power B^I the subgroup generated by the elements α and β given by

$$\alpha(i) = a \quad \text{and} \quad \beta(i) = c^i \qquad (i \in I).$$

One checks that the conjugates of α by all powers β^n of β are independent; hence $\operatorname{gp}(\alpha, \beta) = \operatorname{gp}(\alpha) \operatorname{wr} \operatorname{gp}(\beta)$. This group generates $\mathfrak{A}^2$, and as its base group is of infinite rank, it is clearly not polycyclic.

3. A Lemma on Words with an Application to Free Products

Some of the results on words which will be needed now have close analogies in free products. As these, and a structural lemma on free products arising out of them, will be used in Chapter 5 we develop these tools immediately in the more general setting of free products. Only the special case where the free product is the free group X_∞, thought of as the free product of the cyclic groups generated by the x_i, will be used in this chapter.

We introduce some special endomorphisms in the free group X_∞: the *translations* τ_k $(k>0)$ given by

$$x_i \tau_k = x_{i+k} \quad \text{for all} \quad i \in I;$$

the *deletions* δ_k $(k>0)$ given by

$$x_k \delta_k = 1, \qquad x_i \delta_k = x_i \quad \text{for} \quad i \neq k.$$

Clearly

$$\delta_k^2 = \delta_k, \qquad \delta_i \delta_j = \delta_j \delta_i \quad \text{when} \quad i \neq j.$$

Next we define *special commutators**.

33.11 **Definition.** (i) *x_1 and x_1^{-1} are special commutators of weight* 1;

(ii) *if u and v are special commutators, of weight k and l respectively, then $[u, v\tau_k]$ is a special commutator of weight $k+l$.*

One deduces inductively:

33.12 *The weight of a special commutator equals the number of variables occurring in it.*

33.13 *If u is a special commutator of weight n, then $u\delta_i = 1$ for $i \leqq n$, $u\delta_i = u$ for $i > n$.*

Now let $A = \Pi^* A_i$ be a free product of a finite or a countably infinite number of groups. For temporary use only we define *specializations:*

33.21 **Definition.** *A homomorphism σ: $X_\infty \to A$ is a specialization if there exists an integer $n>0$ such that*

$$\begin{aligned} &x_i \sigma = 1 && \textit{for } i > n, \\ &x_i \sigma \in A_{\lambda(i)} && \textit{for some subscript } \lambda(i), \\ &x_i \sigma \neq 1 && \textit{for } i \leqq n. \end{aligned}$$

We also use *deletions* ϑ_i defined on the free product A: ϑ_i is that endomorphism of A that maps A_i trivially and the other factors identically.

33.22 *For a given specialization σ and an integer k such that $I(k) = \{i \in I \mid \lambda(i) = k\}$ is not empty, one has*

$$\Big(\prod_{i \in I(k)} \delta_i\Big)\sigma = \sigma \vartheta_k.$$

---

* Only very slightly more special than the *outer commutators* of P. Hall defined by Turner-Smith [*1*].

Proof. Note that the left hand side is unambiguous as different δ's commute. As a homomorphism of X_∞ is determined by the images of the x_i, one merely has to check the assertion for these, distinguishing between $i \in I(k)$ and $i \notin I(k)$. //

We can now explain our terminology in free products:

33.31 **Definition.** (i) *An element $c \neq 1$ of $A = \Pi^* A_i$ is a commutator of weight n if there exists a special commutator u,* wt $u = n$, *and a specialization σ such that $u\sigma = c$;*

(ii) *the commutator c involves the members of a finite subset J of I if u and σ can be so chosen that $J \subseteq \{\lambda(1), \ldots, \lambda(n)\}$ where $n =$* wt *u.*

Note that 33.31 (i) defines a commutator of weight n in an arbitrary group while part (ii) is significant only when the number of constituents A_i of A is greater than one.

33.32 *$c\vartheta_k = 1$ if c involves k, $c\vartheta_k = c$ otherwise.*

Proof. If c involves k, choose u, σ according to the definition; then $c = u\sigma$ and $I(k)$ contains an element, j say, such that j is at most equal to the weight of u. Now apply 33.22:

$$c\vartheta_k = u\sigma\vartheta_k = u\Big(\prod_{i \in I(k)} \delta_i\Big)\sigma = 1 \quad \text{as} \quad u\delta_j = 1 \quad \text{by} \quad 33.13.$$

If c does not involve k and $c = u\sigma$, then $k \notin \{\lambda(1), \ldots, \lambda(n)\}$ where $n =$ wt u, hence every syllable of $u\sigma$ belongs to a factor other than A_k; that is $u\sigma\vartheta_k = c\vartheta_k = c$. //

33.33 *If the commutators c and c_1 involve the elements of the subsets J and J_1 of I respectively, then $[c, c_1]$ is either* 1 *or it is a commutator involving the elements of $J \cup J_1$.*

Proof. Choose u, σ and u_1, σ_1 so that $c = u\sigma$ and $c_1 = u_1\sigma_1$. If u has weight k and u_1 has weight l, we may assume that σ maps x_i $(i > k)$ trivially and σ_1 maps x_i $(i > l)$ trivially. Then define σ' by

$$x_i\sigma' = x_i\sigma \qquad \text{for } i = 1, \ldots, k,$$

$$x_i\sigma' = x_{i-k}\sigma_1 \qquad \text{for } i = k+1, \ldots, k+l,$$

$$x_i\sigma' = 1 \qquad \text{for } i > k+l.$$

Now $[c, c_1] = [u, u_1\tau_k]\sigma'$ and the assertion follows. //

33.34 *Commutator identities:*

(1) $$[xy, zt] = [x,t]^y [y,t] [x,z]^{yt} [y,z]^t,$$

hence

(2) $[x^{-1}, z] = [z, x]^{x^{-1}}$, $[x, y^{-1}] = [y, x]^{y^{-1}}$, $[x^{-1}, y^{-1}] = [x, y]^{y^{-1}x^{-1}}$;

the Witt identity:

(3) $$[x, y^{-1}, z]^y [y, z^{-1}, x]^z [z, x^{-1}, y]^x = 1,$$

and

(4) $$[x, y^z] = [x, z]\,[x, y]^z [x, z^{-1}]^{yz}.$$

The first one is most frequently used in the cases when either $y=1$ or $t=1$. The proof can be given by means of a straight check. Using these identities, we prove:

33.35 **Lemma.** *Every commutator of weight n of a group A is a product of left-normed commutators and their inverses; hence it belongs to* $A_{(n)}$.

Proof. We use induction over n. The statements are trivial for $n=1, 2$. Then consider $c=[u, v]$ where u and v are commutators of weight k and l respectively with $k+l=n$, and assume the assertion to be true for all commutators of weight less that n. The first two identities of 33.34 allow us to assume that both u and v are left-normed: by the induction assumption they are products of left-normed commutators and their inverses of weights k and l respectively; hence repeated application of (1) and (2) represents c as a product $c=\Pi\,[u_i, v_i]^{w_i}$ where u_i and v_i are left-normed. But the conjugates of commutators are commutators of the same type. Thus it suffices to consider $[u, v]$ where both u and v are left-normed as asserted.

Write $[u, v]=[u, [v_1, t]]$ where $\operatorname{wt} v_1 = l-1$, $l \neq 1$ and use (3) with $z=u$, $x=v_1$, $y=t^{-1}$:

$$\begin{aligned}[u,[v_1,t]]^{t^{-1}} &= [t^{-1}, u^{-1}, v_1]^u [u, v_1^{-1}, t^{-1}]^{v_1}\\ &= [[u, t^{-1}]^{u^{-1}}, v_1]^u [[u, v_1^{-1}], t^{-1}]^{v_1}\\ &= [[u, t^{-1}], v_1^u]\,[[v_1, u], t^{-v_1}].\end{aligned}$$

The second term is of the form $[c', t']$ where c' is of weight $n-1$, hence is a product of left-normed commutators of weight $n-1$, and as before, application of (1) and (2) shows that this term is a product of left-normed commutators of weight n. The first term is of the form $[u', v']$ where u' is left-normed of weight $k+1$ and v' is left-normed of weight $l-1$. Hence $l-2$ repetitions of this procedure complete the proof. //

Together with 33.12, this gives:

33.36 *If the commutator* $c \in A$ *involves the distinct integers* $i_1, \dots, i_n$ *then* $c \in A_{(n)}$. //

We now put

$$D_k = \ker \vartheta_k \quad \text{and} \quad D_J = \bigcap_{k \in J} D_k,$$

where $D_J = A$ when J is the empty set. Then

33.37 **Lemma.** *If* $1 \neq a \in D_J$ *where* J *is finite, then* a *can be written as a product of commutators each of which involves every element of* J.

Proof. Use induction over $|J|$: The lemma is vacuously true when J is empty. Assume it to be true when $|J| = n-1$ and write $J = \{i_1, \ldots, i_{n-1}, i\}$. As $a \in D_J$ implies $a \in D_{J'}$, where $J' = \{i_1, \ldots, i_{n-1}\}$, we know that $a = c_1 c_2 \ldots c_s$ where each factor involves each element of J'. If they all also involve i, we have finished. Assume c_j involves i but c_{j+1} does not; then write

$$c_j c_{j+1} = c_{j+1} c_j [c_j, c_{j+1}],$$

and by 33.33 the factors involving i now follow those not involving i. This shows that we may assume $a = c_1 \ldots c_s$ to be such that $c_1, \ldots, c_r$ do not involve i, but $c_{r+1}, \ldots, c_s$ do; and all factors involve the elements of J'. Now apply ϑ_i: as $a\vartheta_i = 1$ by assumption, we obtain by 33.32:

$$1 = (c_1 \ldots c_r)\,\vartheta_i (c_{r+1} \ldots c_s)\,\vartheta_i = c_1 \ldots c_r,$$

so that $a = c_{r+1} \ldots c_s$, and here each factor involves every element of J. //

Using 33.36 this shows:

33.38 **Corollary.** *If* $|J| = n$, *then* $D_J \subseteq A_{(n)}$. //

Now let $w \neq 1$ be an element of A. We write $w(1-\vartheta_i) = w(w\vartheta_i)^{-1}$. As $\vartheta_i^2 = \vartheta_i$,

33.41 $w(1-\vartheta_i)\,\vartheta_i = 1$, *that is* $w(1-\vartheta_i) \in D_i$.

Also, as $\vartheta_i \vartheta_j = \vartheta_j \vartheta_i$, one checks easily that $(1-\vartheta_j)\,\vartheta_i = \vartheta_i(1-\vartheta_j)$; therefore, if $v \in D_i$, then $v(1-\vartheta_j)\,\vartheta_i = 1$ so that $v(1-\vartheta_j) \in D_i$. Using 33.41 we obtain $w(1-\vartheta_i)(1-\vartheta_j) \in D_i \cap D_j$. By induction:

33.42 $w(1-\vartheta_{i(1)})(1-\vartheta_{i(2)}) \ldots (1-\vartheta_{i(c+1)}) \in D_J$ *where*

$$J = \{i(1), \ldots, i(c+1)\}.$$

On the other hand

$$w(1-\vartheta_i)(1-\vartheta_j) = w(w\vartheta_i)^{-1} w\vartheta_i\vartheta_j (w\vartheta_j)^{-1},$$

and again by induction:

$$w(1-\vartheta_{i(1)}) \ldots (1-\vartheta_{i(c+1)}) = w\,\Pi\, w^{(-1)^r \vartheta_{j(1)} \ldots \vartheta_{j(r)}}$$

where the product is taken over all non-empty subsequences of the sequence $i(1), \ldots, i(c+1)$. Therefore 33.42 and 33.37, 33.38 now give:

33.43 **Lemma** (Powell [*1*]). *Let* $w \neq 1$ *be an element of* $A = \Pi^* A_i$ *and* $c \geqq 1$. *Then* w *can be written in the form*

$$w = u v_1 \ldots v_t$$

where $u \in D_{\{1,\dots,c+1\}} \subseteq A_{(c+1)}$ *and each* v_i *is of the form*

$$v_i = w^{(-1)^{r-1}\vartheta_{j(1)}\dots\vartheta_{j(r)}}, \quad 1 \leqq j(1) < \dots < j(r) \leqq c+1 . \quad //$$

Applied in the special case where $A = X_\infty$:

33.44 **Corollary** (HIGMAN [2]). *Every word* w *can, for every* $c \geqq 1$, *be written in the form:*

$$w = u\, v_1 \dots v_t$$

where u *is in the* $(c+1)$*-st lower central term and each* v_i *is of the form*

$$v_i = w^{(-1)^{r-1}\delta_{j(1)}\dots\delta_{j(r)}}, \quad 1 \leqq j(1) < \dots < j(r) \leqq c+1 . \quad //$$

In both cases the side condition on the subscripts comes from applying the factors $1-\vartheta_j$ on the left in order of their subscripts. Other orders are, of course, admissible and may give a different representation.

It is convenient to digress at this point to draw attention to a slightly different formulation of 33.44 which has proved a useful tool in many instances.

Assume that w is a word in n variables; then

$$\begin{aligned} w &= w(1-\delta_1)\, w\delta_1 \\ &= w(1-\delta_1)(1-\delta_2)\, w(1-\delta_1)\delta_2\, w\delta_1(1-\delta_2)\, w\delta_1\delta_2 \\ &= w(1-\delta_1)(1-\delta_2)\, w(1-\delta_1)\delta_2\, w(1-\delta_2)\delta_1\, w\delta_1\delta_2 . \end{aligned}$$

Inductively one obtains

$$w = u\, w_1^* \dots w_s^*$$

where

$$u = w(1-\delta_1)\dots(1-\delta_n) \in X_{(n)}$$

by 33.38 and each factor w_σ^* is of the form (we omit the subscript):

$$w^* = w \prod_{i \in M} (1-\delta_i) \prod_{j \in N \setminus M} \delta_j \quad \text{with} \quad M \subset N = \{1, 2, \dots, n\} .$$

But the δ_j commute and $\delta_j^2 = \delta_j$, hence

$$w^*\delta_j = w^* \quad \text{for} \quad \delta_j \in N \setminus M ;$$

and using 33.41:

$$w^*\delta_i = 1 \quad \text{for} \quad \delta_i \in M .$$

Thus by 33.37, w^* is a word involving precisely the variables x_i, $i \in M$, and can be written as a product of commutators each of which involves every x_i. Finally, by the definition of the operators $1-\delta$, each w^* as well as u is a product of endomorphic images of w, that is they are consequences of w. As $w = u w_1^*, \dots w_s^*$, w is conversely a consequence of the set $\{u, w_1^*, \dots, w_s^*\}$. Thus we have proved

33.45 **Theorem.** *Every word w in n variables $x_1, \dots, x_n$ is equivalent to a set of words each of which is a product of commutators involving precisely the variables x_i, $i \in M$, for some subset M of $\{1, 2, \dots, n\}$.* //

4. The Laws of a Nilpotent Variety and Related Topics

We use Lemma 33.44: Assume w is a word in n variables and keep $c \geqq 1$ fixed. Then $w = u v_1 \dots v_t$ where each $v_\tau = w^{\pm 1} \beta_\tau$ is a consequence of w. Hence u also is a consequence of w. But conversely, w is clearly a consequence of u and $v_1, \dots, v_t$; therefore $\{u, v_1, \dots, v_t\}$ is equivalent to w. Here each v_τ contains at least one variable less than w. If one or more of the v_τ still contain more than c variables, we can by the same lemma replace each one by a word in the $(c+1)$-st lower central term and a finite set of words involving at least one variable less than the original. After a finite number of steps we arrive at a finite set of words which is equivalent to w and consists of words that either involve at most c variables, or belong to the $(c+1)$-st lower central term. These latter may be replaced by a single equivalent word by taking their product after first writing them with non-overlapping variable sets using 12.11. The former may, again by 12.11, be written as words in $x_1, \dots, x_c$. The procedure that has led to them shows that they are simply images of w under certain endomorphisms of X_∞ of the following kind:

To each sequence $1 \leqq m_1 < \dots < m_k \leqq c$ of integers denote by $\pi(m_1, \dots, m_k)$ the endomorphism of X_∞ given by

34.11 $$x_i \pi(m_1, \dots, m_k) = x_j \quad \textit{if} \quad 1 \leqq j \leqq k \quad \textit{and} \quad m_j = i,$$
$$x_i \pi(m_1, \dots, m_k) = 1 \quad \textit{otherwise}.$$

Thus we have obtained the following generalization of Theorem 12.12:

34.12 **Theorem** (HIGMAN [2]). *Every word w is equivalent to the set of all words $w\pi(m_1, \dots, m_k)$ (where $\pi(m_1, \dots, m_k)$ is given by* 34.11) *and a word in the* $(c+1)$-st *lower central term.* //

34.13 **Corollary.** *Let $\mathfrak{U}$ be nilpotent of class c; then all the laws of $\mathfrak{U}$ follow from $[x_1, x_2, \dots, x_{c+1}]$ and c-variable laws.* //

From this we deduce the key result of this section:

34.14 **Theorem** (LYNDON [1]). *The laws of a nilpotent variety have a finite basis.*

Proof. By 34.13, U is the closure of $U(X_{c+1})$ which contains $(X_{c+1})_{(c+1)} = N$, say. Now X_{c+1}/N is finitely generated, nilpotent of class c, hence by 31.13 the subgoup $U(X_{c+1})/N$ is also finitely generated, that is $U(X_{c+1})$ is finitely generated modulo N. But then all the words in $U(X_{c+1})$ are consequences of $[x_1, x_2, \ldots, x_{c+1}]$ and a set of counter images of these generators, that is they are consequences of a finite set. //

Moreover we have as a further consequence of 34.13 that a nilpotent variety of class c is defined by its $(c+1)$-variable laws; in the notation of 16.21:

34.15 **Theorem.** *If $\mathfrak{U}$ is nilpotent of class c then $\mathfrak{U}=\mathfrak{U}^{(c+1)}$; that is, a group belongs to $\mathfrak{U}$ if and only if all its $(c+1)$-generator subgroups belong to $\mathfrak{U}$.* //

The arguments leading up to these theorems have been used by Graham Higman [2] to prove the finite basis property for a rather larger class of varieties. First some auxiliary remarks:

34.21 *If $\mathfrak{x}$ is a free generating set of the free group X, then $X_{(c)}$ is the normal closure of the set of left-normed commutators*

$$[x_{i(1)}^{\varepsilon(1)}, x_{i(2)}^{\varepsilon(2)}, \ldots, x_{i(c)}^{\varepsilon(c)}], \qquad x_{i(j)} \in \mathfrak{x}, \qquad \varepsilon(j) = \pm 1.$$

Proof. By induction over c: $X_{(c)}=[X_{(c-1)}, X]$ is generated by all elements $[u, v]$ where u is, by assumption, a product of conjugates of left normed-commutators $[x_{i(1)}^{\varepsilon(1)}, \ldots, x_{i(c-1)}^{\varepsilon(c-1)}]$ and v is a word. This can, by repeated application of the identity 33.34(1), be written as a product of conjugates of commutators of the form

$$[[x_{i(1)}^{\varepsilon(1)}, \ldots, x_{i(c-1)}^{\varepsilon(c-1)}]^w, x_{i(c)}^{\varepsilon(c)}] = [x_{i(1)}^{\varepsilon(1)}, \ldots, x_{i(c-1)}^{\varepsilon(c-1)}, x_{i(c)}^{\varepsilon(c)\, w^{-1}}]^w.$$

Now use the identity 33.34 (4), that is

$$[x, y^z] = [x, z]\,[x, y]^z\,[x, z^{-1}]^{yz},$$

to remove the transforming element w^{-1} from inside the commutator; if w is a word of length >1, the identities 33.34 (1) have then got to be applied once more to expand $[x_{i(1)}^{\varepsilon(1)}, \ldots, x_{i(c-1)}^{\varepsilon(c-1)}, w^{\pm 1}]$ in a product of conjugates of commutators of the required form. //

Next a remark on the laws of a product variety:

34.22 *If U is the closure of the m-variable word u, V is the closure of the n-variable word v, then $U(V)$ is the closure of a set of words of the form*

$$u(v_1^{\varepsilon(1)} \ldots v_l^{\varepsilon(l)}, v_{l+1}^{\varepsilon(l+1)} \ldots v_{2l}^{\varepsilon(2l)}, \ldots, v_{(m-1)l+1}^{\varepsilon((m-1)l+1)} \ldots v_{ml}^{\varepsilon(ml)})$$

where l runs through a sequence of positive integers that tends to infinity, $\varepsilon(i)=\pm 1$ and the $v_i = v\tau_n^{i-1}$ are copies of v with disjoint variable sets obtained by repeated use of the translation τ_n: $x_j \to x_{j+n}$.

Proof. The set of words $U(V)$ consists of all words in U with arbitrary words of V substituted for the variables; it is therefore the closure of the set of words obtained from u by substituting arbitrary words of V for the variables. An arbitrary word of V is obtainable by taking sufficiently many copies of v with non-overlapping variable sets, forming products with these and their inverses and only then substituting arbitrary words for the variables. If therefore we substitute these products into u first, we obtain a set of words from which $U(V)$ is obtained by substitution and multiplicative closure, that is we obtain a basis for $U(V)$. Finally we may clearly take each of these products to have the same number of factors by putting in 'dummy' factors. //

34.23 **Theorem** (HIGMAN [2]). *If $\mathfrak{U}$ is nilpotent of class c, defined by the single law u in m variables and if $\mathfrak{V}$ is defined by the single law v in n variables, then $\mathfrak{U}\mathfrak{V}$ is defined by the set of laws*

$$u(v_1^{\varepsilon(1)}\dots v_c^{\varepsilon(c)},\, v_{c+1}^{\varepsilon(c+1)}\dots v_{2c}^{\varepsilon(2c)},\, \dots,\, v_{(m-1)c+1}^{\varepsilon((m-1)c+1)}\dots v_{mc}^{\varepsilon(mc)}), \qquad \varepsilon(i)=\pm 1,$$

and the law $[v_1, v_2, \dots, v_{c+1}]$, *with* $v_i = v\tau_n^{i-1}$ *as before.*

Proof. As $\mathfrak{U}$ is nilpotent of class c, u implies $[x_1, x_2, \dots, x_{c+1}]$. Therefore 34.22 shows that the words

$$u(v_1^{\varepsilon(1)}\dots v_l^{\varepsilon(l)}, \dots, v_{(m-1)l+1}^{\varepsilon((m-1)l+1)}\dots v_{ml}^{\varepsilon(ml)}) \quad \text{for} \quad l=1,2,\dots \text{ and } \varepsilon(i)=\pm 1$$

form a basis for the laws of $\mathfrak{U}\mathfrak{V}$; moreover $[v_{i(1)}, v_{i(2)}, \dots, v_{i(c+1)}]$ is a law in $\mathfrak{U}\mathfrak{V}$ for every selection of copies $v_{i(j)} = v\tau_n^{i(j)-1}$ of v.

Now let Y_∞ be the free group freely generated by $y_1, y_2, \dots$ and let η: $Y_\infty \to X_\infty$ be the homomorphism defined by $y_i\eta = v_i = v\tau_n^{i-1}$. Consider the set $\mathfrak{y}$ of words in Y_∞ consisting (i) of all

$$u(y_1^{\varepsilon(1)}\dots y_l^{\varepsilon(l)}, \dots, y_{(m-1)l+1}^{\varepsilon((m-1)l+1)}\dots y_{ml}^{\varepsilon(ml)}) \quad \text{for} \quad l=1,2,\dots$$

and (ii) of the words $[y_{i(1)}, y_{i(2)}, \dots, y_{i(c+1)}]$. Then the basis of the laws $U(V)$ of $\mathfrak{U}\mathfrak{V}$ given above is simply $\mathfrak{y}\eta$. We now apply 34.12 to this set $\mathfrak{y}$ of words in Y_∞:

Denote by $\pi^*(m_1, \dots, m_k)$ the endomorphism of Y_∞ that maps y_i onto y_j if $m_j = i$, and y_i onto 1 otherwise, where $1 \leqq m_1 < \dots < m_k \leqq c$; then each word of $\mathfrak{y}$ of the first kind is equivalent to the set of all its images under the endomorphisms $\pi^*(m_1, \dots, m_k)$ and a word in $(Y_\infty)_{(c+1)}$ which is a consequence of the words of the second kind in $\mathfrak{y}$ in any case. As $Y_\infty \pi^*(m_1, \dots, m_k) \subseteq Y_c$, this means we need only consider values of l up to $l=c$ inclusive, and then simply the one value $l=c$. Thus $\mathfrak{y}$ is, in Y_∞, equivalent to the set $\mathfrak{y}^*$ consisting of the words

$$u(y_1^{\varepsilon(1)}\dots y_c^{\varepsilon(c)}, \dots, y_{(m-1)c+1}^{\varepsilon((m-1)c+1)}\dots y_{mc}^{\varepsilon(mc)})$$

and $[y_1, y_2, \dots, y_{c+1}]$. Note that $\mathfrak{y}^*$ is a finite set.

It remains to show that the original set $\mathfrak{y}\eta$ is, in X_∞, equivalent to $\mathfrak{y}^*\eta$. Of the operations by means of which one set is a consequence of the other, multiplication and inversion are preserved under η. In general, however, substitutions for the y_i – that is, endomorphisms of Y_∞ – are not necessarily induced by endomorphisms of X_∞. However, the argument used to prove 34.12 shows that to establish the equivalence of $\mathfrak{y}$ and $\mathfrak{y}^*$ only endomorphisms of the type $\pi^*(m_1, \ldots, m_k)$ are used and these correspond to endomorphisms of X_∞ which map blocks of generators $x_{i(n-1)+1}, \ldots, x_{in}$ simultaneously onto other such blocks, or onto 1's, since the sets of variables occurring in the $v_i = y_i\eta$ are non-overlapping. As, by the same kind of endomorphisms, $[y_1, \ldots, y_{c+1}]\eta$ implies in X_∞ all the words $[y_{i(1)}, \ldots, y_{i(c+1)}]\eta$ and as $(Y_\infty)_{(c+1)}$ is the *normal* closure of these words by 34.21, also $(Y_\infty)_{(c+1)}\eta$ is a consequence in X_∞ of $[y_1, \ldots, y_{c+1}]\eta$ and hence equivalent to it. //

34.24 **Corollary** (HIGMAN [2]). *If $\mathfrak{U}$ is nilpotent and $\mathfrak{V}$ is finitely based, then $\mathfrak{U}\mathfrak{V}$ is finitely based.*

Proof. This follows from 34.14 together with the usual argument that a finite set of laws is equivalent to a single law, namely the product of the words in the finite set after writing the latter with non-overlapping variable sets. //

34.25 **Example.** Consider $\mathfrak{B}_r\mathfrak{B}_s$; here we may take $u \equiv x^r$ and $v \equiv x^s$. As v is a one-variable word it suffices to take in 34.22 all exponents $\varepsilon(i) = 1$. Thus:

A basis for the laws of $\mathfrak{B}_r\mathfrak{B}_s$ is given by the set

$$\{(x_1^s x_2^s \ldots x_l^s)^r \mid l \in I\}.$$

Under certain conditions a finite subset is sufficient:

If $r=2$, $\mathfrak{B}_2$ is abelian, that is nilpotent of class $c=1$; therefore 34.23 gives:

The product $\mathfrak{B}_2\mathfrak{B}_s$ is defined by the laws x^{2s} and $[x^s, y^s]$.

If $r=3$, $\mathfrak{B}_3$ is nilpotent of class $c=3$ (LEVI [2]). Hence, again by 34.23:

The product $\mathfrak{B}_3\mathfrak{B}_s$ is defined by the laws $(x^s y^s z^s)^3$ and $[x^s, y^s, z^s, t^s]$.

In one further case an ad hoc argument gives a finite basis:

If $(r, s) = 1$ then $\mathfrak{B}_r\mathfrak{B}_s$ is defined by the single law $(x^s y^s)^r$.

Proof. As r and s are coprime, an element of order r is an s-th power; thus $(x^s y^s)^r = 1$ implies that there is an element t such that $x^s y^s = t^s$, hence $(x^s y^s z^s)^r = (t^s z^s)^r = 1$. Inductively, $(x_1^s x_2^s \ldots x_l^s)^r$ follows in this way from $(x^s y^s)^r$. //

Beyond this nothing seems to be known. In particular one would ask

Problem 11. *Is $\mathfrak{B}_4\mathfrak{B}_2$ finitely based?*

We return to Theorem 34.15 in order to show that this can be sharpened. We first recall the case $c=2$. (For proofs of these statements cf. MARSHALL HALL 18.2):

34.31 **Theorem** (LEVI [2]). *The law* $[x, y, x]$ *implies* $[x, y, z, t]$ *and* $[x, y, z]^3$; *that is, a group whose two-generator subgroups are nilpotent of class two is nilpotent of class three and the third term of its lower central series has exponent three.*

However,

34.32 **Theorem** (LEVI and VAN DER WAERDEN [1]). *The groups* $B_{n,3}=F_n(\mathfrak{B}_3)$ *are of class exactly three when* $n>2$; *the law* $[x, y, x]$ *holds in them, hence* $[x, y, x]$ *does not imply* $[x, y, z]$.

When $c>2$ we can say more:

34.33 **Theorem** (HEINEKEN [3], MACDONALD [1], [2]). *For* $c>2$, *the laws* $[x_1, x_2, \ldots, x_c, x_{c+1}]$ *and* $[x_1, x_2, \ldots, x_c, x_1]$ *are equivalent.*

34.34 **Corollary.** *If* $\mathfrak{U}$ *is nilpotent of class* $c>2$ *then* $\mathfrak{U}=\mathfrak{U}^{(c)}$; *that is, a group belongs to* $\mathfrak{U}$ *if and only if all its c-generator subgroups belong to* $\mathfrak{U}$.

This is the promised sharpening of 34.15; it follows from 34.33 in view of Corollary 34.13.

The proof of 34.33 needs several preliminary steps.

34.41 *The commutator* $[x_1, x_2, \ldots, x_n, y]$ *can be written as a product of commutators of the form* $[y, x'_1, \ldots, x'_n]^{\pm t}$, *where each* x'_i *is the conjugate of some* $x_j^{\pm 1}$.

Proof. Clearly this is true for $n=1$. Assume it true for n and write $[x_1, x_2, \ldots, x_n]=v$. Then consider $[v, x_{n+1}, y]$; by 33.34 (3),

$$\begin{aligned}[v, x_{n+1}, y] &= [y, v^{-1}, x_{n+1}^{-1}]^{-v x_{n+1}} [x_{n+1}^{-1}, y^{-1}, v]^{-y x_{n+1}} \\ &= [v, y, x_{n+1}^{-v}]^{-x_{n+1}} [y, x_{n+1}^{-1}, v^y]^{-x_{n+1}}.\end{aligned}$$

We deal with the two factors separately.

By the induction assumption

$$[v, y] = [x_1, \ldots, x_n, y] = \Pi [y, x'_1, \ldots, x'_n]^{\pm t},$$

hence $[v, y, x_{n+1}^{-v}]$ is a product of conjugates of commutators of the form

$$[[y, x'_1, \ldots, x'_n]^t, x_{n+1}^{-v}] = [y, x'_1, \ldots, x'_n, x_{n+1}^{-v t^{-1}}]^t$$

or

$$[[y, x'_1, \ldots, x'_n]^{-1}, x_{n+1}^{-v t^{-1}}]^t.$$

The latter can be put into the required form using the identity $[y^{-1}, x]=[y, x^{-1}]^{x y^{-1}}$

To deal with the second factor, write

$$[y, x_{n+1}^{-1}, v^y]^{-1} = [v^y, [y, x_{n+1}^{-1}]] = [x_1^y, \ldots, x_n^y, [y, x_{n+1}^{-1}]].$$

By the induction assumption this is a product of conjugates of commutators of the form $[y, x_{n+1}^{-1}, x_1', \ldots, x_n']$ as required. //

34.42 *The words* $[x_1, x_2, \ldots, x_c, x_1]$ *and* $[x_1, x_2, \ldots, x_c, x_1^{\pm y}]$ *are equivalent.*

Proof. The former is trivially a consequence of the latter. For the reverse implication use 33.34 (1) to obtain

$$[x_1, x_2, \ldots, x_{c-1}, x_c y] = [x_1, x_2, \ldots, x_{c-1}, y]\,[x_1, x_2, \ldots, x_{c-1}, x_c]^y.$$

But in a group where $[x_1, x_2, \ldots, x_c, x_1]$ is a law, both

$$[x_1, \ldots, x_{c-1}, x_c y] \quad \text{and} \quad [x_1, \ldots, x_{c-1}, y]$$

permute with x_1 and so also with x_1^{-1}. Therefore also $[x_1, \ldots, x_{c-1}, x_c]^y$ permutes with x_1 and with x_1^{-1}, that is $[x_1, \ldots, x_{c-1}, x_c]$ permutes with $x_1^{y^{-1}}$ and $x_1^{-y^{-1}}$. Replacing y by y^{-1} gives the required result. //

From 34.41 and 34.42:

34.43 *The law* $[x_1, x_2, \ldots, x_c, x_1]$ *implies the law*

$$[y_1, y_2, \ldots, y_{c-1}, x_1^z, x_1^{\pm 1}].$$

Proof. The latter is equivalent to $[y_1^{z^{-1}}, y_2^{z^{-1}}, \ldots, y_{c-1}^{z^{-1}}, x_1, x_1^{\pm z^{-1}}]$. By 34.41, we can express $[y_1^{z^{-1}}, \ldots, y_{c-1}^{z^{-1}}, x_1]$ as a product of conjugates of $[x_1, y_1', \ldots, y_{c-1}']^{\pm 1}$. But by 34.42 the law $[x_1, x_2, \ldots, x_c, x_1]$ implies that $x_1^{\pm z^{-1}}$ commutes with each of these conjugates and therefore with their product. //

34.44 *The law* $[x_1, \ldots, x_c, x_1]$ *implies the law* $[x_1, \ldots, x_{c-1}, x_1, x_c]$.

Proof. We put $x_1 = uv$ in the given law and consider $[uv, x_2, \ldots, x_c]$. Now

$$[uv, x_2] = [u^v, x_2^v]\,[v, x_2],$$

and continuing in this way we obtain

$$[uv, x_2, \ldots, x_c] = c_1 c_2 \quad \text{where} \quad c_1 = [u', x_2', \ldots, x_c']$$

and u' and x_i' denote conjugates of u and x_i respectively, and $c_2 = [v, x_2, \ldots, x_c]$. Now use 33.34 (1):

$$[uv, x_2, \ldots, x_c, uv] = [c_1 c_2, uv] = [c_1, v]^{c_2}\,[c_2, v]\,[c_1, u]^{c_2 v}\,[c_2, u]^v.$$

By 34.42 $[c_2, v]$ and $[c_1, u]$ are consequences of $[x_1, \ldots, x_c, x_1]$; hence so is the product $[c_1, v]^{c_2} \cdot [c_2, u]^v$, or written in full:

$$[v, x_2, \ldots, x_c, u] = [u', x_2', \ldots, x_c', v]^{-c_2 v^{-1}}.$$

But by 34.43 the right hand side is a consequence of $[x_1, \ldots, x_c, x_1]$ for the special choice $x_c = v$; so therefore is the left hand side, that is: $[v, x_2, \ldots, x_{c-1}, v, u]$ is a consequence of $[x_1, \ldots, x_c, x_1]$, and 34.44 follows by re-naming the variables. //

The implication 34.44 will enable us to prove Theorem 34.33 by induction. We therefore supply the starting point, which must be the case $c=3$ as the theorem is false when $c=2$ (by 34.32).

34.45 *If the law* $[x, y, z, x]$ *holds in a group* A *then* A *is nilpotent of class three.*

Proof. From 34.44 we know $[x, y, z, x] = [x, y, x, z] = 1$ in A. Hence, if $Z(A)$ is the centre of A, 34.31 shows that $A/Z(A)$ is nilpotent of class three and the third term of its lower central series has exponent three. Thus A is nilpotent of class four and $[[x, y, z]^3, t]$ is a law in A, that is

(i) $[x, y, z, t]^3 = 1$ holds in A.

Next we use $[uv, y, z, uv] = 1$ and expand it by means of 33.34(1). Using the law $[x, y, z, x]$ again, one obtains

(ii) $[u, y, z, v]\,[v, y, z, u] = 1$ in A.

In the same way one deduces from $[x, y, x, z] = 1$ that

(iii) $[u, y, v, z]\,[v, y, u, z] = 1$ in A.

Further, as A is nilpotent of class four,

(iv) $[x, y, u, v]\,[y, x, u, v] = 1$ in A.

Moreover, replacing any variable by its inverse replaces the commutator $[x, y, z, t]$ by its inverse.

Now we use 33.34 (3):

$$[x, y, z]^{y^{-1}} = [z, x^{-1}, y^{-1}]^{-x}\,[y^{-1}, z^{-1}, x]^{-z}.$$

If we take $z = [u, v]$, then each term is of weight four and therefore equal to its conjugates in A.

$$\begin{aligned}[][[x, y], [u, v]] &= [u, v, x^{-1}, y^{-1}]^{-1}\,[y^{-1}, [v, u], x]^{-1} \\ &= [u, v, x, y]^{-1}\,[v, u, y, x]^{-1}.\end{aligned}$$

Now, by (ii), (iii), (iv) and the rule about inverses:

$$[v, u, y, x] = [u, v, y, x]^{-1} = [y, v, u, x] = [x, v, u, y]^{-1} = [u, v, x, y];$$

therefore

(v) $[[x, y], [u, v]]=[u, v, x, y]^{-2}$.

Interchanging the variables in (v):

$$[[u, v], [x, y]]=[x, y, u, v]^{-2}.$$

Now, using (ii), (iii), (iv) again,

$$[x, y, u, v]=[u, y, x, v]^{-1}=[y, u, x, v]=[v, u, x, y]^{-1}=[u, v, x, y];$$

hence

(vi) $[[u, v], [x, y]]=[u, v, x, y]^{-2}$,

hence from (v) and (vi):

$$[u, v, x, y]^4=1,$$

which together with (i) gives $[u, v, x, y]=1$. //

Proof of 34.33. Assume $[x_1, x_2, \ldots, x_c, x_1]=1$ holds in A; if $c=3$, 34.45 shows that $[x_1, x_2, x_3, x_4]=1$ holds in A, so 34.33 is true when $c=3$. We make the induction assumption that $[x_1, x_2, \ldots, x_{c-1}, x_1]=1$ in A implies $[x_1, x_2, \ldots, x_c]=1$ and assume that $[x_1, x_2, \ldots, x_c, x_1]=1$ in A. By 34.44 this implies

$$[x_1, \ldots, x_{c-1}, x_1, x_c]=1 \quad \text{so that} \quad [x_1, \ldots, x_{c-1}, x_1]$$

is central in A and by the induction assumption $A/Z(A)$ is nilpotent of class $c-1$. Thus A is nilpotent of class c. //

Finally we show that no further improvement on Corollary 34.34 is possible. First a simple and frequently used fact on metabelian groups:

34.51 **Lemma.** *If A is metabelian, $x \in A'$, then*

$$[x, y_1, \ldots, y_n]=[x, y_{\pi(1)}, \ldots, y_{\pi(n)}]$$

for every permutation $i \to \pi(i)$.

Proof. It suffices to show $[x, y_1, y_2]=[x, y_2, y_1]$ when x is in the derived group. Now

$$\begin{aligned}[x, y_1, y_2]\,[x, y_2, y_1]^{-1}&=[x, y_1]^{-1}[x, y_1]^{y_2}[x, y_2]\,[x, y_2]^{-y_1}\\ &=[x, y_1 y_2]\,[x, y_2 y_1]^{-1}\end{aligned}$$

by 33.34 (1) and the assumption that the group is metabelian.

But

$$[x, y_1 y_2]\,[x, y_2 y_1]^{-1}=[x^{-1}, [y_1^{-1}, y_2^{-1}]]^{-y_2 y_1 x}=1,$$

as $x \in A'$ which is abelian. //

34.52 (M. F. NEWMAN and J. WIEGOLD, unpublished). *If A is metabelian, and if for $k=2$ and $k=3$ all the k-generator subgroups of A are nilpotent of class $k+1$, then the same is true for all values of k.*

Proof. It is sufficient to show that all left-normed commutators of weight $k+2$ whose entries are taken from a set of k variables have value 1 in A.

If $[x_1, x_2, \ldots, x_{k+1}, x_{k+2}]$ involves k variables only, then either at least one variable is repeated three times or at least two variables are repeated twice. Using 34.51, this leads to the following typical situations which cover all cases:

(i) $[x_1, x_2, x_1, x_1, \ldots]$. This takes value 1 in A, because

$$[x_1, x_2, x_1, x_1]=1$$

as two-generator subgroups are of class three;

(ii) $[x_1, x_2, x_3, x_3, x_3, \ldots]$; this is 1 as three-generator subgroups are nilpotent of class four;

(iii) $[x_1, x_2, x_1, x_2, \ldots]=1$ as in (i);

(iv) $[x_1, x_2, x_1, x_3, x_3, \ldots]=1$ as in (ii);

(v) $[x_1, x_2, x_3, x_3, x_4, x_4, \ldots]=[u, x_3, x_3, x_4, x_4, \ldots]=1$ as in (ii). //

We deduce:

34.53 **Theorem** (M. F. NEWMAN and J. WIEGOLD, unpublished). *In the variety $\mathfrak{A}_2^2$, every $(c-1)$-generator group is nilpotent of class c for every $c \geqq 3$.*

Proof. Because of 34.52 we need to prove this only for $c=3$ and $c=4$.

Let $B \in \mathfrak{A}_2^2$; then B has a normal subgroup N of exponent two and the factor group B/N also is of exponent two. Take $a \in N$; then for every $b \in B$ $[a, b^2]=1$. But $[a, b^2]=[a, b]^2\,[a, b, b]$ and $[a, b]^2=1$, so that

(i) $[a, b, b]=1$ in B whenever $a \in N$.

We now deal with the case $c=3$: we have to consider commutators of the form $[x_1, x_2, x_3, x_4]$ in which only two distinct variables occur. Using 34.51 again, all possibilities reduce to the following typical cases: $[x, y, x, x]$, which is a law by (i), and $[x, y, x, y]=[x, y, y, x]$. But by (i), $[x^2, y, y]$ is a law in B, and $[x^2, y, y]=[[x, y]^2\,[x, y, x], y]=[x, y, x, y]$. Thus

(ii) $[x, y, x, y]$ is a law in B.

Next the case $c=4$: we have to consider commutators

$$[x_1, x_2, x_3, x_4, x_5]$$

in which at most three distinct variables occur. As before, 34.51 reduces this to the following typical cases which we describe briefly:

$[x, y, x, x, z]$ is a law as $[[x, y], x, x]$ is a law by (i);
$[x, y, z, z, z]$ is a law by (i), as $[x, y] \in N$;
$[x, y, x, y, z]$ is a law as $[x, y, x, y]$ is a law by (ii);
$[x, y, x, z, z]$ is a law by (i), as $[x, y, x] \in N$.
This completes the proof. //

34.54 **Corollary.** *There exists a group, namely the wreath product* $P = C_2 \text{ wr } C_2^{(I)}$ *(where* C_2 *is the cycle of order two) which is not nilpotent, but every* $(c-1)$*-generator subgroup of* P *is nilpotent of class* c *for* $c \geqq 3$.

Proof. Clearly $P \in \mathfrak{A}_2^2$, hence 34.53 applies. And by 24.23, P has trivial centre and therefore is not nilpotent. //

It should be mentioned that this particular wreath product has been used by various authors in similar contexts (cf. for example GRUENBERG [*3*]), in particular in connection with the Engel laws:

34.61 **Definition.** *The k-th Engel law is the law* $[x, y, y, \ldots, y]$, *where* y *is* k *times repeated.*

The preceding arguments show:

34.62 *The k-th Engel law does not imply nilpotency of any class when* $k > 2$.

In fact it may not even imply local nilpotency; evidence supplied recently by GOLOD and ŠAFAREVIČ points that way:

34.63 (GOLOD [*1*]). *To each k, there is a* $(k+1)$*-generator group that is not nilpotent but all whose k-generator subgroups are nilpotent.*

And in fact the methods show:

34.64 *There are two-generator Engel groups* that are not nilpotent.*

Much work is being done on groups satisfying an Engel law with some subsidiary condition (see in particular GRUENBERG [*1*], [*3*] and HEINEKEN [*2*]). R. C. BRUCK and his pupils are considering groups called 'of type $[k \to c]$', that is groups in which every k-generator subgroup is nilpotent of class c. In this context H. HEINEKEN has shown (cf. [*4*]) that groups of type $[n \to (2n-2)]$ without elements of order two are nilpotent of class $3n-3$.

The commutator manipulations used in the latter part of this paragraph have led to a number of interesting results attempting to derive properties of a variety from the laws defining it, and attempting to recognize the interdependence of different *commutator laws*. This seems a

* That is groups where every pair of elements satisfies an Engel condition whose length may depend on the pair.

convenient place to report these results briefly; connections between them are tenuous, and the arguments leading to them are ad hoc.

We write $[x_1, \ldots, x_k; x_{k+1}, \ldots, x_n]$ for $[[x_1, \ldots, x_k], [x_{k+1}, \ldots, x_n]]$. I. D. MACDONALD ([*1*], [*2*]) studies varieties defined by commutator laws with repeated variables, generalizing 34.33. For example: The variety defined by the law $[x, y_1, \ldots, y_n; x, z_1, \ldots, z_m]$, $n \geqq m \geqq 1$, is nilpotent-by-nilpotent: the lower central term $G_{(m+1)}$ is nilpotent of class at most $n-m+2$. There are more precise results in special cases; in particular $[x, y; x, z]$ defines the *variety of 3-metabelian groups*, that is of all groups whose 3-generator subgroups are metabelian (cf. 16.21 and 16.24). This variety may also be defined by the law $[x, y, z]\,[y, z, x]\,[z, x, y]$ (BACHMUTH and LEWIN [*1*]) or by the law $[x, y; y, z]\,[y, z; z, x]\,[z, x; x, y]$ (MACDONALD [*4*]). Various generalizations of this can be found in MACDONALD [*2*] where one finds inter alia a single law defining the variety of groups all whose (2^l-1)-generator subgroups are soluble of length l, as well as a law in less than the expected number of variables for the variety of groups whose derived groups are nilpotent of class c. Again generalizing the metabelian law, which is equivalent to

$$[x, y, z, t]\,[x, y, t, z]^{-1},$$

I. D. MACDONALD proves in [*5*] that the laws $[x, y, z, t]\,[x, y, t, z]^{-n-1}$ and $[x, y; z, t]\,[x, y, z, t]^n$ $(n \geqq 0)$ are equivalent and define a variety where G'' is in the centre of G and has exponent two; for odd n it is metabelian. Going in a slightly different direction, F. LEVIN [*1*] shows the law $[x_1, \ldots, x_n, x_{n+1}, x_{n+2}]\,[x_1, \ldots, x_n, x_{n+2}, x_{n+1}]^{-1}$ to be equivalent to $[x_1, \ldots, x_n; x_{n+1}, x_{n+2}]$.

For an application of commutator calculus to *groups of exponent* p, especially metabelian ones, see the series of papers by MEIER-WUNDERLI, which contain the much used result:

34.7 (MEIER-WUNDERLI [*3*]) *A metabelian group of prime exponent* $p>2$ *has class* p.

5. Generating Groups of Finite Rank

The basic facts on the defining laws of a nilpotent variety serve to establish another 'finiteness' property of nilpotent varieties:

35.11 **Theorem.** *Let* $\mathfrak{U}$ *be any nilpotent variety of class* c, $G_c = F_c(\mathfrak{U})$ *the* $\mathfrak{U}$*-free group of rank* c *freely generated by* $g_1, g_2, \ldots, g_c$. *Let* J *be the set of sequences* j: $1 \leqq m_1 < m_2 < \cdots < m_c \leqq n$ *for some fixed integer* $n > c$. *Then the elements* $t_1, \ldots, t_n$ *of the direct power* G_c^J *defined by*

$$t_{m_i}(j) = g_i \in G_c \quad \textit{when} \quad m_i \in j,$$
$$t_i(j) = 1 \quad \textit{when} \quad i \notin j,$$

generate a subgroup of G_c^J *that is isomorphic to* $G_n = F_n(\mathfrak{U})$.

35.12 **Corollary.** *Every nilpotent variety* $\mathfrak{U}$ *of class* c *is generated by its* c-*generator groups. The free group* $F_n(\mathfrak{U})$, $n > c$, *is a subdirect product of at most* $\binom{n}{c}$ *copies of* $F_c(\mathfrak{U})$.

Proof of 35.11. Put $G = \mathrm{gp}(t_1, \ldots, t_n) \subseteq G_c^J$. By 13.21 it suffices to show that every relator of the generators $t_1, \ldots, t_n$ is a law in $\mathfrak{U}$. Assume therefore a relation $r(t_1, \ldots, t_n) = 1$ in G. This holds if and only if it holds component wise, i.e. for the values at j of the functions t_i for each $j \in J$. Therefore, if the endomorphism $\pi(m_1, \ldots, m_c)$ of X_∞ is defined as in 34.11:

$$x_i \pi(m_1, \ldots, m_c) = x_j \quad \text{if} \quad m_j = i$$

and

$$x_i \pi(m_1, \ldots, m_c) = 1 \quad \text{otherwise,}$$

then $r\pi(m_1, \ldots, m_c)$ is a relator in G_c for every such endomorphism $\pi(m_1, \ldots, m_c)$ corresponding to the sequences $j \in J$. But a relator of the free generators of G_c is a law in $G_c = F_c(\mathfrak{U})$, and therefore a law in $\mathfrak{U}$ (as c-variable laws of $F_c(\mathfrak{U})$ are laws of $\mathfrak{U}$ for any variety $\mathfrak{U}$). By 34.12, every law u of $\mathfrak{U}$ is equivalent to the laws $u\pi(m_1, \ldots, m_c)$ and the nilpotency law. As $r\pi(m_1, \ldots, m_c)$ and $[x_1, x_2, \ldots, x_{c+1}]$ are laws in $\mathfrak{U}$, it follows that the n-variable word r is a law in $\mathfrak{U}$ as required. //

Proof of 35.12. There clearly are $\binom{n}{c}$ sequences j, so that G_c^J has $\binom{n}{c}$ factors. Also the functions t_i are defined so that their components in the factor corresponding to $j \in J$ include every free generator of that factor; hence the projections of $G = \mathrm{gp}(t_1, \ldots, t_n)$ into the factors of G_c^J are in fact onto these factors; that is, G is a subdirect power of G_c. //

We now combine Theorem 25.31 with 32.23 and 35.12 to obtain:

35.13 **Theorem.** *If* $\mathfrak{U} \neq \mathfrak{O}$ *and* $c > 1$ *then* $\mathfrak{U}\mathfrak{N}_c$ *is discriminated by its free group of rank* c. //

35.14 **Corollary.** *The polynilpotent variety* $\mathfrak{N}_{c_l} \ldots \mathfrak{N}_{c_2} \mathfrak{N}_{c_1}$ *is discriminated by its* k-*generator group where* $k = \max(2, c_1)$. //

It is, of course, quite feasible for a variety $\mathfrak{U}$ of class c to be generated by its k-generator groups for some $k < c$. In that case Lemma 32.31, or 32.32, still ensures that the free groups of rank $n > k$ are subgroups of finite direct powers of $F_k(\mathfrak{U})$:

35.15 *If* $F_k(\mathfrak{U})$ *generates the nilpotent variety* $\mathfrak{U}$, *then* $F_n(\mathfrak{U})$ *is a subgroup of a finite direct power of* $F_k(\mathfrak{U})$ *for every* $n > k$. //

As one might expect, the minimal rank of a generating group of a nilpotent variety is in general a non-decreasing function of the class:

35.21 *Let* $\mathfrak{U}_{c+1}$ *be a variety of class* $c+1$ *with the property that the centre of* $F_{c+1}(\mathfrak{U}_{c+1})$ *is exactly the* $(c+1)$*-st term of the lower central series, and let* $\mathfrak{U}_c$ *be the subvariety of all groups of class* c *in* $\mathfrak{U}_{c+1}$. *If* $F_k(\mathfrak{U}_{c+1})$ *generates* $\mathfrak{U}_{c+1}$, *then* $F_k(\mathfrak{U}_c)$ *generates* $\mathfrak{U}_c$.

Then 31.63 shows:

35.22 **Corollary.** *If* $\mathfrak{N}_{c+1}$, *the variety of all nilpotent groups of class* $c+1$, *is generated by its k-generator groups then so is* $\mathfrak{N}_c$. //

Proof of 35.21. Assume $F_k(\mathfrak{U}_c)$ does not generate $\mathfrak{U}_c$; then there is a word w which is a law in $F_k(\mathfrak{U}_c)$ but not in $\mathfrak{U}_c$. By 34.13 we may assume that w involves at most c variables. Form $w^* = [w(x_1, \ldots, x_c), x_{c+1}]$; as w is a law in $F_k(\mathfrak{U}_c)$, it is central in $F_k(\mathfrak{U}_{c+1})$; hence w^* is a law in $F_k(\mathfrak{U}_{c+1})$. But w^* is not a law in $\mathfrak{U}_{c+1}$: if it were, w would be central in every free group of $\mathfrak{U}_{c+1}$, in particular in $F_{c+1}(\mathfrak{U}_{c+1})$. By the assumption on the latter, w would belong to the $(c+1)$-st term of the lower central series of $F_{c+1}(\mathfrak{U}_{c+1})$, that is it would be a law in $F_{c+1}(\mathfrak{U}_c)$. But by 35.12 $\mathfrak{U}_c$ is generated by $F_c(\mathfrak{U}_c)$, hence certainly by $F_{c+1}(\mathfrak{U}_c)$, so that w would be a law in $\mathfrak{U}_c$, contradicting the choice of w. //

Remark. There are nilpotent varieties other than the varieties $\mathfrak{N}_c$ that satisfy the assumptions of 35.21. In fact it will be a by-product of arguments contained in the next section that the varieties $\mathfrak{N}_c \wedge \mathfrak{A}^2$ of all metabelian groups that are nilpotent of class c have the property, analogous to 31.63, that the k-th term of the upper central series equals the $(c-k+1)$-st term of the lower central series. Recently M. A. WARD has devised a generalized commutator collecting process (WARD [*1*]) which establishes the corresponding fact for a large class of nilpotent varieties including in particular the varieties $\mathfrak{N}_c \wedge \mathfrak{S}_l$ of all nilpotent groups of class c that are soluble of length l. But a complete characterization of the nilpotent varieties satisfying the hypothesis of 35.21 is outstanding :

Problem 12. *Characterize those nilpotent varieties* $\mathfrak{U}_{c+1}$ *with the property that the centre of* $F_{c+1}(\mathfrak{U}_{c+1})$ *is exactly the* $(c+1)$*-st term of the lower central series.*

Moreover:

Problem 13. *Is the condition that the centre of* $F_{c+1}(\mathfrak{U}_{c+1})$ *is the* $(c+1)$*-st lower central term of that group necessary to ensure the truth of* 35.21?

In the case of the varieties $\mathfrak{N}_c$ a little more information is available. We denote by $d(c)$ the least value of k such that $F_k(\mathfrak{N}_c)$ generates $\mathfrak{N}_c$. We state the following conjecture in the form of a problem and follow it by some supporting evidence.

Problem 14. *Prove that $d(c)=[c/2]+1$; that is: if $k<[c/2]+1$, $F_k(\mathfrak{N}_c)$ generates a proper subvariety of $\mathfrak{N}_c$, but if $k\geqq[c/2]+1$, $F_k(\mathfrak{N}_c)$ generates $\mathfrak{N}_c$.*

It was pointed out by W. MAGNUS that certain invariants in Lie rings translate into non-trivial commutator expressions of weight c in n variables which take value 1 modulo terms of higher weight when words in less than n variables are substituted for the original variables. The weight c of such invariants is necessarily a multiple of the number n of variables and M. BURROW [*1*] has shown that such invariants exist for all values $c=mn$ with $m\geqq 2$, $n\geqq 4$. To use this information to best advantage, take $m=2$. Then it means that for all even $c\geqq 8$ there exist non-trivial commutator expressions of weight c in $n=c/2$ variables which are laws in every group of $\mathfrak{N}_c$ that can be generated by less than n elements; hence $F_{n-1}(\mathfrak{N}_c)$ does not generate $\mathfrak{N}_c$ when $c=2n\geqq 8$. Combining this with 35.22 shows that $F_{n-1}(\mathfrak{N}_{c+1})$ does not generate $\mathfrak{N}_{c+1}$ when $c=2n$ and $c\geqq 8$; hence

35.31 $d(c)\geqq[c/2]$ *for* $c\geqq 8$.

For the remaining values of c, more precise information can be obtained directly:

35.32 $d(c)\geqq[c/2]+1$ *for* $2\leqq c\leqq 7$.

Proof. The cases $c=2, 3$ are trivial, since $[c/2]=1$, and a one-generator group can not generate a non-abelian variety.

The other cases will be covered, using 35.22 again, if we deal with $c=4$ and $c=6$. This is achieved by proving:

35.33 *The free group $F_2(\mathfrak{N}_4)$ is metabelian, hence does not generate $\mathfrak{N}_4$ which is not metabelian.*

35.34 *In the free group $F_3(\mathfrak{N}_6)$ the word*

$$[[x_4,x_3],[x_2,x_1],[x_2,x_1]]\,[[x_4,x_2],[x_2,x_1],[x_3,x_1]]^{-1}\times$$
$$\times[[x_4,x_1],[x_2,x_1],[x_3,x_2]]\,[[x_3,x_2],[x_2,x_1],[x_4,x_1]]\times$$
$$\times[[x_3,x_1],[x_2,x_1],[x_4,x_2]]^{-1}$$

is a law, but it is not a law in $F_4(\mathfrak{N}_6)$, hence not a law in $\mathfrak{N}_6$; hence $F_3(\mathfrak{N}_6)$ does not generate $\mathfrak{N}_6$.

Proof of 35.33. Let $F_2(\mathfrak{N}_4)$ be freely generated by a and b. The derived group consists of elements of the form $[a,b]^\alpha s$ where s is a product of commutators of higher weight. Hence the second derived group is generated by commutators of the form $\left[[a,b]^\alpha s, [a,b]^\beta t\right]$ where s and t are products of commutators of weight $\geqq 3$. By 33.34 (1), this equals $\left[[a,b]^\alpha, [a,b]^\beta\right] u$ where u is a product of commutators of weight $\geqq 5$, hence equal to 1 in $\mathfrak{N}_4$. Thus every second commutator is trivial in $F_2(\mathfrak{N}_4)$. On the other hand the second commutator $[[c, b], [c, a]]$ is basic, hence non-trivial in $F_3(\mathfrak{N}_4)$. //

Proof of 35.34. We remark first that the given expression is a product of distinct basic commutators and their inverses, hence non-trivial in $F_4(\mathfrak{N}_6)$.

To prove that it is a law in $F_3(\mathfrak{N}_6)$, it suffices to show – again using 33.34 (1) and the fact that conjugates need not be considered – that it becomes trivial when a single one of the four variables, x_i, is replaced by a product of powers of the other three: $x_i = x_j^\alpha x_k^\beta x_l^\gamma$. Now note that the expression is unchanged when x_1 and x_2 are interchanged, and it merely changes into its inverse when x_3 and x_4 are interchanged. Hence it suffices to put in it $x_1 = x_2^\alpha x_3^\beta x_4^\gamma$, and then $x_4 = x_1^\alpha x_2^\beta x_3^\gamma$, and check in these cases that, on expansion, one obtains the identity. This is easily confirmed. //

Finally we mention that it has been checked that up to $c=6$ the conjectured value for $d(c)$ is in fact correct:

35.35 *For* $2 \leqq c \leqq 6$, $F_k(\mathfrak{N}_c)$ *generates* $\mathfrak{N}_c$ *whenever* $k \geqq [c/2]+1$.

We merely give an indication of a possible procedure: For $c=2, 3$, $\mathfrak{N}_c$ is metabelian, and we shall show in the next paragraph that the variety of all metabelian groups of class c is generated by its two-generator groups for every value of c.

In general, to show that $\mathfrak{N}_c$ is generated by $F_k(\mathfrak{N}_c)$, it suffices to show that $F_c(\mathfrak{N}_c)$ – which generates $\mathfrak{N}_c$ by 35.12 – is a subgroup of a direct power of $F_k(\mathfrak{N}_c)$, or equivalently, that the kernels of all homomorphisms of $F_c(\mathfrak{N}_c)$ into $F_k(\mathfrak{N}_c)$ have trivial intersection. In the cases mentioned here, that is $c=4, 5, 6$, it is easy to pick out a small number of such homomorphisms whose kernels have trivial intersection. A typical example is the case $c=4$: the following seven homomorphisms of $F_4(\mathfrak{N}_4)$, generated freely by d_1, d_2, d_3, d_4, into $F_3(\mathfrak{N}_4)$, generated by a, b, c, have kernels that intersect trivially:

$$
\begin{array}{lllllll}
d_1 \to 1 & a & a & a & a & a & a \\
d_2 \to a & 1 & b & b & a & b & b \\
d_3 \to b & b & 1 & c & b & b & c \\
d_4 \to c & c & c & 1 & c & c & c.
\end{array}
$$

This is confirmed without much trouble by means of the unique representation of the elements of $F_4(\mathfrak{N}_4)$ in terms of basic commutators in the generators d_i. //

6. The Variety of All Metabelian Nilpotent Groups of Class c

We shall use in this paragraph a little of certain techniques developed by W. MAGNUS [3] for the investigation of metabelian groups. These same techniques are the starting point for very recent work on metabelian varieties by D. E. COHEN [1] who proves:

36.11 **Theorem.** *The laws of every metabelian variety have a finite basis.*

We therefore insert at this point a description of Magnus' method and a very brief indication of the gist of the argument leading to Theorem 36.11, before we prove what little of these methods are needed for our purposes.

Let $A = \mathrm{gp}(\mathfrak{a})$ be any group generated by the set $\mathfrak{a}$ and $A \cong X/R$ a presentation of it. Let ZA be the group ring of A over the integers, and $(ZA)^k$ the direct sum of k copies of ZA, where $k = |\mathfrak{a}| = \operatorname{rank} X$. Then the matrices of degree two of the form

$$\begin{pmatrix} a & 0 \\ \alpha & 1 \end{pmatrix}, \quad a \in A, \quad \alpha \in (ZA)^k,$$

form a group under 'ordinary' matrix multiplication. Let α_i be that element of $(ZA)^k$ which is the 1 of ZA in the i-th component and 0 everywhere else. Then:

36.12 **Theorem** (cf. Fox [1] for a proof). *The mapping of X into the group of matrices given by*

$$x_i \to \begin{pmatrix} a_i & 0 \\ \alpha_i & 1 \end{pmatrix}$$

for all $x_i \in \mathfrak{x}$, the free generating set of X, induces a monomorphism on $X/[R, R]$.

Thus one has in particular a faithful representation by matrices of this kind for the free metabelian groups of every finite or countably infinite rank. Starting from this representation D. E. COHEN shows that the free metabelian group $F_\infty(\mathfrak{A}^2)$ satisfies the maximum condition for certain normal subgroups, namely those that admit the automorphisms induced by permutations of the free generators. Thus it certainly satisfies the maximum condition for fully invariant, that is (by 13.31) for verbal, subgroups. For the proof one notices first that the only relevant subgroups causing difficulty are those contained in the derived group. This allows one to translate the problem into one on chains of admissible sub-modules in the operator module formed by the α's, the operators being essentially the elements of X/X' and the permutations of the generators. A modification of the operator domain – replacing the group X/X' by the abelian semigroup freely generated by the $x_i X'$, $x_i \in \mathfrak{x}$ – further translates the problem into one on chains of ideals admitting the permutations of the x_i in a polynomial ring. The final step reduces this to the validity of the maximum condition for certain ideals in the abelian semigroup, namely those ideals that admit 'order-preserving' mappings of the set of generators. But this situation is covered by results of GRAHAM HIGMAN [*1*].

Finally, M. F. NEWMAN noticed that results by A. I. MAL'CEV [*2*], independently proved by B. H. NEUMANN and TEKLA TAYLOR [*1*], on nilpotent semigroups achieve the following generalization:

36.13 *The laws of every subvariety of the variety* $\mathfrak{A}\mathfrak{N}_c \wedge \mathfrak{N}_c\mathfrak{A}$ $(c \geqq 1)$ *have a finite basis.*

In a metabelian group, only left-normed basic commutators are non-trivial. We want to use the matrix representation to establish the independence of the left-normed basic commutators in a free metabelian group of rank two. This is all we shall use; their independence in a free metabelian group of any rank will then follow as a by-product of the main result of this paragraph. We therefore prove:

36.21 **Lemma.** *Let* $A_1 = F_2(\mathfrak{A})$ *be freely generated by* a_1 *and* b_1, *denote by* α *and* β *the elements of* $(ZA_1)^2$ *whose components are* (1, 0) *and* (0, 1) *respectively. Then the mapping* μ *given by*

$$x_1\mu = \begin{pmatrix} a_1 & 0 \\ \alpha & 1 \end{pmatrix} \quad \textit{and} \quad x_2\mu = \begin{pmatrix} b_1 & 0 \\ \beta & 1 \end{pmatrix}$$

defines a homomorphism of X_2/X_2'' *into the matrix group.*

Proof. To prove that μ is a homomorphism one only has to check that the two matrices generate a metabelian group, that is that the conjugates of the commutator $[x_1\mu, x_2\mu]$ commute. One computes:

$$[x_1\mu, x_2\mu] = \begin{pmatrix} 1 & 0 \\ (b_1-1)\alpha + (1-a_1)\beta & 1 \end{pmatrix}$$

Moreover, generally, for $c \in A_1$ and $\gamma, \delta \in (ZA_1)^2$:

$$\begin{pmatrix} c & 0 \\ \gamma & 1 \end{pmatrix}^{-1} \begin{pmatrix} 1 & 0 \\ \delta & 1 \end{pmatrix} \begin{pmatrix} c & 0 \\ \gamma & 1 \end{pmatrix} = \begin{pmatrix} 1 & 0 \\ \delta c & 1 \end{pmatrix};$$

hence every conjugate of $[x_1\mu, x_2\mu]$ has the form $\begin{pmatrix} 1 & 0 \\ * & 1 \end{pmatrix}$, and any two matrices of this form commute. //

36.22 **Lemma.** *If* $A = F_2(\mathfrak{A}^2)$ *is freely generated by* a *and* b *then all the left-normed basic commutators in* a *and* b *are independent elements in the derived group* A' *of* A.

36.23 **Corollary.** *In $F_2(\mathfrak{A}^2 \wedge \mathfrak{N}_c)$ the left-normed basic commutators of weight at most c are independent for every $c \geqq 2$.*

Proof. Assuming that a precedes b, a left-normed basic commutator is of the form $[b, a, a, \dots, a, b, \dots, b]$ with $k+1$ repetitions of a and l repetitions of b for all integers $k \geqq 0$, $l \geqq 0$. We abbreviate this as $[b, (k+1)\,a, lb]$. Its matrix representation is found to be

$$\begin{pmatrix} 1 & 0 \\ (a_1-1)^k(b_1-1)^l((1-b_1)\alpha+(a_1-1)\beta) & 1 \end{pmatrix}.$$

To show that the left-normed basic commutators are independent it is sufficient, by 36.21, to show that the forms

$$(a_1-1)^k(b_1-1)^l((1-b_1)\alpha+(a_1-1)\beta), \quad k \geqq 0, l \geqq 0,$$

as forms in indeterminates a_1, b_1, α, β, are independent over the integers. But a relation

$$\sum n_{kl}(a_1-1)^k(b_1-1)^l((1-b_1)\alpha+(a_1-1)\beta)=0,$$

with integral coefficients implies that the terms with α and those with β are separately zero:

$$\sum n_{kl}(a_1-1)^k(b_1-1)^{l+1} = \sum n_{kl}(a_1-1)^{k+1}(b_1-1)^l = 0.$$

But these are now polynomial identities in the indeterminates $u=a_1-1$ and $v=b_1-1$ which give $n_{kl}=0$ for all $k \geqq 0$, $l \geqq 0$. //

We add a caution:

36.24 *The basic commutators in $A=F_2(\mathfrak{A}^2)$ do not generate the derived group A' even though (by 31.52 and 31.53) they generate A' modulo every term of the lower central series.*

Proof. Consider $[b, a^{-1}]$: for every $m \geqq 1$

$$[b,a^{-1}]=[b,a]^{-1}[b,a,a]\dots[b,(m-1)\,a]^{(-1)^{m-1}} \times$$
$$\times [b,(m-1)\,a, a^{-1}]^{(-1)^{m-1}}$$

If $[b, a^{-1}]$ can be expressed in terms of basic commutators, let m be the highest occurring weight. Then by 36.23 this expression must be identical to that part of the one above which is of weight $\leqq m$; hence

$$[b, (m-1)\,a, a^{-1}]=1$$

in A would follow. But this implies $[b, ma]=1$ in A contradicting 36.22. //

We now turn to the free groups of the variety $\mathfrak{N}_c \wedge \mathfrak{A}^2$ of all nilpotent groups of class c that are metabelian. When $c=2, 3$ this variety is, of course, identical with the whole of $\mathfrak{N}_c$. In any group of such a variety, every element can, by 31.52, be expressed as product of left-normed basic commutators, $g = c_1^{\alpha_1} \dots c_l^{\alpha_l}$ say, where the c_i are distinct left-normed basic commutators of weight $\leqq c$.

36.31 **Lemma.** *Let* $G = F_k(\mathfrak{N}_c \wedge \mathfrak{A}^2)$ *be generated freely by* $g_1, \dots, g_k$ *and* $k > 2$, *and let now* $A = F_2(\mathfrak{N}_c \wedge \mathfrak{A}^2)$, *freely generated by* a *and* b. *Let* $g \in G$, $g = c_1^{\alpha_1} \dots c_l^{\alpha_l}$ *where the* c_i *are distinct basic left-normed commutators; if* $g\varphi = 1$ *for every homomorphism* $\varphi: G \to A$, *then all exponents* α_i *in the representation of* g *are zero.*

Before we prove the lemma, we state its consequences:

36.32 **Theorem** (W. MAGNUS, unpublished). *Every element of the free group* $F_k(\mathfrak{N}_c \wedge \mathfrak{A}^2)$ *is uniquely representable as product* $c_1^{\alpha_1} \dots c_l^{\alpha_l}$ *of left-normed basic commutators where* $c_1 < \dots < c_l$ *in the ordering of the basic commutators.* //

Equivalently, using 31.52:

36.33 **Theorem.** *In every free group* $F(\mathfrak{A}^2)$ *the left-normed basic commutators of weight* $\geqq 2$ *freely generate a free abelian subgroup of the derived group.* //

Further:

36.34 **Theorem** ($B+3N$). *Every variety* $\mathfrak{N}_c \wedge \mathfrak{A}^2$, *where* $c > 1$, *is generated by its two-generator groups.*

Proof. Lemma 36.31 implies that the kernels of all homomorphisms $\varphi: F_c(\mathfrak{N}_c \wedge \mathfrak{A}^2) \to F_2(\mathfrak{N}_c \wedge \mathfrak{A}^2)$ intersect trivially. Thus $F_c(\mathfrak{N}_c \wedge \mathfrak{A}^2)$ is a subgroup of a cartesian power of $F_2(\mathfrak{N}_c \wedge \mathfrak{A}^2)$. Thus the free group of rank two of the variety generates the c-generator groups of the variety and so, by 35.12, the whole variety. //

Proof of Lemma 36.31. In the case $c=2$, the variety in question is simply $\mathfrak{N}_2$. By 35.12 $F_2(\mathfrak{N}_2)$ generates it, hence $F_k(\mathfrak{N}_2) \leqq (F_2(\mathfrak{N}_2))^m$ for some m. The projections of $F_k(\mathfrak{N}_2)$ into the factors of the direct power provide homomorphisms whose kernels intersect trivially. As in $F_k(\mathfrak{N}_2)$ the representation in terms of basic commutators is unique, by 31.53, the lemma follows in this case.

This forms the basis for an induction on the class and we now assume that the lemma is true for class $c-1$; it follows that all the basic commutators of weight $\leqq c-1$ in the representation of g must occur with exponent zero. We may therefore assume that only basic commutators of weight c occur. If any of these do actually occur, then we shall prove that there exists a homomorphism of G into A in which g has a non-trivial image.

Each commutator that occurs in $g = c_1^{\alpha_1} \dots c_l^{\alpha_l}$ involves a certain subset of the free generators $g_1, \dots, g_k$. Consider those amongst the c_i

that involve the least number of free generators, r say. Then there is an automorphism γ of G, given by a permutation of the generators, such that there occur in the representation of $g\gamma$ basic commutators involving precisely $g_1, \ldots, g_r$. Apply the endomorphism, π say, given by $g_i\pi = g_i$ for $i=1, \ldots, r$ and $g_i\pi = 1$ for $i=r+1, \ldots, k$. Then $g\gamma\pi$ is a product of basic commutators all of which involve precisely $g_1, \ldots, g_r$ and it is sufficient to find a homomorphism of G into A such that $g\gamma\pi$ has a non-trivial image.

Every left-normed basic commutator involving precisely $g_1, \ldots, g_r$ is of the form $[g_j, g_1, \ldots, g_1, g_2, \ldots, g_2, \ldots, g_r, \ldots, g_r]$ where g_i occurs $n_i > 0$ times and $2 \leqq j \leqq r$. By applying, possibly, another automorphism which permutes the free generators, γ' say, we can ensure that $g\gamma\pi\gamma'$ involves basic commutators starting with g_r, that is of the form

$$[g_r, g_1, \ldots, g_1, \ldots, g_r, \ldots, g_r]$$

where g_i occurs $n_i > 0$ times. Put $g\gamma\pi\gamma' = h$. We show that there is a homomorphism $\mu\colon G \to A$ such that $h\mu \neq 1$; then $g\gamma\pi\gamma'\mu \neq 1$ in A and we have finished.

We define μ by setting

$$g_i\mu = a^{m_i} \quad \text{for} \quad 1 \leqq i \leqq r-1,$$
$$g_r\mu = b^{m_r},$$
$$g_i\mu = 1 \quad \text{for} \quad i > r,$$

leaving the exponents m_i to be determined. With this μ, every basic commutator occurring in h that does not start with g_r is mapped on 1. Moreover

$$[g_r, g_1, \ldots, g_1, \ldots, g_r, \ldots, g_r]\mu = [b, a, \ldots, a, b, \ldots, b]^m$$

where the number of times that a occurs is $n(a) = n_1 + \cdots + n_{r-1}$, the number of times that b occurs is $n(b) = n_r$, and the exponent m is

$$m = m_1^{n_1} m_2^{n_2} \ldots m_r^{n_r},$$

using again the commutator expansion 33.34 (1) and the fact that we are operating in the c-th lower central term of a nilpotent group of class c.

We now pick out basic commutators occurring in h for which the value $n(b)$, and therefore also $n(a) = c - n(b)$, is constant. Let all these, for some fixed $n(b)$ that does occur, be $c_1, \ldots, c_s$ say. Then the images $c_1\mu, \ldots, c_s\mu$ are powers $d^{p_1}, \ldots, d^{p_s}$ of the same basic commutator $d = [b, n(a)\, a, (n(b)-1)\, b]$ in A. Now

$$h = c_1^{\alpha_1} \ldots c_s^{\alpha_s} h_1,$$

where the basic commutators occurring in h_1 have, under μ, images that are basic commutators different from d in A. By 36.23, the basic commutators in A are independent; hence to ensure that $h\mu \neq 1$ it suffices to ensure that $(c_1^{\alpha_1} \dots c_s^{\alpha_s})\,\mu = d^\delta \neq 1$ where

$$\delta = \alpha_1 p_1 + \dots + \alpha_s p_s.$$

But the p_i are products of powers of $m_1, \dots, m_r$ and the α_i are non-zero integral coefficients. Thus δ is the value of a non-trivial polynomial in r indeterminates, hence $m_1, \dots, m_r$ can be so chosen that $\delta \neq 0$. This completes the proof. //

We remark without giving details that close analysis of the last step of the proof (or use of 42.35) shows that the homomorphisms can be taken so that each one maps G onto A. This then shows that $F_k(\mathfrak{N}_c \wedge \mathfrak{A}^2)$ is in fact a subcartesian power of $F_2(\mathfrak{N}_c \wedge \mathfrak{A}^2)$. Using the fact that the free metabelian groups are residually nilpotent (cf. 26.32), one deduces, in confirmation of the remark on p. 69, that

36.35 *The free metabelian groups are residually two-generator metabelian groups.*

Chapter 4

Miscellaneous Properties of Relatively Free Groups

1. Remarks on Automorphisms and the Hopf Property

We consider free groups of finite rank and write F_k for the absolutely free group of rank k, freely generated by $\mathfrak{f}=\{f_1, \ldots, f_k\}$. An automorphism of F_k maps a verbal subgroup $U(F_k)$ onto itself; hence:

41.11 *Every automorphism of F_k induces an automorphism of the relatively free group $F_k(\mathfrak{U})\cong F_k/U(F_k)$ for every variety $\mathfrak{U}$.*

We listed in 11.41 a generating set of automorphisms of F_k and stated (11.42) that in the case of a free abelian group of rank k every automorphism is induced by an automorphism of the absolutely free group. This is clearly not true in general for relatively free groups; one certainly has:

41.12 *If $\mathfrak{U}$ has finite exponent m, then the endomorphism β of F_n defined by $f_i\beta=f_i^{n_i}$ $(i=1, \ldots, k)$ induces an automorphism of $F_k(\mathfrak{U})$ provided all n_i are relatively prime to m.*

Proof. For each i, $1\leqq i\leqq k$, there is an integer n_i' such that $n_i n_i'\equiv 1 \bmod m$. Hence if β' is the endomorphism of F_k defined by $f_i\beta'=f_i^{n_i'}$ $(i=1, \ldots, k)$, then $\beta\beta'$ and $\beta'\beta$ induce the identity on $F_k/U(F_k)$. //

41.21 **Theorem** (Mostowski [2]). *Let $G_k=F_k(\mathfrak{U})$; then every automorphism of the factor commutator group G_k/G_k' is induced by an automorphism of G_k.*

Proof. First assume the exponent of $\mathfrak{U}$ to be zero. Then $G_k/G_k'\cong F_k/F_k'$; using the natural isomorphism between these factor groups one sees from 11.42 that every automorphism α of G_k/G_k' is induced by an automorphism, α_1 say, of F_k. But α_1 induces an automorphism, α_2 say, on G_k, and α_2 induces α on the factor group.

Next let $\mathfrak{U}$ have exponent $m>0$ and let α be an automorphism of G_k/G_k'. If $g_1, \ldots, g_k$ generate G_k freely, then α is given by

$$g_i\alpha=\prod_j g_j^{a_{ij}} \mod G_k'.$$

Let A be the matrix of exponents a_{ij}; then there exist elementary row and column operations that transform A into diagonal form; equivalently, there exist automorphisms β_1 and β_2 of G_k – and these are even induced by automorphisms of F_k – such that $\beta_1 \alpha \beta_2$ is represented by a diagonal matrix modulo G_k', say

$$\beta_1 \alpha \beta_2 \leftrightarrow \operatorname{diag}(n_1, n_2, \dots, n_k).$$

As $\beta_1 \alpha \beta_2$ is an automorphism of G_k/G_k', all the integers n_i are relatively prime to m. By 41.12 there exists an automorphism δ of G_k such that $\beta_1 \alpha \beta_2 \delta$ is the identity on G_k/G_k'. Therefore α is induced by $\beta_1^{-1} \delta^{-1} \beta_2^{-1}$ which is an automorphism of G_k. //

41.22 **Corollary.** *If the exponent of* $\mathfrak{U}$ *is zero, there exists to each automorphism of* $F_k(\mathfrak{U})$ *an automorphism of* F_k *such that both induce the same automorphism on* $F_k(\mathfrak{A})$.

If the exponent of $\mathfrak{U}$ *is* $m>0$, *there exists to each automorphism of* $F_k(\mathfrak{U})$ *an automorphism of* $F_k(\mathfrak{B}_m)$ *such that both induce the same automorphism on* $F_k(\mathfrak{A}_m)$.

This is immediate from Theorem 41.21 and its proof. //

Little is known on the automorphisms of specific relatively free groups except in the case of free nilpotent groups whose automorphism groups have been described in fair detail by A. W. Mostowski [*2*] and S. Andreadakis [*1*]. Recently S. Bachmuth [*1*], [*2*] has investigated the automorphism group of a free metabelian group of finite rank finding in particular which automorphisms of its nilpotent free factor groups are induced by those of the whole group.

A group is said to be a *Hopf group*, or to have the *Hopf property*, if every ependomorphism (that is endomorphism onto the whole group) is an automorphism. Trivially:

41.31 *Every finite group is a Hopf group.*

41.32 *No free group* $F_\infty(\mathfrak{U})$, $\mathfrak{U} \neq \mathfrak{E}$, *is a Hopf group.*

Proof. Let $\mathfrak{g}$ be a set of free generators of $F_\infty(\mathfrak{U})$ indexed by I, then the mapping

$$g_1 \to 1 \quad \text{and} \quad g_i \to g_{i-1} \, (i>1)$$

defines an ependomorphism with non-trivial kernel. //

41.33 *A relatively free group* $F_k(\mathfrak{U})$ *is a Hopf group if and only if every set of* k *elements that generates the group generates it freely.*

Proof. Let $g_1, \dots, g_k$ be a set of free generators of $G_k = F_k(\mathfrak{U})$ and $G_k = \operatorname{gp}(a_1, \dots, a_k)$. Then the mapping α defined by $g_i\alpha = a_i$ $(i=1, \dots, k)$ is an ependomorphism of G_k. Conversely, for every ependomorphism α the images $g_i\alpha = a_i$ generate G_k. If w is a word, then $w(\mathfrak{g})\alpha = w(\mathfrak{a})$; therefore there exists an ependomorphism α with non-trivial kernel if and only if for some generating set $a_1, \ldots, a_k$ of G_k and some word $w \notin U$ one has $w(a_1, \ldots, a_k)=1$. But then, by 13.25, $\mathfrak{a}=\{a_1, \ldots, a_k\}$ does not generate G_k freely. //

We summarize what little is known about relatively free groups as regards the Hopf property.

41.41 **Lemma.** *A group A has the Hopf property if and only if it possesses a set of fully invariant subgroups whose factor groups have the Hopf property and whose intersection is trivial.*

Proof. The necessity is trivial. To prove sufficiency, let μ be an ependomorphism of A and N a fully invariant subgroup of A whose factor group is a Hopf group. As $N\mu \subseteq N$ and $A\mu = A$, μ induces an ependomorphism on A/N. By assumption this is an automorphism of A/N so that $\ker \mu \subseteq N$ follows. Hence the intersection of every set of such fully invariant subgroups contains $\ker \mu$. If the intersection is trivial, then $\ker \mu$ is trivial and μ is an automorphism. //

41.42 **Lemma.** *A finitely generated group is residually finite if and only if its fully invariant subgroups of finite index have trivial intersection.*

Proof. By 17.72, a group A is residually finite if and only if the normal subgroups of finite index have trivial intersection. Thus A is certainly residually finite if the fully invariant subgroups of finite index have trivial intersection. The converse will follow provided we know:

41.43 *In a finitely generated group every normal subgroup of finite index contains a fully invariant subgroup of finite index.*

Proof of 41.43. Let $A = F_k\alpha$ be a presentation of A, let N be normal of finite index in A and let S be the complete inverse image of N in F_k so that $S\alpha = N$. As S is of finite index in F_k, the free group of rank k of the variety var (F_k/S) is finite by 15.71; moreover F_k/S is a factor group of this free group. Hence, putting $F_k(\text{var}\,(F_k/S)) \cong F_k/V$, V is a verbal subgroup of F_k, of finite index in F_k and contained in S. Then $V\alpha$ is a verbal, hence fully invariant, subgroup of $F_k\alpha$ which is of finite index in $F_k\alpha = A$ and contained in $S\alpha = N$. //

Combining 41.31, 41.41 and 41.42 gives

41.44 **Corollary.** *A finitely generated residually finite group is a Hopf group.* //

Now we know (26.33) that the free polynilpotent groups are residually finite – in fact residually finite p-groups for every prime p; moreover:

41.51 *The absolutely free groups are residually finite p-groups for every prime p.*

Proof. If suffices to prove this for the case of finite rank. Consider, for given p, the varieties $\mathfrak{A}_p^m$ $(m>0)$. Each one is locally finite by 21.14, so that $F_k(\mathfrak{A}_p^m)$ is finite. Also, by 21.71,the powers $\mathfrak{A}_p^m$, $m=1, 2, \ldots$, generate $\mathfrak{O}$; therefore the verbal subgroups of F_k corresponding to the free groups $F_k(\mathfrak{A}_p^m)$ for all $m>0$ intersect in the trivial group. As each group $F_k(\mathfrak{A}_p^m)$ is a finite p-group, F_k is residually a finite p-group. //

Consequently:

41.52 **Theorem.** *The absolutely free groups of finite rank and the free polynilpotent groups of finite rank are Hopf groups.* //

This seems to be all that is known; in particular no relatively free Hopf groups other than residually finite ones are known.

The results of A. I. Kostrikin and P. S. Novikov together show (cf. 15.75, 15.76) that for a large enough prime p, $F_2(\mathfrak{B}_p)$ is not residually finite. Whether it has the Hopf property is not known.

Problem 15. *Are there relatively free groups of finite rank that are not Hopf groups?*

The following remark due to Peter M. Neumann is of interest in this context:

41.53 If $\mathfrak{B}$ *is soluble and* $F_k(\mathfrak{B})$ *is not a Hopf group, then the set of non-isomorphic k-generator groups in* $\mathfrak{B}$ *is not countable.*

Proof. If $H=F_k(\mathfrak{B})$ is non-Hopf, there exists a number l such that $H/H^{(l)}$ is a Hopf group but $H/H^{(l+1)}$ is not. By reducing modulo the term $H^{(l+1)}$ of the derived series we obtain a soluble free group of rank k in $\mathfrak{B}$ – in fact in a subvariety of $\mathfrak{B}$, but this is irrelevant – which is non-Hopf and the kernel of every proper ependomorphism lies in the last term of the derived series. Assume from now on that H itself has this property and that $H=F_k(\mathfrak{B})$. Let $N\subseteq H^{(l)}$ be the relevant kernel, so that $H/N\cong H$. We prove inductively that $H^{(l)}$ contains a direct power $N^{(I)}$ of countably many subgroups $N(i)$, each isomorphic to N and normal in H, such that every part product $N(1)\times\cdots\times N(n)$ has factor group isomorphic to H. Putting $N(1)=N$ gives the start of the induction. Assume that $L(m)=N(1)\times\cdots\times N(m)$ with the required properties has been found in $H^{(l)}$; then $H/L(m)\cong H$. Anticipating the result 44.21 (with 44.22 and 44.23) that every extension of a group in the variety by a relatively free group in the variety splits, we obtain that $L(m)$ is complemented in H by a subgroup H_1 isomorphic to H. Let N_1 be the subgroup corresponding to $N=N(1)$ in H under this isomorphism.

Now $N_1\subseteq H_1^{(l)}\subseteq H^{(l)}$, which is abelian; hence N_1 is centralized by $L(m)\subseteq H^{(l)}$. As N_1 is normal in H_1 and $H=H_1L(m)$, N_1 is normal in H. Clearly $N_1\cap L(m)=\{1\}$, hence N_1 and $L(m)$ generate their direct product.

Putting $N(m+1)=N_1$ and $L(m+1)=L(m)\times N(m+1)$ completes the inductive step as $L(m+1)$ is normal in H and

$$H/L(m+1)\cong H/L(m)/L(m+1)/L(m)\cong H_1/N_1\cong H.$$

Now take $N^{(I)}$ to be the direct limit of the direct products $L(m)$, $m\in I$; then $N^{(I)}$ is normal in H, every one of its constituents is normal in H, so therefore is $N^{(J)}$ for every subset $J\subseteq I$. Thus there are $2^{\aleph_0}$ different homomorphic mappings of H. But a fixed k-generator group of $\mathfrak{V}$ is the epimorphic image of $H=F_k(\mathfrak{V})$ in at most a countable number of ways as the epimorphism is determined by the image of a fixed free generating set of H. Thus there must be uncountably many non-isomorphic k-generator groups in $\mathfrak{V}$. //

It is worth while at this point to reflect on the following facts: the variety $\mathfrak{N}_2\mathfrak{A}$ contains uncountably many non-isomorphic finitely generated groups and contains finitely generated non-Hopf groups (B. H. NEUMANN and HANNA NEUMANN [*1*]); the variety $[\mathfrak{C}, \mathfrak{A}^2]$ of all 'centre-extended-by-metabelian' groups has the same two properties (P. HALL [*3*] and [*5*]). Finitely generated metabelian groups are Hopf groups and there are only countably many finitely generated metabelian groups (P. HALL [*3*]). This suggests the question:

Problem 16 (PETER M. NEUMANN). *Is it true that a locally soluble variety contains finitely generated non-Hopf groups if and only if it contains uncountably many non-isomorphic finitely generated groups?*

2. Free Subgroups of Free Groups

Schreier's result that every subgroup of an absolutely free group is absolutely free is classical. Similarly, every subgroup of a free abelian group is free abelian, and – trivially – every subgroup of an $\mathfrak{A}_p$-free group is $\mathfrak{A}_p$-free. Thus:

42.1 *The varieties $\mathfrak{O}$, $\mathfrak{A}$, $\mathfrak{A}_p$ (p a prime) have the property that every subgroup of a free group of the variety is free in the variety.*

We say, $\mathfrak{O}$, $\mathfrak{A}$, $\mathfrak{A}_p$ are *Schreier varieties*. It has long been conjectured but only very recently been proved by PETER M. NEUMANN and JAMES WIEGOLD (cf. Section 3 of this chapter) that these are the only Schreier varieties. It is however obvious that most well known varieties are not Schreier varieties. In these the question arises under what condition a subset of a free group generates freely a group that is free in the same variety. One has immediately, from 13.21, say:

42.2 *If $\mathfrak{s}$ is a subset of the free group $F(\mathfrak{U})$, then $\mathfrak{s}$ generates freely a $\mathfrak{U}$-free group if and only if every finite subset of $\mathfrak{s}$ has this property.* //

The following two subgroup theorems 42.31 and 42.35 are closely related but neither follows from the other.

42.31 **Theorem** (P. Hall [2], Mostowski [2]). *Let $\mathfrak{U}$ be a variety whose free groups are residually nilpotent. If $\mathfrak{s}$ is a subset of $F(\mathfrak{U})$ that generates $(\mathfrak{U} \wedge \mathfrak{A})$-freely modulo $F'(\mathfrak{U})$ a direct factor of $F(\mathfrak{U})/F'(\mathfrak{U})$ then $\mathfrak{s}$ generates freely a $\mathfrak{U}$-free subgroup of $F(\mathfrak{U})$.*

Proof. We have to consider several cases. First assume $\mathfrak{s}=\{s_1, \ldots, s_k\}$ and $G=F_k(\mathfrak{U})$. In this case the data mean that $\mathfrak{s}$ generates G modulo G'. If therefore $g_1, \ldots, g_k$ are free generators of G, then there is an automorphism of G/G' that takes g_i into s_i modulo G' for $i=1, \ldots, k$. By 41.21 this automorphism of G/G' is induced by an automorphism of G. Thus after applying this automorphism and renaming the generators we may assume $g_i \equiv s_i$ modulo G', that is $s_i = g_i c_i$ with $c_i \in G'$ for $i=1, \ldots, k$. Put $g_i \sigma = s_i$; this defines an endomorphism of G which induces the identity on G/G'. To show that σ is mono, take $g \in G$ such that $g\sigma = 1$; then trivially $g\sigma$ lies in every lower central term $G_{(m+1)}$ of G. But for every m, $G_{(m)}/G_{(m+1)}$ is generated, modulo $G_{(m+1)}$, by the left-normed commutators $[g_{i(1)}, \ldots, g_{i(m)}]$ of the free generators. As

$$[g_{i(1)}, \ldots, g_{i(m)}]\sigma = [g_{i(1)} c_{i(1)}, \ldots, g_{i(m)} c_{i(m)}] \equiv [g_{i(1)}, \ldots, g_{i(m)}] \bmod G_{(m+1)},$$

σ induces the identity on each central factor $G_{(m)}/G_{(m+1)}$. Thus $g\sigma \in G_{(m+1)}$ implies $g \in G_{(m+1)}$ for every m. But $\bigcap_m G_{(m)} = \{1\}$ as G is residually nilpotent, therefore $g=1$ as required.

Next assume $G=F_k(\mathfrak{U})$ as before, but $\mathfrak{s}=\{s_1, \ldots, s_l\}$ with $l<k$. By assumption $\mathfrak{s}$ can be completed by elements $s_{l+1}, \ldots, s_k$ to a set of elements of G that form a basis modulo G'. Using the first step we know that $s_1, \ldots, s_k$ generate freely a free subgroup of G, so therefore do the elements $s_1, \ldots, s_l$ which form a subset of this set.

Finally let $G=F(\mathfrak{U})$ be of arbitrary infinite rank and let $\mathfrak{s}$ be any set generating freely modulo G' a direct factor of G/G'. We complete $\mathfrak{s}$ to a set generating freely the whole of G/G' modulo G'; then by 42.2 it suffices to show that every finite subset of this completed set generates freely a free subgroup of G. Thus we may assume $\mathfrak{s}=\{s_i, \ldots, s_k\}$ to be finite. If $\mathfrak{g}$ is a set of free generators of G, there exists l such that $S=\operatorname{gp}(s_1, \ldots, s_k) \subseteq \operatorname{gp}(g_1, \ldots, g_l)$. Then $G_l = \operatorname{gp}(g_1, \ldots, g_l) \cong F_l(\mathfrak{U})$ and $SG'/G' \subseteq G_l G'/G'$; as a direct factor of G/G' contained in $G_l G'/G'$, SG'/G' is also a direct factor of $G_l G'/G'$. Moreover $SG'/G' \cong S/S \cap G' = S/S \cap G_l'$ and by 13.41 and 13.42 $G_l G'/G' \cong G_l/G_l'$, so that $\mathfrak{s}$ generates modulo G_l' a direct factor of G_l and we are in the situation of the previous case. This shows that $\mathfrak{s}$ generates freely a free subgroup of G_l, hence of G. //

42.32 **Corollary.** *If $\mathfrak{U}$ is a variety whose free groups are residually nilpotent and have the property that a subset $\mathfrak{s}$ which generates $F(\mathfrak{U})$ modulo $F'(\mathfrak{U})$ generates the whole of $F(\mathfrak{U})$, then an endomorphism of $F(\mathfrak{U})$ that induces an automorphism on $F(\mathfrak{U})/F'(\mathfrak{U})$ is an automorphism of $F(\mathfrak{U})$.* //

By 31.25 this applies in particular to every nilpotent variety.

The following example shows that in Theorem 42.31 it is not sufficient to assume that the set $\mathfrak{s}$ freely generates a free subgroup of $F(\mathfrak{U})/F'(\mathfrak{U})$:

42.33 **Example** (Mostowski [2]). Take $G=\text{gp}(a, b)$ nilpotent of class two with derived group of exponent two; that is G is the free group of rank two of the variety defined by the laws $[x, y, z]$ and $[x, y]^2$. As G is of exponent zero, G/G' is free abelian generated by a and b modulo G'. The elements a^2 and b generate modulo G' a free subgroup, but they do not generate freely a free subgroup of G, because $[a^2, b]=[a, b]^2=1$ and so $\text{gp}(a^2, b)$ is abelian.

However, in this case of a set $\mathfrak{s}$ consisting of elements of G that are merely independent modulo G', different conditions on $\mathfrak{U}$ provide the desired result.

42.34 **Lemma.** *Let $\mathfrak{U}$ be a variety whose free groups are residually finite p-groups. Let $G=F_k(\mathfrak{U})$ be freely generated by $g_1, \ldots, g_k$ and $s_i=g_i^{m_i} c_i$ with m_i prime to p and $c_i \in G'$ for $i=1, \ldots, k$. Then $s_1, \ldots, s_k$ freely generate a $\mathfrak{U}$-free subgroup of G.*

Proof. Define the endomorphism σ of G by setting $g_i \sigma=s_i$ $(i=1, \ldots, k)$; we show that it is a monomorphism. Assume $g\sigma=1$ for some $g \neq 1$. Then there is a normal subgroup N of G avoiding g such that G/N is of order p^r, say, and so nilpotent, of class c, say. Let $V(G)$ be the verbal subgroup of G defined by the words x^{p^r} and $[x_1, x_2, \ldots, x_{c+1}]$; then $V(G) \subseteq N$ so that $V(G)$ also avoids g. Now $H=G/V(G)$ is a finite relatively free group; let μ be the natural epimorphism $\mu\colon G \twoheadrightarrow H$. As σ is an endomorphism of G, $\sigma\mu$ is a homomorphism of G into H and $g\sigma\mu=1$. On the other hand the elements $g_i\mu$ are free generators of H so that putting $g_i\mu\sigma^*=g_i\sigma\mu$ defines an endomorphism σ^* of H. From the definition of σ,

$$g_i \mu \sigma^* = g_i \sigma \mu = (g_i^{m_i} c_i) \mu = (g_i \mu)^{m_i} c_i \mu .$$

As each m_i is prime to the exponent of H, the elements $(g_i\mu)^{m_i} c_i\mu$ generate H modulo H'; as H is nilpotent, they generate H (31.25). Thus σ^* is a mapping of H onto H, hence an automorphism since H is finite. Next use again that the g_i generate G to see that $g_i\mu\sigma^*=g_i\sigma\mu$ for all i implies $g'\mu\sigma^*=g'\sigma\mu$ for every $g' \in G$. Take in particular the element g with $g\sigma=1$; then $g\mu\sigma^*=1$ and so $g\mu=1$. But this contradicts the choice of μ since $\ker \mu=V(G)$ avoids g. //

This gives

42.35 **Theorem** (BAUMSLAG [3]). *Let* $\mathfrak{U}$ *be a variety whose free groups are residually finite p-groups for infinitely many primes p. If* $\mathfrak{s}$ *is a subset of* $F(\mathfrak{U})$ *that generates freely modulo* $F'(\mathfrak{U})$ *a free subgroup of* $F(\mathfrak{U})/F'(\mathfrak{U})$*, then* $\mathfrak{s}$ *generates freely a* $\mathfrak{U}$*-free subgroup of* $F(\mathfrak{U})$.

Proof. As in the proof of Theorem 42.31 the general case can be reduced to the situation where $\mathfrak{s}=\{s_1, \ldots, s_k\}$ is a finite subset of $G=F_n(\mathfrak{U})$ $(n \geqq k)$ that is independent modulo G'. Next note that $\mathfrak{s}$ may be replaced by any set $\mathfrak{s}\alpha$ where α is the result of 'Nielsen operations' as described in 11.41 (i.e. α is an operation on a set of k elements that induces an automorphism of the free group on k elements); for in any group $\mathfrak{s}$ and $\mathfrak{s}\alpha$ generate the same subgroup and $\mathfrak{s}$ generates it freely if and only if $\mathfrak{s}\alpha$ does. Consider $\mathfrak{s}$ modulo G'. In the free abelian group G/G' bases of G/G' and $\mathrm{gp}(\mathfrak{s})$ can be chosen so that the basis of $\mathrm{gp}(\mathfrak{s})$ consists of powers of basis elements of G/G'. Hence in G an equivalent set $\mathfrak{s}\alpha$ and a new basis of G can be chosen so that

$$s_i \alpha = g_i^{m_i} c_i, \qquad c_i \in G', \qquad \text{for } i=1, \ldots, k.$$

If $k<n$, add $n-k$ elements $s_j = g_j$ for $j=k+1, \ldots, n$. By the assumption on $\mathfrak{U}$ there is a prime p such that p does not divide the m_i and G is residually a finite p-group. Hence Lemma 42.34 shows that the set of all elements $s_i\alpha$ and s_j generates freely a $\mathfrak{U}$-free group; so therefore does the subset $\mathfrak{s}\alpha$, and therefore also $\mathfrak{s}$. //

A slight modification of the argument gives the following further variation on Theorems 42.31 and 42.35:

42.36 **Theorem** (PETER M. NEUMANN [3]). *If the free groups of* $\mathfrak{U}$ *are residually nilpotent* π*-groups for some fixed non-empty set* π *of primes, and if* $\mathfrak{s}$ *is a subset of* $F(\mathfrak{U})$ *that is independent modulo* $F'(\mathfrak{U})$ *and such that the periodic subgroup of* $F(\mathfrak{U})/F'(\mathfrak{U})\ \mathrm{gp}(\mathfrak{s})$ *is a* π'*-group*★*, then* $\mathfrak{s}$ *generates freely a* $\mathfrak{U}$*-free subgroup of* $F(\mathfrak{U})$. //

These results, or the arguments leading up to them, help to give similar information also in the case of certain product varieties, though additional tools are needed. Firstly the result of BAUMSLAG [2] that for a normal subgroup R of F, $F/U(R)$ is residually a finite p-group, provided F/R and $R/U(R) \cong F(\mathfrak{U})$ have this property (cf. the remark following 22.47), will be wanted at least in the special case when F/R is $\mathfrak{V}$-free (but not necessarily free on the generators obtained from free generators of F). Secondly we need the following remark that is useful in various contexts:

★ If π is a set of primes, π' is the complementary set of primes; a group is a π-group if the orders of its elements are divisible only by primes in π.

42.41 *If F^* is a free factor of the absolutely free group F, R is normal in F and W a set of words then $W(R)\cap F^*=W(R\cap F^*)$ and $W(R\cap F^*)$ is a free factor of $W(R)$.*

Proof. By Kurosh's subgroup theorem applied to a normal subgroup of a free product (KUROSH, Vol. 2, p. 17; MARSHALL HALL, p. 315) the intersection of a free factor of F with a normal subgroup is a free factor of the normal subgroup. Hence $R=(R\cap F^*)*T$ for some $T\subseteq R$. Then, by 12.62, or 18.22, $W(R)\cap(R\cap F^*)=W(R\cap F^*)$ and the left hand side is $W(R)\cap F^*$ as required. Applying the subgroup theorem once more to the normal subgroup $W(R)$ of F we see that $W(R)\cap F^*$ is a free factor of $W(R)$. //

Now we can prove

42.42 **Lemma** (BAUMSLAG [5]). *Let $\mathfrak{U}$ and $\mathfrak{V}$ be varieties whose free groups are residually finite p-groups for the same prime p; let R be a normal subgroup of the absolutely free group F such that F/R is $\mathfrak{V}$-free, freely generated modulo R by the subset $\mathfrak{s}$ of F. Then $\mathfrak{s}$ generates freely, modulo $U(R)$, a $\mathfrak{U}\mathfrak{V}$-free group.*

Proof. As before it is sufficient, by 42.2, to prove the conclusion for every finite subset $\mathfrak{s}^*$ of $\mathfrak{s}$. Replace F by the (free) subgroup $F^*=\mathrm{gp}(\mathfrak{s}^*)\,R$ of F; then the assumptions of the lemma are restored and the conclusion shows that $\mathfrak{s}^*$ generates freely modulo $U(R)$ a $\mathfrak{U}\mathfrak{V}$-free group in F^*, hence in F. Thus we now assume $\mathfrak{s}=\{s_1,\dots,s_k\}$.

Now $\mathfrak{s}$ is contained in some free factor F_n of finite rank n. Then, as $\mathrm{gp}(\mathfrak{s})\,R=F$, one has $\mathrm{gp}(\mathfrak{s})\,(R\cap F_n)=F_n$. As, by 42.41,

$$F_n\,U(R)/U(R)\cong F_n/U(R)\cap F_n=F_n/U(R\cap F_n),$$

replacing F by F_n and R by $R\cap F_n$ shows that we may assume that F has finite rank $n\geqq k$.

The next step is to choose suitable free generators of F. As $\mathfrak{s}$ generates freely the $\mathfrak{V}$-free group F/R, it generates freely modulo $F'R$ the factor commutator group $F/F'R$ of this $\mathfrak{V}$-free group of rank k. As $\mathfrak{V}$-free groups are residually finite p-groups, $F/F'R$ is either free abelian of rank k, and then a direct factor of F/F', or free abelian of exponent p^r (for some $r>0$) of rank k. Therefore $\mathfrak{s}$ generates freely modulo F' either a direct factor of F/F' or of F/F' modulo its subgroup of all p^r-th powers. Hence, as in the proof of 42.35, we can replace $\mathfrak{s}$ by an equivalent set $\mathfrak{s}\alpha$ and choose a set $\mathfrak{f}=\{f_1,\dots,f_n\}$ of free generators of F so that

(1) $$s_i\alpha=f_i^{m_i}c_i,\quad c_i\in F',\quad i=1,\dots,k,$$

(2) $$f_i\in RF',\quad i=k+1,\dots,n,$$

where $m_i = 1$ if $\mathfrak{V}$-free groups have exponent zero, m_i prime to p otherwise. That is, we may assume

$$(2') \qquad f_i c_i \in R \quad \text{for some} \quad c_i \in F', \quad i = k+1, \dots, n.$$

Now put $F_k = \mathrm{gp}(f_1, \dots, f_k)$ so that F_k is a free factor of F. As the $s_i\alpha$ generate freely a $\mathfrak{V}$-free group modulo R, which is certainly residually nilpotent, Theorem 42.31 shows that $f_1, \dots, f_k$ generate freely modulo R a $\mathfrak{V}$-free subgroup of F/R. But then

$$F_k R/R \cong F_k/F_k \cap R \cong F_k/V(F_k),$$

so that $F_k \cap R \supseteq V(F_k)$. As $\mathfrak{V}$-free groups of finite rank are Hopf groups by 41.44, $R \cap F_k = V(F_k)$ follows. Now 42.41 gives $U(R) \cap F_k = U(R \cap F_k) = U(V(F_k))$, so that

$$F_k U(R)/U(R) \cong F_k/U(R) \cap F_k = F_k/U(V(F_k)),$$

showing that $f_1, \dots, f_k$ generates freely, modulo $U(V(F_k))$, a $\mathfrak{U}\mathfrak{V}$-free group. As $\mathrm{gp}(\mathfrak{s})U(R)/U(R)$ certainly belongs to $\mathfrak{U}\mathfrak{V}$, the mapping φ defined by

$$\varphi\colon \; f_i \to f_i^{m_i} c_i = s_i \alpha, \qquad i = 1, \dots, k,$$

induces an epimorphism

$$\varphi\colon \; F_k U(R)/U(R) \twoheadrightarrow \mathrm{gp}(\mathfrak{s})\, U(R)/U(R).$$

It remains to show that this is a monomorphism.

Assume then that $g \in F_k$ does not belong to $U(R)$. We have to show: $g\varphi \notin U(R)$, and this is achieved by reducing the situation to one in a finite p-group by means of the fact that $F/U(R)$ is residually a finite p-group. There exists therefore a normal subgroup L of F containing $U(R)$ such that $g \notin L$ and F/L is a finite p-group. Let F/L have class c and exponent p^d, then RL/L and F/RL are finite p-groups of class at most c and exponent p^d. We denote, temporarily, the variety of all nilpotent groups of class at most c and exponent p^d by $\mathfrak{N}_{c,d}$. Then $N_{c,d}(F) \subseteq L$; also

$$RL/L \in \mathfrak{U} \cap \mathfrak{N}_{c,d} = \mathfrak{U}_1, \qquad \text{say},$$

$$F/RL \in \mathfrak{V} \cap \mathfrak{N}_{c,d} = \mathfrak{V}_1, \qquad \text{say},$$

so that further $F/L \in \mathfrak{U}_1 \mathfrak{V}_1$. We now use $S = RN_{c,d}(F)$ in place of R. Certainly $S \subseteq RL$; hence, as $U_1(RL) \subseteq L$, also $U_1(S) \subseteq L$. Therefore we are sure that $g \notin U_1(S)$.

Also, as F/R is $\mathfrak{V}$-free, of rank k, F/S – by definition of S – is $\mathfrak{V}_1$-free of rank k. As $f_1, \dots, f_k$ generate F/R modulo the derived group, they also generate F/S modulo $F'S$. But F/S is nilpotent, hence $f_1, \dots, f_k$ generate it modulo S. Now F/S is a finite free group, hence a Hopf group;

so, by 41.33, $f_1 S, \ldots, f_k S$ are free generators of F/S. Now $F/S = F_k S/S \cong F_k/F_k \cap S$, and so $F_k \cap S = V_1(F_k)$ follows. By 42.41, $U_1(F_k \cap S) = F_k \cap U_1(S) = U_1(V_1(F_k))$, so that $F_k U_1(S)/U_1(S)$ is a $\mathfrak{U}_1 \mathfrak{V}_1$-free group freely generated modulo $U_1(S)$ by $f_1, \ldots, f_k$. Now $g \notin U_1(S)$ means that g is non-trivial in $F_k U_1(S)/U_1(S) \cong F_k/U_1(V_1(F_k))$.

Consider now $F/U_1(V_1(F)) = K$, say. Let ν: $F \twoheadrightarrow K$ be the natural epimorphism. K is a finite p-group, freely generated by the elements $f_i \nu$, $i = 1, \ldots, n$. As K is nilpotent, modifying the generators by factors in the derived group gives again a set of generators. Going back to (2′), this shows that K is also generated, hence freely generated, by the elements $f_i \nu$, $i = 1, \ldots, k$ and $(f_i c_i)\nu$, $i = k+1, \ldots, n$, where the c_i were so chosen that $f_i c_i \in R \subseteq S$ for $i > k$. Hence the kernel of the projection of K onto the subgroup generated by $f_1 \nu, \ldots, f_k \nu$ is contained in $S\nu$. Thus, as $U_1(V_1(F)) \subseteq S$ by definition of S, the complete inverse image P of this kernel in F is contained in S. By definition of P, F/P is a free $\mathfrak{U}_1 \mathfrak{V}_1$-group, freely generated modulo P by $f_1, \ldots, f_k$; hence $g \notin P$. As F/P is a free finite p-group freely generated by $f_1 P, \ldots, f_k P$ it follows from (1) that the elements $f_1^{m_1} c_1 P, \ldots, f_k^{m_k} c_k P$ also generate F/P freely. Thus φ induces an automorphism of F/P and so $g\varphi \notin P$.

Finally, as F/S is $\mathfrak{V}_1$-free, $S/P = V_1(F/P)$ follows, and $S/P \in \mathfrak{U}_1$. Hence $U_1(S) \subseteq P$. By definition of S, $U(R) \subseteq U_1(R) \subseteq U_1(S) \subseteq P$, and $g\varphi \notin P$ implies $g\varphi \notin U(R)$ as required. //

This leads to:

42.43 **Theorem** (Baumslag [5]). *Let $\mathfrak{U}$ and $\mathfrak{V}$ be varieties whose free groups are residually finite p-groups for the same prime p; let $\mathfrak{s}$ be a subset of $K = F(\mathfrak{U}\mathfrak{V})$ which generates freely modulo $V(K)$ a $\mathfrak{W}$-free group. Then $\mathfrak{s}$ generates freely a $\mathfrak{U}\mathfrak{W}$-free subgroup of K.*

Proof. The $\mathfrak{W}$-free subgroup of $K/V(K)$ freely generated by $\mathfrak{s}$ modulo $V(K)$ is residually a finite p-group, since $K/V(K)$ is residually a finite p-group.

Take a presentation $K \cong F/U(V(F))$ and in F take a set $\mathfrak{s}^*$ of counter images of $\mathfrak{s}$; then $V(F)\,\mathrm{gp}(\mathfrak{s}^*) = F^*$ is as subgroup of F absolutely free. Also $V(F)$ is normal in F^*, and $F^*/V(F)$ is isomorphic to the $\mathfrak{W}$-free group generated by $\mathfrak{s}$ in $K/V(K) \cong F/V(F)$. Thus one wants to apply Lemma 42.42 with F^* in place of F, $V(F) \lhd F^*$ in place of R and $\mathfrak{W}$ in place of $\mathfrak{V}$. However, we do not know that $\mathfrak{W}$-free groups are residually finite p-groups; we know it only of the one $\mathfrak{W}$-free group of rank $|\mathfrak{s}|$. If $\mathfrak{s}$ is finite, $|\mathfrak{s}| = k$ say, and $F_k(\mathfrak{W})$ does not generate $\mathfrak{W}$, we consider the subvariety $\mathfrak{W}_1 = \mathrm{var}(F_k(\mathfrak{W}))$ of $\mathfrak{W}$. Its free groups, as subgroups of cartesian powers of $F_k(\mathfrak{W})$, are residually finite p-groups, like $F_k(\mathfrak{W})$. Therefore, with $\mathfrak{W}_1$ in place of $\mathfrak{W}$ the lemma applies and shows that $\mathfrak{s}$

generates freely a $\mathfrak{U}\mathfrak{W}_1$-free subgroup of K. But this is an extension of a $\mathfrak{U}$-free group by $F_k(\mathfrak{W}_1)$ and as $\mathfrak{W}_1$ is generated by $F_k(\mathfrak{W})$, we have $F_k(\mathfrak{W}_1)=F_k(\mathfrak{W})$ (cf. 16.52). Hence in fact $\mathrm{gp}(\mathfrak{s})\cong F_k(\mathfrak{U}\mathfrak{W}_1)=F_k(\mathfrak{U}\mathfrak{W})$ as required. //

The conditions imposed on $\mathfrak{U}$ and $\mathfrak{V}$ in Theorem 42.43 are necessary:

42.44 **Example** Take $\mathfrak{U}=\mathfrak{A}_3$ and $\mathfrak{V}=\mathfrak{A}_2$. The group $F_2(\mathfrak{A}_3\mathfrak{A}_2)$ is, as the two factor varieties have coprime exponents, a splitting extension of $F_5(\mathfrak{A}_3)$ – the rank is given by Schreier's formula – by $F_2(\mathfrak{A}_2)$. The complement of $F_5(\mathfrak{A}_3)$ in $F_2(\mathfrak{A}_3\mathfrak{A}_2)$ is a four-group, that is isomorphic to $F_2(\mathfrak{A}_2)$, freely generated by two elements of order two which are independent modulo $F_5(\mathfrak{A}_3)$ but which commute and so do not generate an $\mathfrak{A}_3\mathfrak{A}_2$-free subgroup. One checks further that the centre of this group is of rank two and contained in the subgroup $F_5(\mathfrak{A}_3)$. Its direct product with a complement of $F_5(\mathfrak{A}_3)$ is an abelian free subgroup of rank two, order 6^2, of $F_2(\mathfrak{A}_3\mathfrak{A}_2)$. This also is generated by two elements that modulo $F_5(\mathfrak{A}_3)$ generate an $\mathfrak{A}_2$-free group; this shows incidentally that $F_2(\mathfrak{A}_3\mathfrak{A}_2)$ contains $\mathfrak{A}_6$-free subgroups.

In some cases the sufficient condition in the preceding theorems can be shown to be necessary. This can of course not be expected without some restriction on the variety: the absolutely free groups are residually nilpotent, and residually finite p-groups for every prime p, but sets of elements generating freely a free subgroup can be found anywhere in an absolutely free group. The converses we discuss refer to nilpotent and polynilpotent varieties.

42.51 **Theorem** (Mostowski [*1*]). *Let $G=F(\mathfrak{N}_c)$; the subset $\mathfrak{s}$ of G consisting of at least two elements generates freely an $\mathfrak{N}_c$-free group if and only if it is independent modulo G'.*

Proof. The sufficiency follows from 42.35 since G is residually a finite p-group for all p, by 32.22.

Assume then that $\mathfrak{s}$ generates freely the subgroup H of G. Then it generates freely modulo H' a free abelian group. As G/G' is free, $\mathfrak{s}$ is independent modulo G' if and only if $H'=G'\cap H$.

Suppose that $H'\subset G'\cap H$ and take $h\in H\cap G'$ such that $h\notin H'$. As H/H' is of rank $\geqq 2$, we can find $h_1\in H$ such that h and h_1 are independent modulo H'. By Theorem 42.35, $\mathrm{gp}(h, h_1)$ is free nilpotent of class c precisely, and freely generated by h and h_1; hence in particular the commutator $[h, (c-1)h_1]$ is non-trivial in H. But $h\in G'$, so that this commutator belongs to $G_{(c+1)}=\{1\}$, which is a contradiction. //

To establish similar theorems for free polynilpotent groups, we need some preparation.

42.52 **Lemma** (GILBERT BAUMSLAG, unpublished). *If* $\mathfrak{U} \neq \mathfrak{E}$ *and the free groups of* $\mathfrak{B}$ *are torsion-free then a non-cyclic nilpotent subgroup of* $K = F(\mathfrak{U}\mathfrak{B})$ *that has non-trivial intersection with* $G = V(K)$ *lies in* G.

If moreover the free groups of $\mathfrak{U}$ *and* $\mathfrak{B}$ *are residually finite p-groups for the same prime p, then every non-cyclic nilpotent subgroup of K lies in G.*

Proof. Let $N \subseteq K$ be nilpotent, non-cyclic, and $N \nsubseteq G$. Take $a \in N \backslash G$; $N \cap G$ is a non-trivial normal subgroup of N, hence intersects the centre non-trivially. Thus there is an element $b \neq 1$ of $N \cap G$ such that $[a, b] = 1$. As K/G is $\mathfrak{B}$-free, it is torsion-free and so a has infinite order modulo G; hence by 25.63, the centralizer of a intersects $V(K) = G$ trivially, giving a contradiction.

Assume now that $N \cap G = \{1\}$, but that $F(\mathfrak{U})$ and $F(\mathfrak{B})$ are residually finite p-groups for some p. Take a and b in N such that $\text{gp}(a, b)$ is abelian, non-cyclic. Then a and b generate a free abelian group modulo $V(K)$, and by Theorem 42.43 they generate freely a $\mathfrak{U}\mathfrak{A}$-free group, contradicting the assumption that $\text{gp}(a, b)$ is abelian. //

Note that the restrictions on $\mathfrak{U}$ and $\mathfrak{B}$ in the lemma are stronger than really necessary. However, this is all we need; the proof of a more general lemma is rather more tedious.

42.53 **Corollary.** *If* $K = F(\mathfrak{N}_{c_l} \ldots \mathfrak{N}_{c_1})$ *is free polynilpotent and the verbal subgroups* K_λ $(\lambda = 0, \ldots, l)$ *are defined by* $K = K_0$, $K_\lambda = (K_{\lambda-1})_{(c_\lambda+1)}$ *so that* $K_l = \{1\}$, *then every nilpotent non-cyclic subgroup lies in* K_{l-1}. //

We recall the following concepts: The *upper nilpotent series* (if it exists) of a group A is defined to be the series $\{1\} = A_0 \subset A_1 \subset \ldots$ where A_{i+1}/A_i is the unique maximal normal nilpotent subgroup of A/A_i. The *lower nilpotent series* (if it exists) of a group B is defined to be the series $B = B_0 \supset B_1 \supset \ldots$ where B_i is the minimal normal subgroup of B_{i-1} such that B_{i-1}/B_i is nilpotent. Now 42.53 shows:

42.54 **Theorem.** *If* $K = F(\mathfrak{N}_{c_l} \ldots \mathfrak{N}_{c_1})$, *then the verbal subgroup series* $K = K_0 \supset K_1 \supset \ldots \supset K_l = \{1\}$ *is the upper nilpotent series of K.* //

Observe however that K does not possess a lower nilpotent series: as K is residually nilpotent, its normal subgroups with nilpotent factor groups have trivial intersection.

We can now prove

42.55 **Theorem** (BAUMSLAG [5]). *Let* $K = F(\mathfrak{N}_{c_l} \ldots \mathfrak{N}_{c_1})$, $l \geqq 1$. *A subset* $\mathfrak{s}$ *of K containing at least two elements generates freely a free polynilpotent subgroup of K if and only if it generates freely modulo some term* $K_m (m \geqq 1)$ *of the upper nilpotent series a free nilpotent group, of class d say, and then* $\text{gp}(\mathfrak{s}) \cong F(\mathfrak{N}_{c_l} \ldots \mathfrak{N}_{c_{m+1}} \mathfrak{N}_d)$.

Proof. The sufficiency follows from Theorem 42.43 with

$$\mathfrak{U}=\mathfrak{N}_{c_l}\ldots\mathfrak{N}_{c_{m+1}} \quad\text{and}\quad \mathfrak{V}=\mathfrak{N}_{c_m}\ldots\mathfrak{N}_{c_1}$$

using the structure of the free groups of a product variety (21.13).

Assume conversely that $\mathfrak{s}$ generates freely a free polynilpotent subgroup of K and assume that $\mathfrak{s}$ is contained in K_{m-1} but not in K_m; then $m\geqq 1$. As K_{m-1} is the free group, of some rank, of $\mathfrak{N}_{c_l}\ldots\mathfrak{N}_{c_m}$ we may without loss of generality assume $m=1$. Put $\operatorname{gp}(\mathfrak{s})=H$; by 42.54, H has a unique maximal normal nilpotent subgroup which is non-trivial as H is free polynilpotent; by 42.52 it lies in K_{l-1}. As $K_{l-1}\cap H$ is a normal nilpotent subgroup of H, it follows that $H_{l-1}=H\cap K_{l-1}$ is the maximal normal nilpotent subgroup of H, hence verbal by 42.54. Therefore reducing K modulo K_{l-1} reduces H modulo H_{l-1} giving the free polynilpotent subgroup H/H_{l-1} of the free polynilpotent group K/K_{l-1}. As the theorem is trivial for $l=1$, induction completes the proof. //

Combining 42.55 and 42.51 gives:

42.56 **Theorem** (Šmel'kin [*2*]). *Let* $K=F(\mathfrak{P})$ *where* $\mathfrak{P}=\mathfrak{N}_{c_l}\ldots\mathfrak{N}_{c_1}$. *A subset* $\mathfrak{s}$ *of* K *consisting of at least two elements generates freely a* $\mathfrak{P}$*-free subgroup of* K *if and only if it is independent modulo* K'. //

42.57 **Corollary** (Baumslag [*3*], Šmel'kin [*2*]). *A subset* $\mathfrak{s}$ *consisting of at least two elements of a free soluble group* $G=F(\mathfrak{A}^l)$ *generates freely a free soluble subgroup if and only if it is independent modulo some term of the derived series of* G.

This is immediate from either 42.55 or 42.56. //

These results leave unanswered, even in the limited range of varieties considered, the question what relatively free groups may be subgroups of a $\mathfrak{U}$-free group. Detailed investigation of the subgroups of free nilpotent groups (Gol'dina [*1*], [*2*], Gol'dina and Golovin [*1*], Mal'cev [*2*], Moran [*4*]) shows that the only reduced free subgroups of free nilpotent groups $F(\mathfrak{N}_c)$ are free nilpotent groups $F(\mathfrak{N}_d)$ with $d\leqq c$. Again 42.57 can be strengthened to show that relatively free subgroups of a free soluble group are free soluble and therefore of the kind described by 42.57 (Šmel'kin [*2*]). Corresponding information on free polynilpotent groups has very recently been obtained, also by A.L.Šmel'kin. I have no indication as yet of the methods used. The published work in this direction (Šmel'kin [*3*]) uses his embedding theorem 22.48 to prove inter alia:

42.61 *If* R *is normal in* F, *then a non-cyclic nilpotent subgroup* B *of* $F/R_{(c+1)}$ *is a finite extension of* $B\cap R/R_{(c+1)}$; *it is of class at most* c *and is embeddable in a free nilpotent group.*

Clearly many of the results mentioned in this section may also be obtained from 42.61. Compare also 43.24 in this context. Finally we mention (ŠMEL'KIN [5]):

42.62 *The only free soluble normal subgroups of a free soluble group are the terms of the derived series and subgroups of the last term of the derived series.*

42.63 *The only free nilpotent normal subgroups of a free nilpotent group are free abelian or the whole group.*

42.64 *The only free polynilpotent normal subgroups of a free polynilpotent group are the terms of the upper nilpotent series and free abelian subgroups of the lowest term.*

It is well known, and clear from Schreier's formula (11.22), that an absolutely free group of rank two contains free subgroups of every finite and of countably infinite rank. The results of this section have, by contrast, exhibited only $\mathfrak{V}$-free subgroups of $\mathfrak{V}$-free groups whose rank is at most that of the whole group; in fact in the cases of nilpotent and polynilpotent free groups, for example, no subgroups of higher rank can occur. Following PETER M. NEUMANN [*3*], we call the variety $\mathfrak{V}$ *regular* if $F_{n+1}(\mathfrak{V})$ cannot be embedded in $F_n(\mathfrak{V})$ for any $n>1$. His results (op. cit.) which we report here seem to be all that is known in this context.

42.71. **Lemma.** *If $F_{n+1}(\mathfrak{V})$ is embeddable in $F_n(\mathfrak{V})$ where $n>1$ and $\mathfrak{V}\neq\mathfrak{E}$, then $F_{n+1}(\mathfrak{V})$ is also embeddable in $F_n'(\mathfrak{V})$.*

Proof. The assumption implies that $H=F_n(\mathfrak{V})$ contains proper subgroups isomorphic to itself. We show that at least one of these can be found in the derived group H'; then using the assumption again, H' also contains an isomorphic copy of $F_{n+1}(\mathfrak{V})$.

Assume that no embedding $H\lambda\subseteq H$, $H\lambda\cong H$, is contained in H'. Then $(H\lambda)H'/H'$ is a non-trivial subgroup of the finitely generated abelian group H/H', hence itself finitely generated. Consider in particular an embedding $H\lambda_1=H_1$, say, for which the minimum number of generators modulo H' is as small as possible, m say. By assumption H_1 contains a subgroup $K\cong F_{n+1}(\mathfrak{V})$. Then KH'/H' as subgroup of H_1H'/H' needs at most m generators; on the other hand it is generated modulo H' by any set of $\mathfrak{V}$-free generators of K. Using 41.21 again, these free generators $k_1, \ldots, k_{n+1}$ may be chosen so that $k_{m+1}, \ldots, k_{n+1}$ are trivial modulo H'. But then the subgroup $\text{gp}(k_2, \ldots, k_{n+1})\subset K$ is a $\mathfrak{V}$-free subgroup of rank n of H which modulo H' has rank at most $m-1$, contradicting the choice of H_1. //

42.72 **Lemma.** *If $F_{n+1}(\mathfrak{V})$ is embeddable in $F_n(\mathfrak{V})$ where $n>1$, $\mathfrak{V}\neq\mathfrak{E}$, then $F_{n+1}(\mathfrak{V})$ is also embeddable in every subgroup of finite index in $F_n(\mathfrak{V})$.*

Proof. We use induction over the index. The lemma is true for index 1 by assumption. Assume it true for every subgroup of index less than l in $H=F_n(\mathfrak{B})$, and let L be a subgroup of index l in H. Let K be an isomorphic copy of $F_{n+1}(\mathfrak{B})$ in H, and assume $K \nsubseteq L$. Choose a set of free generators for K such that as many as possible belong to L:

$$K = \mathrm{gp}(k_1, \ldots, k_m, k_{m+1}, \ldots, k_{n+1}), \text{ where } k_1, \ldots, k_m \in L, k_{m+1}, \ldots, k_{n+1} \notin L$$

and m is maximal with this property; clearly $m<n+1$ as $K \nsubseteq L$. Consider the subgroup $H_1 = \mathrm{gp}(k_1, \ldots, k_m, k_{m+2}, \ldots, k_{n+1})$ which is isomorphic to $F_n(\mathfrak{B})$. Then the index of $H_1 \cap L$ in H_1 is at most l. If it were equal to l, a transversal for $H_1 \cap L$ in H_1 would also serve as transversal for L in H. Hence we could write $k_{m+1} = h_1 k$, $h_1 \in H_1$, $k \in L$.

But then

$$k_1, \ldots, k_m, \quad h_1^{-1} k_{m+1}, \quad k_{m+2}, \ldots, k_{n+1}$$

also is a set of free generators for K, because h_1 only involves the k_i with $i \neq m+1$, and of this set $m+1$ elements belong to L, contradicting the choice of our original set. Hence $H_1 \cap L$ has index less than l in H_1; as $H_1 \cong F_n(\mathfrak{B})$, the induction assumption shows that $H_1 \cap L$ and therefore L contains an isomorphic copy of $F_{n+1}(\mathfrak{B})$. //

The two lemmas give

42.73 **Theorem** (Peter M. Neumann [*3*]). *If $\mathfrak{B} \neq \mathfrak{E}$ has the property that every group $F_n(\mathfrak{B})$ possesses a finite subnormal series whose factors are either locally finite or locally soluble, then $\mathfrak{B}$ is regular.*

Proof. We use that every subgroup of a group with a subnormal series of the specified kind also has such a subnormal series obtained from the series of the whole group by intersection with the subgroup.

Let $H=F_n(\mathfrak{B})$ and consider a series $H=H_0 \supset \ldots \supset H_m = \{1\}$, where each factor H_i/H_{i+1} $(0 \leqq i < m)$ is locally soluble or locally finite and the series is as short as possible. As H_0 is finitely generated, H_0/H_1 is soluble or finite. Assume $F_{n+1}(\mathfrak{B}) \leqq H$; if H_0/H_1 is soluble, repeated application of Lemma 42.71 shows the existence of an isomorphic copy of $F_{n+1}(\mathfrak{B})$ in H_1; if H_0/H_1 is finite, Lemma 42.72 gives the same conclusion. But then $F_n(\mathfrak{B})$ also is embeddable in H_1 and so possesses a normal series of the required kind of length at most $m-1$, contradicting the minimality of m. Hence $F_{n+1}(\mathfrak{B})$ is not embeddable in $F_n(\mathfrak{B})$. //

42.74 **Corollary.** *Every non-trivial subvariety of a product variety all whose factors are locally finite or locally soluble is regular.* //

There remains the problem:

Problem 17. *Are all non-trivial varieties other than $\mathfrak{O}$ regular?*

3. Theorems like Auslander and Lyndon's: the Schreier Property

The monotonicity of variety multiplication established in 23.23 means for the corresponding verbal subgroups of F_∞: if $U \neq \{1\}$ and $U(V_1(F)) \supseteq U(V_2(F))$ then $V_1(F) \supseteq V_2(F)$, with equality occurring in one if and only if it occurs in the other. One expects that in this theorem the fact that $V_1(F)$ and $V_2(F)$ are verbal subgroups is irrelevant, and that it would hold for arbitrary normal subgroups. In fact MAURICE AUSLANDER and R.C. LYNDON [*1*] confirmed this for the case of the derived group: $S' \subseteq R'$ implies $S \subseteq R$ for arbitrary normal subgroups R, S of a free group F of any rank greater than 1. Since then the corresponding fact, that $V(S) \subseteq V(R)$ implies $S \subseteq R$, has been established for many varieties $\mathfrak{V}$, but the general problem remains unsolved. This section will provide a summary of results often with no more than brief indications of the – frequently involved – arguments. We shall not need any of these results. More frequently needed is the special case where $S = F$ is the whole free group; this we discuss in full.

We introduce a convenient name for those varieties that have the property in question: We call $\mathfrak{V}$ *monotone* if for any two normal subgroups R, S of a free group F of arbitrary rank >1 the inclusion $V(S) \subseteq V(R)$ implies $S \subseteq R$.

Since a verbal subgroup of a normal subgroup of F is normal in F, one has at once that $\mathfrak{U}\mathfrak{V}$ is monotone if $\mathfrak{U}$ and $\mathfrak{V}$ are. Hence by induction

43.1 *A product variety is monotone if every one of its factors is monotone.* //

The first extension of AUSLANDER and LYNDON's result is due to B.H. NEUMANN [*6*] who proved that $\mathfrak{N}_c$ is monotone for every c. This is obtained as a consequence of a much stronger result whose proof used 'twisted wreath products' (B.H. NEUMANN [7]).

43.21 **Theorem** (B. H. NEUMANN). *If R and S are normal subgroups of the non-abelian free group F and if $S_{(c)} \subseteq R'$ for some $c > 1$ then $S \subseteq R$.*

43.22 **Corollary.** *If $S_{(c)} \subseteq R_{(c)}$ for $c > 1$ then $S \subseteq R$.*

43.23 **Corollary.** *The polynilpotent varieties $\mathfrak{P} = \mathfrak{N}_{c_l} \ldots \mathfrak{N}_{c_1}$ are monotone.*

We shall use, for the proof of 43.21, the following lemma which is of interest in itself.

43.24 **Lemma.** *If R is normal in F and F/R' is nilpotent, then $R = F$.*

Proof. Assume first that $F' \subseteq R$. We use the matrix representation 36.12 of metabelian groups. Again we only need that the mapping defined by

$$f_i \mu = \begin{pmatrix} a_i & 0 \\ \alpha_i & 1 \end{pmatrix},$$

where f_i are free generators of F, the a_i, $\neq 1$, are corresponding generators of $A=F/R$ and the α_i are basis elements of the direct sum $(ZA)^k$ of $k=$ rank (F) copies of the group ring ZA, induces a homomorphism of F/R' into the matrix group. This is as easily checked as in the special case $R=F'$ which was used in 36.21. As there (cf. the proof of 36.22), one computes

$$[f_2, (c+1) f_1]\mu = \begin{pmatrix} 1 & 0 \\ (a_1-1)^c((1-a_2)\alpha_1+(a_1-1)\alpha_2) & 1 \end{pmatrix}.$$

If $A=F/R$ is non-trivial, this can never be the unit matrix, as the elements $(a_1-1)^c(1-a_2)$ and $(a_1-1)^{c+1}$ cannot both be zero in the group ring ZA.

In the general case put $T=RF'$. Then also F/T' is nilpotent and the first part shows that $T=F$. But also F/R is nilpotent, hence $T=RF'=F$ implies $R=F$, by 31.25. //

Proof of 43.21. Since the rank of F is not mentioned in the statement, we may replace F, if necessary, by RS; that is, we may assume that $F=RS$. Then it is sufficient to deduce from the assumption that $R=F$, since $RS=R$ implies $S\subseteq R$.

We first deduce from $S_{(c)}\subseteq R'$ that $F_{(c+1)}\subseteq R'$, as follows. The commutator identities 33.34 imply for mutual commutator groups that

(i) $[X, YZ]=[X, Y]\,[X, Z]$,
(ii) $[X, Y, Z]\subseteq[Y, Z, X]\,[Z, X, Y]$.

Now writing $[R, kS]=[R, (k-1)\,S, S]$, we have inductively from $[R, S]\subseteq S$ that $[R, kS]\subseteq S_{(k)}$, hence in our case

(iii) $[R, cS]\subseteq S_{(c)}\subseteq R'$.

Now $F_{(2)}=[RS, RS]=[R, R]\,[R, S]\,[S, S]$,
hence $F_{(3)}=[R, R, R]\,[R, S, R]\,[S, S, R]\,[R, R, S]\,[R, S, S]\,[S, S, S]$.

Here the first, second and fourth terms lie in R'; from (ii)

$$[S, S, R]\subseteq[R, S, S];$$

hence
$$F_{(3)}\subseteq R'[R, 2S]\,S_{(3)}.$$

Inductively: $F_{(k+1)}\subseteq R'[R, kS]\,S_{(k+1)}$, hence from (iii): $F_{(c+1)}\subseteq R'$ as asserted. Lemma 43.24 now completes the proof. //

A number of other cases can be dealt with by relatively simple arguments (for the case of $\mathfrak{A}_p$ see Hanna Neumann [3], for nilpotent varieties whose exponent is zero or contains at least two distinct prime factors see Peter M. Neumann [3], p. 15), but all these cases are covered by the following far reaching result:

43.25 **Theorem** (PETER M. NEUMANN [*3*]). *If $\mathfrak{B}$ is a variety whose free group of rank two has a finite subnormal series such that each factor is either locally soluble or locally of finite exponent, then $\mathfrak{B}$ is monotone.*

Summary of proof. Comparison with Theorem 42.73 indicates that there is a link between monotonicity and regularity.

Assume $\mathfrak{B}$ is not monotone and choose R and S in some non-abelian free group so that $V(S) \subseteq V(R)$, but $S \nsubseteq R$. A fairly elementary argument reduces the general case to that where R and S are normal subgroups of a free group F of rank two such that $F = RS$ and $F/R \cong S/S \cap R$ is cyclic of prime power order, p^r say. After this essential reduction, define inductively subvarieties of $\mathfrak{B}$ as follows:

Put $\mathfrak{D}_0 = \mathfrak{E}$, $\mathfrak{D}_n = \text{var}\left(S/D_{n-1}(R) \cap S\right)$ for $n > 1$, and $\mathfrak{D} = \vee \mathfrak{D}_n$. The special choice of R and S implies that each $\mathfrak{D}_n$ is generated by a finite p-group (proof by induction) so that free groups of $\mathfrak{D}$ are residually finite p-groups. Again inductively one shows $\mathfrak{D}_n \subseteq \mathfrak{B}$, hence $\mathfrak{D} \subseteq \mathfrak{B}$, and finally $D(S) \subseteq D(R)$. Thus $\mathfrak{B}$ has been replaced by a subvariety with the same property relative to R and S, but more manageable as it is explicitly defined in terms of R and S. This makes it possible to derive the following properties of $\mathfrak{D}$: $F_2(\mathfrak{D})$ is embeddable in its own derived group, as well as in its subgroup generated by all k-th powers for every $k \geqq 1$. Now an argument like the proof of Theorem 42.73 shows that $F_2(\mathfrak{B})$ can have no finite subnormal series whose factors are locally soluble or locally of finite exponent.

As $\mathfrak{D} \subseteq \mathfrak{B}$, the same applies to $\mathfrak{B}$. From this the result follows. //

Problem 18. *Is every variety $\mathfrak{B} \neq \mathfrak{O}$ monotone, that is, does $V(R) \supseteq V(S)$ for two normal subgroups R, S of some nonabelian free group imply $R \supseteq S$?*

There remains the question whether imposing restrictions on R and S, less severe than requiring them to be verbal subgroups of F, produces useful results. PETER M. NEUMANN (loc. cit.) remarks:

43.31 *If $S/S \cap R$ contains elements of infinite order, or even: if it does not have finite exponent, then $V(S) \subseteq V(R)$ and $\mathfrak{B} \neq \mathfrak{O}$ implies $S \subseteq R$.*

Finally, the condition that R and S are normal in F is not dispensable:

43.32 **Example** (DUNWOODY [*1*]). Let F be freely generated by a and b, let $R = \text{gp}(a, b^2, bab^{-1})$ and $S = \text{gp}(ba, b^2)$. Then R is normal in F and $S \nsubseteq R$. Now S' is generated by $[ba, b^2]$ and its conjugates; since $[ba, b^2] = [a, b^2] \in R'$, and R' is normal in F since R is normal in F, $S' \subseteq R'$ follows.

We now turn to the special case mentioned above.

43.41 **Theorem** (PETER M. NEUMANN [*3*]). *If $V(R) = V(F)$ for some proper normal subgroup R of a non-abelian free group F, then $\mathfrak{B} = \mathfrak{O}$.*

We need two lemmas:

43.42 **Lemma.** *If R is normal in F and F/R is cyclic of order m, then there exist free generators $\mathfrak{f}$ of F such that R is the normal closure of $f_1^m, f_2, f_3, \ldots$ and R can be freely generated either by f_1^m and $f_1^{-i} f_k f_1^i$ for all $k \geqq 2$ and $i=0, \ldots, m-1$, or by f_1^m and $f_k, [f_k, f_1], \ldots, [f_k, (m-1) f_1]$ for all $k \geqq 2$. All such normal subgroups R of F are equivalent under automorphisms of F.*

Proof. As $F' \subset R$, the basis theorem for free abelian groups shows that $\mathfrak{f}$ can be so chosen that $f_1^m \in R$ and $f_k \in R$ $(k \geqq 2)$. Thus, in particular, an automorphism of F takes an arbitrary normal subgroup with cyclic factor group of order m into the normal closure of these elements, which proves the final statement.

Now use the Schreier-Reidemeister procedure (Marshall Hall p. 94) to calculate free generators of R, using the obvious transversal of F modulo R with the Schreier property consisting of the elements f_1^i, $i=0, \ldots, m-1$. This gives the free generating set for R mentioned first.

Now the subset $\{f_k, f_1^{-i} f_k f_1^i, 1 \leqq i \leqq m-1\}$ is equivalent to the set $\{f_k, [f_k, f_1^i], 1 \leqq i \leqq m-1\}$ by 11.41. But

$$[f_k, f_1^2] = [f_k, f_1]^2 [f_k, f_1, f_1],$$

so that $[f_k, f_1^2]$ can be replaced by $[f_k, 2f_1]$. Now induction completes the proof with the aid of the two identities:

$$[f_k, f_1^i] = [f_k, f_1] [f_k, f_1^{i-1}]^{f_1}$$

and

$$[f_k, l f_1]^{f_1} = [f_k, l f_1] [f_k, (l+1) f_1]. \quad //$$

We shall need the second of these two generating sets only later, in the proof of Theorem 43.6.

43.43 **Lemma.** *If $\mathfrak{B} = \operatorname{var} A$ and, for each $n \in I$, D_n is a group containing a subgroup isomorphic to A — and again denoted by A — and an element d such that the conjugates $d^{-k} A d^k$, $k=0, \ldots, n$, are distinct and generate their direct product, then $\mathfrak{B}\mathfrak{A} \subseteq \operatorname{var} \{D_n, n \in I\}$.*

Proof. This lemma is clearly a straight generalization of the fact (22.44) that A wr C generates $\mathfrak{B}\mathfrak{A}$ whenever A generates $\mathfrak{B}$ and C is an infinite cycle. It will be proved by 'imitating' the value of a word w in A wr C by a value of w in a group D_n for large enough n, using the method and notation of 22.34 and of the proof of 22.31. We have to show that a non-law in $\mathfrak{B}\mathfrak{A}$, that is, a non-law of A wr C, also fails to be a law in some group D_n. Let w, involving m variables, have the non-trivial value

$$1 \neq w(c^{\alpha_1} f_1, \ldots, c^{\alpha_m} f_m) = w(c^{\alpha_1}, \ldots, c^{\alpha_m}) \prod_\mu f_{i(\mu)}^{\varepsilon_{i(\mu)} c^{\beta(\mu)}}$$

in A wr C. If the first factor is non-trivial, then for large enough N, $w(d^{\alpha_1}, \dots, d^{\alpha_m})$ is non-trivial in D_N as the powers $1, \dots, d^{N-1}$ are clearly distinct in D_N. Hence assume the first factor is trivial so that the second factor is a non-trivial function in the base group of A wr C. Then at some argument $c^{\delta} \in C$ it takes a non-trivial value:

$$\prod_{\mu} f_{i(\mu)}^{\varepsilon_{i(\mu)} c^{\beta(\mu)}}(c^{\delta}) = \prod_{\mu} f_{i(\mu)}^{\varepsilon_{i(\mu)}}(c^{\delta-\beta(\mu)}) = a \neq 1 .$$

Choose the positive integer γ so that $\gamma+\delta \geqq 0$ and $\gamma+\delta-\beta(\mu) \geqq 0$ for all μ and then take N greater than every one of these integers $\gamma+\delta$ and $\gamma+\delta-\beta(\mu)$. Then define elements $\varphi_i\,(i=1, \dots, m)$ in the subgroup $A \times A^d \times \dots \times A^{d^{N-1}}$ of D_N by setting

$$\varphi_{i(\mu)}(d^{\gamma+\delta-\beta(\mu)}) = f_{i(\mu)}(c^{\delta-\beta(\mu)})$$

and giving these functions value 1 in every factor of the direct product not covered by this rule. Then in D_N:

$$\begin{aligned} w(d^{\alpha_1}\varphi_1, \dots, d^{\alpha_m}\varphi_m) &= w(d^{\alpha_1}, \dots, d^{\alpha_m})\, \Pi\, \varphi_{i(\mu)}^{\varepsilon_{i(\mu)}\, d^{\beta(\mu)}} \\ &= \Pi\, \varphi_{i(\mu)}^{\varepsilon_{i(\mu)}\, d^{\beta(\mu)}}, \end{aligned}$$

as $w(c^{\alpha_1}, \dots, c^{\alpha_m})=1$ in C implies $w(d^{\alpha_1}, \dots, d^{\alpha_m})=1$. But

$$(\Pi\, \varphi_{i(\mu)}^{\varepsilon_{i(\mu)}\, d^{\beta(\mu)}})\,(d^{\gamma+\delta}) = \Pi\, \varphi_{i(\mu)}^{\varepsilon_{i(\mu)}}(d^{\gamma+\delta-\beta(\mu)}) = a \neq 1$$

by definition of the φ_i. //

Proof of 43.41. First step: This consists in reducing the general case of an arbitrary proper normal subgroup R of a non-abelian free group of arbitrary rank to a very special case. Let $f \in F$ be an element not in R; then f will have infinite order modulo R or order pm for some prime p. In either case take $F_1 = \text{gp}(f, R)$ and $R_1 = \text{gp}(f^p, R)$. Then R_1 is normal in the free group F_1; also $R \subseteq R_1 \subseteq F_1 \subseteq F$ so that $V(R) = V(F)$ implies $V(R_1) = V(F_1)$. Moreover F_1 is nonabelian, as it contains R, and F_1/R_1 is cyclic of order p. Using Lemma 43.42 we may assume a set $\mathfrak{f}$ of free generators of F_1 so chosen that R_1 is the normal closure of $f_1^p, f_2, \dots$. Now use the projection $\pi_2 : f_i\pi_2 = f_i$ for $i=1, 2$, $f_i\pi_2 = 1$ for $i>2$. Then $R_1\pi_2$ is the normal closure of f_1^p and f_2 in $F_1\pi_2$ which is freely generated by f_1 and f_2, and

$$V(R_1\pi_2) = V(R_1)\pi_2 = V(F_1)\pi_2 = V(F_1\pi_2) .$$

Hence we assume from now on that F has rank two, $F = \text{gp}(f_1, f_2)$, that R is such that F/R is cyclic of order p and R is the normal closure of f_1^p and f_2. We have to show that in this situation $V(R) = V(F)$ implies $\mathfrak{B} = \mathfrak{O}$.

Second step: Consider $G=F/V(F)$, a $\mathfrak{B}$-free group of rank two, freely generated by $a=f_1V(F)$ and $b=f_2V(F)$. As R contains $V(F)=V(R)$, the subgroup $S_1=R/V(F)$ of G also is $\mathfrak{B}$-free, and by Lemma 43.42 it is freely generated by

$$s(1,0)=a^p \quad \text{and} \quad s(1,i+1)=a^{-i}ba^i, \qquad 0\leqq i<p.$$

Hence $S_1\cong F_{p+1}(\mathfrak{B})$, and one free generator of S_1 is a^p.

We make this the starting point of an induction which will show that for each $n\geqq 1$ the normal closure S_n of a^{p^n} and b in G contains p^{n-1} copies of $F_{p+1}(\mathfrak{B})$, each having a^{p^n} as one of its free generators.

Apply Lemma 43.42 to the normal closure of $f_1^{p^n}$ and f_2 in F and reduce modulo $V(F)$; this shows that

$$S_n=\mathrm{gp}(a^{p^n}, \quad a^{-i}ba^i \ \text{ for } \ 0\leqq i<p^n).$$

We write $a^{p^n}=s(n,0)$ and $a^{-i}ba^i=s(n,i+1)$; then for each j, $1\leqq j\leqq p^{n-1}$, the subgroup

$$S_{n,j}=\mathrm{gp}\big(s(n,0),s(n,j+ip^{n-1}) \ \text{ for } \ 0\leqq i<p\big)$$

is $\mathfrak{B}$-free, freely generated by the $p+1$ elements exhibited. For $n=1$, $S_{1,1}=S_1$ and this is just the statement that the normal closure of a^p and b is $\mathfrak{B}$-free, freely generated by $s(1,0)$ and $s(1,i+1)$, $0\leqq i<p$. Assume the statement true for $n-1$; then in particular $s(n-1,0)=a^{p^{n-1}}$ and $s(n-1,j)$ generate a $\mathfrak{B}$-free group of rank two in G. Now apply the case $n=1$ to this group to obtain that $s(n-1,0)^p$ and $s(n-1,0)^{-i}s(n-1,j)s(n-1,0)^i$, $0\leqq i<p$, generate freely a $\mathfrak{B}$-free group. Expressing the $s(n-1,i)$ in terms of a and b shows that this is just what was required.

Put $T_{n,j}=\mathrm{gp}\big(s(n,j+ip^{n-1}), 0\leqq i<p\big)$, so that for each $1\leqq j\leqq p^{n-1}$

$$S_{n,j}=\mathrm{gp}(a^{p^n},T_{n,j}), \qquad T_{n,j}\cong F_p(\mathfrak{B}).$$

Next we show that these subgroups $T_{n,j}$ of S_n are 'independent' in the sense that S_n possesses a projection onto $S_{n,j}$, hence also one onto $T_{n,j}$ for each j. Again we use induction over n: As $S_1=S_{1,1}$, the case $n=1$ is obvious. Assume that S_{n-1} possesses projections onto each $S_{n-1,j}$; as the latter are free groups they can be projected onto the free subgroups generated by $s(n-1,0)$ and $s(n-1,k)$ for each $s(n-1,k)$ that occurs in $S_{n-1,j}$. Thus S_{n-1} also possesses projections $\varepsilon_{n-1,k}$ given by

$$s(n-1,0)\,\varepsilon_{n-1,k}=s(n-1,0)$$
$$s(n-1,k)\,\varepsilon_{n-1,k}=s(n-1,k)$$
$$s(n-1,i)\,\varepsilon_{n-1,k}=1 \quad \text{when} \quad i\neq 0,k.$$

Clearly the subgroup S_n of S_{n-1} admits this endomorphism, and a simple check by means of the definition of $S_{n,k}$ shows that the restriction of $\varepsilon_{n-1,k}$ to S_n is a projection of S_n onto $S_{n,k}$.

Final step: We use the information on the subgroups S_n and $T_{n,j}$ of G to exhibit a set of factors of G that fit the assumptions of Lemma 43.43.

Let $\pi_{n,j}: S_n \twoheadrightarrow T_{n,j}$, $1 \leqq j \leqq p^{n-1}$, denote the projection obtained in the previous step. If $\ker \pi_{n,j} = K_{n,j}$ then $K_{n,j}$ contains every commutator group $[T_{n,i}, T_{n,k}]$, $i \neq k$, as well as a^{p^n}. Let K_n be the normal closure of all these mutual commutators and a^{p^n} so that $K_n \subseteq K_{n,j}$ for each j. Any homomorphism δ_n of S_n with kernel K_n maps S_n onto a homomorphic image of the direct product $\Pi T_{n,j}$. As $K_n \subseteq K_{n,j}$, $S_n \delta_n$ possesses projections onto $T_{n,j}$ for each j; hence $S_n \delta_n$ is isomorphic to the direct product. We write

$$S_n \delta_n = \prod_j T_{n,j}.$$

But the kernel K_n is normal not only in S_n but in G. To show this, only transformation by a need be considered as G is generated by a modulo S_n. As a^{p^n} is invariant under a, and as $a^{-1} T_{n,j}\, a = T_{n,j+1}$ as long as $j < p^{n-1}$, only mutual commutator groups involving $T_{n,p^{n-1}}$ need a closer look. But

$$\begin{aligned} a^{-1} T_{n,p^{n-1}}\, a &= \mathrm{gp}(a^{-1} s(n, p^{n-1} + i p^{n-1})\, a,\ 0 \leqq i < p) \\ &= \mathrm{gp}(a^{-1} s(n, i p^{n-1})\, a,\ 1 \leqq i \leqq p) \\ &= \mathrm{gp}(s(n, 1 + i p^{n-1}),\ 1 \leqq i \leqq p). \end{aligned}$$

Here the last generator is $a^{-p^n} s(n,1)\, a^{p^n}$; as generally $S_{n,j} = \mathrm{gp}(a^{p^n}, T_{n,j})$, we get $a^{-1} S_{n,p^{n-1}} a = S_{n,1}$. Now $[T_{n,i}, T_{n,j}] \subseteq [S_{n,i}, S_{n,j}]$ for all pairs i, j and the latter clearly also lie in K_n; as transformation by a only permutes these $[S_{n,i}, S_{n,j}]$, it transforms K_n in itself.

Put $D_n = G/K_n$; D_n contains the direct product $S_n \delta_n$ of p^{n-1} factors isomorphic to $F_p(\mathfrak{B})$. These are transformed cyclically by the element $a K_n$ in D_n giving the p^{n-1} distinct conjugate factors of the direct product. By Lemma 43.43, the variety generated by the set of groups D_n contains the product $\operatorname{var} F_p(\mathfrak{B})\, \mathfrak{A}$. But for each n, $D_n = G/K_n \in \operatorname{var} G \subseteq \operatorname{var} F_p(\mathfrak{B})$ as $G = F_2(\mathfrak{B})$. Hence $\operatorname{var} F_p(\mathfrak{B})\, \mathfrak{A} \subseteq \operatorname{var} F_p(\mathfrak{B})$ and so $\operatorname{var} F_p(\mathfrak{B}) = \mathfrak{O}$ giving $\mathfrak{B} = \mathfrak{O}$. //

In view of this proof it is surprising that a remarkably simple argument due to TEKLA TAYLOR will prove the theorem in a large number of cases without the restriction that R is normal in F. As earlier (cf. the proof of 21.61) we denote by $l(\mathfrak{a})$ the length of a shortest non-trivial element of the subset $\mathfrak{a}$ of F in terms of free generators $\mathfrak{f}$ of F, with $l(\mathfrak{a}) = 0$ if $\mathfrak{a} = \{1\}$.

43.51 **Theorem** (TEKLA TAYLOR; cf. DUNWOODY [*1*]). *If F is a non-abelian free group, R a proper subgroup of F, and if $l(V(F))=l(V(F_\infty))$ then $V(R)=V(F)$ implies $\mathfrak{B}=\mathfrak{D}$.*

43.52 **Corollary.** *If R is a proper subgroup of F_∞ and if $V(R)=V(F_\infty)$ then $\mathfrak{B}=\mathfrak{D}$.*

Proof. Note that in general, by the definition of $l(\mathfrak{a})$, $l(V(F))\geqq l(V(F_\infty))$. In particular, if we indicate reference to length with respect to a set of free generators of R by a subscript, one has $l_R(V(R))\geqq l(V(F_\infty))$. We show that if $\mathfrak{B}\neq\mathfrak{D}$, then $l_R(V(R))<l(V(F))=l(V(F_\infty))$ giving a contradiction.

As $R\subset F$, at least one element of $\mathfrak{f}$, f_1 say, does not belong to R. As $V(F)$ is non-trivial, there is in $V(F)$ an element of minimal positive length $m=l(V(F))$. Let v be such an element, then so is $v\alpha$ for every permutation α of the generators of F. We may therefore assume that the representation of v in terms of $\mathfrak{f}$ starts with f_1 or its inverse. Again, the former may be assumed, so that $v=f_1 a_2 \dots a_m$, where each a_i or its inverse belongs to $\mathfrak{f}$.

We now use again elementary properties of the Schreier-Reidemeister procedure (MARSHALL HALL p. 94): As $f_1\notin R$, f_1 is a shortest element in its coset modulo R; hence there is a transversal T for R in F that has the Schreier property and includes 1 and f_1. Denote by $\tau(x)$ the representative of x in T; then the free generators of R obtained from T are the non-trivial elements $tf\,\tau(tf)^{-1}$, $t\in T$, $f\in\mathfrak{f}$. As $V(F)=V(R)\subseteq R$, $v\in R$; we express v in terms of these free generators by the standard procedure. As the first two letters $f_1 a_2$ in the expression of v are used up in the first step – they are replaced by $(f_1 a_2\,\tau(f_1 a_2)^{-1})\,\tau(f_1 a_2)$ – and as the procedure uses the remaining letters one by one, at most $m-1$ generators of R will occur in the expression for v. Thus $l_R(V(R))\leqq m-1<l(V(F))$ as claimed. //

No set V is known that does not satisfy the conditions of the theorem:

Problem 19. *Does there exist a verbal subgroup $V(F_\infty)$ such that for some $n>1$ a shortest non-trivial element of $V(F_n)$ is longer than a shortest non-trivial element of $V(F_\infty)$?*

Problem 20. *Does Theorem 43.41 hold without the condition of normality; that is, does $V(R)=V(F)$ for some proper subgroup R of the non-abelian free group F imply $\mathfrak{B}=\mathfrak{D}$?*

We now turn to the result on Schreier varieties mentioned earlier.

43.6 **Theorem** (PETER M. NEUMANN and JAMES WIEGOLD [*1*]). *The varieties $\mathfrak{D}$, $\mathfrak{A}$, $\mathfrak{A}_p$ where p is prime are the only Schreier varieties.*

The proof here presented embodies a considerable simplification, due to M. F. NEWMAN, of the original proof in the case of exponent zero. The most recent version of the proof, by PETER M. NEUMANN and M. F. NEWMAN [*1*], is still simpler. It is independent of KOSTRIKIN's deep result and does not use Theorem 43.41 either; in fact, the reasoning employed in that paper might well be refinable to give a simpler proof of 43.41.

Proof of 43.6. The proof is in several steps. The letter $\mathfrak{B}$ always denotes a Schreier variety, and $H=F_2(\mathfrak{B})$.

1. Assume $\mathfrak{B}$ has finite exponent. As every subgroup of a $\mathfrak{B}$-free group is free in the variety, this is true in particular for $F_1(\mathfrak{B})$ and so the exponent must be a prime p. It remains to show that $F_2(\mathfrak{B})$ is abelian; then $\mathfrak{B}$ is abelian.

By A. I. KOSTRIKIN's theorem (cf. [*1*]), the finite factor groups of $H=F_2(\mathfrak{B})$ are of bounded order. Hence there is a unique minimal normal subgroup N of H whose factor group is finite. By assumption, N is $\mathfrak{B}$-free; as it is of finite index in a group of rank two, it is finitely generted. Hence its derived group N' is of finite index in N, hence in H. But N' is characteristic in N, and therefore normal in H. Since N was minimal with these properties, $N'=N$. But a non-trivial free group is distinct from its derived group; hence N is trivial and H is finite.

As a finite p-group, H is nilpotent. Hence its centre contains a non-trivial element c; as H is not cyclic, there exists an element $h\in H$, $h\notin \mathrm{gp}(c)$. Then $\mathrm{gp}(h, c)$ is a noncyclic abelian subgroup of H and as it is $\mathfrak{B}$-free, $\mathrm{gp}(h, c)\cong H$ and H is abelian.

2. We may now assume that $\mathfrak{B}$ has exponent zero. Let N be normal in H and of index p in H for some prime p. Here, and repeatedly later on, we use Lemma 43.42: If $H=\mathrm{gp}(a, b)$, we may assume that N is the normal closure of a^p and b. If N is cyclic, then $a^{mp}=b^n$ for some non-zero integers m and n. But this relation between free generators of H shows that $x^{mp}=y^n$ is a law in H and so also y^n and x^{mp} are laws, contradicting the assumption that $\mathfrak{B}$ has exponent zero. Using Schreier's formula, this shows that the rank of N, r say, satisfies $2\leqq r\leqq p+1$. Again we distinguish several cases:

(i) If every normal subgroup of prime index in H has rank two, then $\mathfrak{B}=\mathfrak{A}$.

Proof. Let N be such a normal subgroup; then N is $\mathfrak{B}$-free, hence $N\cong H$. Also $H'\subseteq N$ and N/H' is a subgroup of index p in the free abelian group H/H' of rank two. Hence N/H' is free abelian of rank two and a factor group of the free abelian group N/N', which is also of rank two. As free abelian groups of finite rank are Hopf groups, we conclude that $H'=N'$.

Now let H/R be any 2-generator finite soluble group in $\mathfrak{B}$. Then there exists a subnormal chain, $R=R_0\lhd R_1\lhd\ldots\lhd R_l=H$, such that each factor group is cyclic of prime order. From the above, $R'_{l-1}=H'$; then $R_{l-1}\cong H$ gives $R'_{l-2}=R'_{l-1}=H'$, hence by induction $R'=H'$. Thus $H'\subseteq R$ and so H/R is abelian. But then every finite soluble group in $\mathfrak{B}$ is abelian, and so every soluble group in $\mathfrak{B}$ is abelian since a finitely generated non-abelian soluble group has finite non-abelian factor groups (using once again 7.2 of B. H. NEUMANN [2]). Therefore $H''=H'$; but H' is $\mathfrak{B}$-free, so that this implies $H'=\{1\}$ and $\mathfrak{B}=\mathfrak{A}$ as asserted.

(ii) If there exists a prime p and a normal subgroup N of index p in H with rank $r\geqq 3$, then $r=p+1$.

Proof. Take a prime q that is a primitive root modulo p – such primes exist for every p. Then the only irreducible representations of a p-cycle over the field of q elements are, by elementary arguments, the trivial representation and a representation of degree $p-1$.

Now H/H' is free abelian of rank two and $H'\subset N$. Hence N/H' as subgroup of index p in H/H' is free abelian of rank two. As N is free, so is N/N'; hence H'/N' is a non-trivial direct factor of rank $r-2$ of N/N'. Let $A_q(N)$ be the verbal subgroup of N generated by N' and all q-th powers of elements of N. Then $N/A_q(N)$, considered in $H/A_q(N)$, has a submodule of rank two corresponding to $N/H'A_q(N)$ on which H/N acts trivially (by conjugation, of course). The complementary direct summand in $N/A_q(N)$ is non-trivial, as N has rank at least 3; its rank is $r-2\leqq p-1$ since $r\leqq p+1$. If the rank is less than $p-1$, it must split into submodules of rank one, acted upon trivially by H/N. But this is impossible as it would make $H/A_q(N)$ an abelian 2-generator group which is a direct product of one p-cycle and $r\geqq 3$ q-cycles. Hence $r-2=p-1$ and $r=p+1$ as required.

(iii) If, for some p, a normal subgroup N of index p in H has rank $p+1$, then $\mathfrak{B}=\mathfrak{O}$.

Proof. Let $\mathfrak{U}$ be the subvariety of $\mathfrak{B}$ generated by all finite p-groups in $\mathfrak{B}$, and let $G=F_2(\mathfrak{U})$. Let M be of index p in G. We use the fact that, by 43.42, all normal subgroups of index p in F, the absolutely free group of rank two, are equivalent under automorphisms of F; thus the normal subgroups of index p in G are equivalent under automorphisms of G induced by those of F and so, in particular, they are isomorphic.

Now $G\cong H/U(H)$; as $H/N\in\mathfrak{U}$, we have $U(H)\subseteq N$ and, of course, $U(N)\subseteq U(H)$. But $H/U(N)$ is an extension of the $\mathfrak{U}$-free group $N/U(N)$ by a p-cycle; it belongs to $\mathfrak{B}$, and as an extension of the residually finite p-group $N/U(N)$ by a finite p-group, it is residually a finite p-group. Thus $H/U(N)\in\mathfrak{U}$ and so $U(H)\subseteq U(N)$, giving $U(H)=U(N)$. Now $N/U(H)$ is of index p in $H/U(H)\cong G$; hence, by the above remark, $N/U(H)\cong M$. As $N/U(H)=N/U(N)$, M is $\mathfrak{U}$-free and of the same rank $p+1$ as N.

Now let R be a complete inverse image of N in F. Then R is of index p, hence of rank $p+1$. As $F/R \in \mathfrak{U}$, we have $R \supseteq U(F) \supseteq U(R)$. Hence $R/U(F)$ is of index p in $F/U(F) \cong G$. Hence $R/U(F) \cong M$ is $\mathfrak{U}$-free of rank $p+1$. But $R/U(R)$ is $\mathfrak{U}$-free of rank $p+1$. As $\mathfrak{U}$-free groups are residually finite p-groups, those of finite rank are Hopf groups; therefore $U(R) = U(F)$ and, by Theorem 43.41, we obtain $\mathfrak{U} = \mathfrak{O}$. But $\mathfrak{U} \subseteq \mathfrak{B}$, hence also $\mathfrak{B} = \mathfrak{O}$.

This completes the proof of step (iii) which, together with (ii), completes the proof of the theorem. //

4. The Splitting Property; Direct Decomposability

There is in the category of abelian groups a well known, pleasing and useful, duality (cf. S. MacLane [*1*]) between *projective* and *injective* groups—we shall recall the definitions below. Furthermore, for abelian groups as well as in some other categories, 'projective' coincides with 'free', so that in such categories a free object may be defined in homological terms. This paragraph contains a report on the position in varieties of groups, following P. Hall [*2*]. The results are negative in the sense that the terms 'free' and 'projective' mean the same in some varieties but certainly not in all; and where they do mean the same they do so for spurious reasons. However, a by-product of these investigations is some very useful insight into structure properties of relatively free groups.

The following definitions are relative to a fixed variety $\mathfrak{U}$, that is all groups are assumed to belong to $\mathfrak{U}$.

44.11 **Definition.** *The group G is projective if whenever $\beta: G \to B$ is a homomorphism and $\alpha: A \twoheadrightarrow B$ is an epimorphism, there exists a homomorphism $\gamma: G \to A$ such that $\gamma\alpha = \beta$.*

44.12 **Definition.** *The group G is injective if whenever $\beta: B \to G$ is a homomorphism and $\alpha: B \rightarrowtail A$ is a monomorphism, there exists a homomorphism $\gamma: A \to G$ such that $\alpha\gamma = \beta$.*

In the case $\mathfrak{U} = \mathfrak{A}$ one proves (cf. for example MacLane, loc. cit.) that a group is projective if and only if it is free, that it is injective if and only if it is divisible; every group in $\mathfrak{A}$ is an epimorphic image of a projective group and is isomorphic to a subgroup of an injective group. In both cases there is a unique minimal such projective, or injective, group.

We turn to projective groups in an arbitrary variety $\mathfrak{U}$.

44.21 **Theorem.** *All $\mathfrak{U}$-free groups are projective.*

Proof. Given $\beta: G \to B$ and $\alpha: A \twoheadrightarrow B$; let $\mathfrak{g}$ be a set of free generators of G; as α is epi, the image $\mathfrak{g}\beta$ possesses a set of counter images under α in A; take $a_i \in A$ such that $a_i\alpha = g_i\beta$ for $g_i \in \mathfrak{g}$. Then define γ by $g_i\gamma = a_i$; as G is free this defines a homomorphism and $\gamma\alpha = \beta$. //

44.22 **Definition** (P. Hall [*2*]). *A group* $S \in \mathfrak{U}$ *is a splitting group for* $\mathfrak{U}$ *if every group* $C \in \mathfrak{U}$ *that is an extension of a group* A *by* S *is a splitting extension of* A *by* S.

Then:

44.23 *A group is projective in* $\mathfrak{U}$ *if and only if it is a splitting group for* $\mathfrak{U}$.

44.24 *A group* S *is projective in* $\mathfrak{U}$ *if and only if for some presentation* $S \cong F(\mathfrak{U})/R$ *the extension* $F(\mathfrak{U})$ *of* R *by* S *splits.*

Proof. (1) If S is projective then S is a splitting group: Let C be an extension of A by S. If α is the natural epimorphism $\alpha: C \twoheadrightarrow S$ and $\iota: S \twoheadrightarrow S$ is the identity, then there exists $\gamma: S \to C$ such that $\gamma\alpha = \iota$. Hence γ is mono and $S\gamma$ is a complement of ker α in C.

(2) Assume S is a splitting group in $\mathfrak{U}$ and $S \cong F(\mathfrak{U})/R$. By definition of a splitting group, this extension $F(\mathfrak{U})$ of R by S splits over R.

(3) Assume $S \in \mathfrak{U}$ has the property that a presentation $S \cong F(\mathfrak{U})/R$ splits over R; we have to show that S is projective, that is if homomorphisms $\beta: S \to B$ and $\alpha: A \twoheadrightarrow B$ are given, we have to find a homomorphism $\gamma: S \to A$ such that $\gamma\alpha = \beta$. Let $G = F(\mathfrak{U})$ be freely generated by $\mathfrak{g}$; let σ be an epimorphism of G onto S with kernel R; then $\mathfrak{g}\sigma$ generates S. If $\mathfrak{g}\sigma\beta = \mathfrak{b}$, take to each $b_i \in \mathfrak{b}$ a counter image $a_i \in A$ such that $a_i\alpha = b_i$. Then define $\rho: G \to A$ by setting $g_i\rho = a_i$ for all $g_i \in \mathfrak{g}$. Then $\rho\alpha = \sigma\beta$. Now use that there is a monomorphism $\tau: S \to G$ such that $S\tau \cap R$ is trivial and $\tau\sigma$ is the identity on S: $\tau\sigma = \iota$. With this injection τ we may put $\gamma = \tau\rho$, for now $\gamma\alpha = \tau\rho\alpha = \tau\sigma\beta = \beta$ as required.

The three steps together prove 44.23 and 44.24. //

44.25 **Theorem** (MacLane [*1*]). *If* $\mathfrak{U}$ *has the Schreier property, a group of* $\mathfrak{U}$ *is projective if and only if it is free.*

Proof. If S is projective, represent S in the form $S \cong F(\mathfrak{U})/R$. By 44.24, $F(\mathfrak{U})$ contains a subgroup isomorphic to S; but subgroups of $\mathfrak{U}$-free groups are $\mathfrak{U}$-free. Hence S is free in $\mathfrak{U}$. //

44.26 **Corollary.** *In* $\mathfrak{O}$, $\mathfrak{A}$ *and* $\mathfrak{A}_p$, *p a prime, the terms 'projective' and 'free' are coextensive.* //

We know from Theorem 43.6 that no further information can come from this approach. In some other varieties the result remains true, but for completely different reasons.

44.31 **Lemma.** *If* S *is projective in* $\mathfrak{U}$ *then* S/S' *is a direct product of cyclic groups.*

Proof. Use 44.24 to represent S in the form $F(\mathfrak{U})/R$ such that $S \leqq F(\mathfrak{U}) = G$, $RS = G$ and $R \cap S = \{1\}$. Then $G' = [G, G] = [RS, RS] = [R, RS]\ [S, R]\ [S, S] \subseteq [R, G]\ S' \subseteq G'$, hence $G' = [R, G]\ S'$.

Now each $g \in G$ is uniquely of the form $g = rs$, hence $G' \cap R = [R, G]$ and $G' \cap S = S'$ follows. But then $G'R \cap G'S = G'$: As $c \in G'R \cap G'S$ implies $c = g_1 r = g_2 s$, $g_1 \in G'$, $g_2 \in G'$, one has $rs^{-1} \in G'$, and so $r \in [R, G]$, $s \in S'$ giving $g_1 r \in G'$, that is $c \in G'$. But from $G'R \cap G'S = G'$ one sees that $G/G' = RS/G' = RG'/G'$. SG'/G' is the direct product of these factors. Hence the factor $SG'/G' \cong S/S \cap G' = S/S'$ is a direct product of cyclic groups. //

44.32 **Theorem** (P. Hall [2]). *If $\mathfrak{U}$ is a variety of exponent zero or p^k whose free groups are residually nilpotent, and if S is a projective group in $\mathfrak{U}$ possessing a generating set $\mathfrak{s}$ such that S/S' has basis $\mathfrak{s}S'$, then S is a $\mathfrak{U}$-free group.*

Proof. By the proof of Lemma 44.31, S/S' is a direct factor of G/G' for some free group $G = F(\mathfrak{U})$ where moreover we may assume $S \subseteq G$, $G = RS$ and $S \cong G/R$. The generators $\mathfrak{s}$ of S are independent generators of this direct factor of G/G'. As G/G' is free abelian of exponent zero or p^k, $\mathfrak{s}$ generates freely modulo G' a direct factor of G/G'. By Theorem 42.31, $\mathfrak{s}$ generates freely in G a $\mathfrak{U}$-free subgroup of G. Thus S is a $\mathfrak{U}$-free group. //

If S is nilpotent every set of elements that generates S modulo S' generates S; hence Lemma 44.31 and Theorem 44.32 give

44.33 **Corollary** (P. Hall, loc. cit.). *The projective groups of a nilpotent variety of exponent zero, or p^k, are precisely the free groups of that variety.* //

44.34 **Corollary.** *If $\mathfrak{U}$ is nilpotent of exponent $m = p_1^{k_1} \dots p_l^{k_l}$, then S is projective if and only if it is of the form*

$$S = F(\mathfrak{U}_1) \times \dots \times F(\mathfrak{U}_l),$$

where each $F(\mathfrak{U}_\lambda)$ is a free group of the subvariety $\mathfrak{U}_\lambda$ consisting of all groups in $\mathfrak{U}$ of exponent dividing $p_\lambda^{k_\lambda}$.

Note that only those products where all factors have the same rank are free groups of $\mathfrak{U}$.

Proof. If C is nilpotent and of exponent m, then $C = \Pi C_\lambda$ where each C_λ has exponent dividing $p_\lambda^{k_\lambda}$. If $R \lhd C$, then $R = \Pi R_\lambda$ where each R_λ is normal in C_λ; and C splits over R if and only if each C_λ splits over R_λ. Thus 44.34 follows from 44.33 and 44.23. //

The examples of non-free projective groups exhibited in 44.34 are in a sense very close to the free groups of the variety. There are however large classes of varieties where other relatively free groups, not free in the variety in question but in some proper subvariety, occur amongst the projective groups.

44.41 **Lemma.** *If $\mathfrak{B} \subseteq \mathfrak{U}$ then $H = F(\mathfrak{B})$ is a splitting group for $\mathfrak{U}$ if and only if $G = F(\mathfrak{U})$, of the same rank as H, contains a subgroup B such that $B \in \mathfrak{B}$ and $G = BV(G)$.*

Proof. Under the assumptions $H \cong G/V(G)$. By 44.24, if H is a splitting group for $\mathfrak{U}$ then $H \leqq G$ and $G = H_1 V(G)$, $H_1 \cong H$.

Conversely, assume $B \in \mathfrak{B}$, $B \leqq G$ and $G = B_1 V(G)$ where $B_1 \cong B$. Then

$$H \cong G/V(G) = B_1\, V(G)/V(G) \cong B_1/V(G) \cap B_1 .$$

As $B \in \mathfrak{B}$, we have a $\mathfrak{B}$-group that is an extension of a $\mathfrak{B}$-group by a $\mathfrak{B}$-free group; by 44.21 and 44.23 the extension splits. By 44.24 H is a splitting group in $\mathfrak{U}$ as the presentation $H \cong G/V(G)$ splits over $V(G)$. //

We now restrict ourselves to locally finite varieties $\mathfrak{U}$ and their free groups of finite rank. Then $G = F(\mathfrak{U})$ is finite. Hence it possesses a lower nilpotent series as defined on p. 122; we use also the *lower p-series* defined as follows:

$$B = \pi_0(B) \supseteq \pi_0'(B) \supseteq \pi_1(B) \supseteq \pi_1'(B) \supseteq \dots,$$

where $\pi_k'(B)$ is the least normal subgroup of $\pi_k(B)$ such that the factor group is a p'-group and $\pi_k(B)$ is the least normal subgroup of $\pi_{k-1}'(B)$ such that the factor group is a p-group.

If B is finite both, the lower nilpotent series and the lower p-series, exist—but they need of course not end in the trivial group. We denote by $M(B)$ an unspecified but fixed term of either of these series. Then

44.42 *$M(B)$ is fully invariant in B.* //

44.43 *If the variety $\mathfrak{B}$ is generated by a finite set of finite groups, $\{A_i\}$ say, such that $M(A_i) = \{1\}$ for all A_i, then $M(B) = \{1\}$ whenever B is a finite group of $\mathfrak{B}$.*

Proof. By 15.73, B is a factor of a finite direct product of groups A_i. But for a finite direct product one confirms that $M(\Pi A_{i(j)}) = \Pi M(A_{i(j)})$. Moreover, if $C \subseteq A$ and $M(A) = \{1\}$, then $M(C) = \{1\}$, and $M(A\vartheta) = M(A)\vartheta$ for a homomorphism ϑ of A. //

44.44 **Lemma.** *If R is a normal subgroup of the finite group B and $M(B) \subseteq R$, then there exists a subgroup L of B such that $M(L) = \{1\}$ and $B = RL$.*

Proof (M. F. Newman). We treat the three possibilities for M separately, abbreviating moreover the recurring Frattini arguments after the first case.

(i) $M(B) = \pi_k(B)$, where $k \geqq 1$ as $k = 0$ is trivial. Put $\pi_k(B) = P$ and $\pi_{k-1}'(B) = Q$; let S be a Sylow p-subgroup of Q. As P is the minimal normal subgroup of Q such that Q/P has p-power order, $Q = SP$. Let N

be the normalizer of S in B; then N has a normal Sylow p-subgroup, which implies $\pi_k(N)=\{1\}$. Therefore we need only show that $B=PN$, for then $P\subseteq R$ implies that $L=N$ satisfies the assertion of the lemma. But for $b\in B$, S^b is a Sylow p-subgroup of $Q^b=Q$, hence it is conjugate in Q to S: there exists an element $c\in Q$ such that $S^b=S^c$, hence $bc^{-1}\in N$ and $B=NQ$ follows. As $Q=SP$, we have $B=NSP=NP$ as required.

(ii) $M(B)=\pi'_k(B)$, $k\geqq 0$. Then $R\supseteq\pi'_k(B)\supseteq\pi_{k+1}(B)$, hence by (i), there exists a subgroup A of B such that $\pi_{k+1}(A)=\{1\}$ and $B=RA$. Now $\pi'_k(A)\subseteq\pi'_k(B)\subseteq R$, hence $\pi'_k(A)\subseteq R\cap A$. Put $\pi'_k(A)=Q$ and $\pi_k(A)=P$; then by the Schur-Zassenhaus Lemma (cf. SCOTT, p. 227) Q is complemented in P and all complements are conjugate in P. Take S as one such complement and let N be its normalizer in A, then $QN=A$ as before, and $\pi'_k(N)=\{1\}$. But $Q\subseteq R\cap A$, hence $(R\cap A)\,N=A$ and so $B=RA=R(R\cap A)\,N=RN$ as required.

(iii) Finally let $B=v_0(B)\supseteq v_1(B)\supseteq\ldots$ be the lower nilpotent series and assume $M(B)=v_k(B)$ with $k\geqq 1$. Denote by $p_1,\ldots,p_s$ all the primes dividing $|v_{k-1}(B)|$, and let S_1 be a Sylow p_1-subgroup of $v_{k-1}(B)$, N_1 its normalizer in B. Then as before $B=RN_1$; besides $v_{k-1}(N_1)$, being contained in $v_{k-1}(B)\cap N_1$, has a normal Sylow p_1-subgroup. Next consider N_1: let S_2 be a Sylow p_2-subgroup of $v_{k-1}(N_1)$, N_2 its normalizer in N_1; then $v_{k-1}(N_2)$ has a normal Sylow p_2-subgroup, and of course also its Sylow p_1-subgroup is normal. Putting $R_1=N_1\cap R$, $R_1\supseteq v_k(N_1)$ follows, and by the standard argument $N_1=R_1N_2$. But then

$$B=RN_1=R(N_1\cap R)\,N_2=RN_2.$$

After at most s steps of this kind, taking the primes $p_1,\ldots,p_s$ in turn, one obtains $B=RN_s$ where N_s has the property that the Sylow p-subgroups of $v_{k-1}(N_s)$ for $p=p_1,p_2,\ldots,p_s$ are all normal in N_s. As these are all the primes that can occur, $v_k(N_s)=\{1\}$, so that putting $L=N_s$ proves the lemma in this case. //

Now we can prove:

44.45 **Theorem** (P. HALL [2]). *If $\mathfrak{U}$ is locally finite, and $M(A)$ denotes a term of the lower nilpotent or the lower p-series of the group A, let $\mathfrak{B}$ be the subvariety generated by all finite groups $A\in\mathfrak{U}$ with $M(A)=\{1\}$. Then $F_r(\mathfrak{B})$, for every finite r, is projective in $\mathfrak{U}$.*

44.46 **Corollary.** *With the same notation, $F_r(\mathfrak{U})$ is a splitting extension of $M(F_r(\mathfrak{U}))$ by $F_r(\mathfrak{B})$ for every choice of M.*

Proof. Put $G=F_r(\mathfrak{U})$ and $H=G/M(G)$. Then H is a relatively free group of rank r in $\mathfrak{U}$. Apply Lemma 44.44 to G with $R=M(G)$: there exists $L\subseteq G$ such that $G=LM(G)$ and $M(L)=\{1\}$.

Now let $\mathfrak{V}$ be the subvariety of $\mathfrak{U}$ generated by all groups $A\in\mathfrak{U}$ with $M(A)=\{1\}$. Then certainly $L\in\mathfrak{V}$, and $H\in\mathfrak{V}$. In fact we show $H\cong F_r(\mathfrak{V})$ as follows:

As $F_r(\mathfrak{V})\in\mathfrak{U}$, we have $F_r(\mathfrak{V})\cong G/N$ for some N. By 44.43 $M(F_r(\mathfrak{V}))=\{1\}$, hence $N\supseteq M(G)$. But also $H\in\mathfrak{V}$ so that $H=G/M(G)$ is a factor group of $F_r(\mathfrak{V})\cong G/N$; hence $M(G)\supseteq N$, giving $M(G)=N$ and $H\cong F_r(\mathfrak{V})$.

Now Lemma 44.41 shows that H is a splitting group for $\mathfrak{U}$. //

The corollary is immediate from the definition of a splitting group. //

P. HALL points out (loc. cit. p. 354) that in the case of soluble finite relatively free groups a number of differently constructed 'lower series' consist of terms over which the whole group splits, giving further splitting groups in such varieties. Moreover

44.47 *There are splitting groups in some locally finite varieties which are not relatively free.*

Proof. By 44.24 one merely has to find an example of a relatively free group with a normal subgroup that is complemented but is not verbal.

Such normal subgroups abound where $F(\mathfrak{U})$ is directly decomposable. As remarked in Chapter 2, Section 1 (p. 41), every free group $F_k(\mathfrak{A}_m\mathfrak{A}_n)$ with m, n relatively prime has a non-trivial centre which is a direct factor and is of exponent m. The complementary direct factor is not free in any subvariety of $\mathfrak{A}_m\mathfrak{A}_n$.

Or again, one derives from Lemma 3.2 of SHEILA OATES [*1*], that the free group of rank two of the variety generated by the icosahedral group A_5 has the direct decomposition

$$F_2(\operatorname{var} A_5)=A_5^{19}\times F_2(\mathfrak{A}_2\mathfrak{A}_3 \vee \mathfrak{A}_3\mathfrak{A}_2 \vee \mathfrak{A}_5\mathfrak{A}_2)$$

into twenty constituent factors, giving a number of non-free splitting groups in that variety and this is just a special case of the fact that the free group of rank k of the variety generated by a non-abelian finite simple group S splits as follows:

$F_k(\operatorname{var} S)=S^{n(k)}\times F_k(\mathfrak{U})$ where $\mathfrak{U}$ is the variety generated by the proper factors of S and $n(k)$ is the number of generating vectors of length k of S that are not equivalent under automorphisms of S.

Problem 21 (P. HALL). *Is every splitting group in a variety of exponent zero or a prime-power free in that variety?*

The known examples of directly decomposable relatively free groups, like those of non-free projective groups, all belong to locally finite varieties of composite exponent. Indeed we saw hints of a possible connection between these two situations.

Problem 22. *Is every non-abelian relatively free group of exponent zero or a prime-power directly indecomposable?*

The answer is certainly positive for many varieties. We collect some evidence.

44.51 **Theorem.** *If $\mathfrak{U}$ and $\mathfrak{V}$ are neither $\mathfrak{E}$ nor $\mathfrak{O}$, and if the non-abelian free groups of $\mathfrak{U}$ and $\mathfrak{V}$ are directly indecomposable, then so are the non-abelian free groups of $\mathfrak{U}\mathfrak{V}$.*

Proof. Assume that, for some rank,

$$K = F(\mathfrak{U}\mathfrak{V}) = A \times B, \quad A \neq \{1\} \neq B.$$

Then $V(K) = V(A) \times V(B) = F(\mathfrak{U})$, where the rank is determined by Schreier's formula from that of $K = F(\mathfrak{U}\mathfrak{V})$, and

$$K/V(K) \cong A/V(A) \times B/V(B) \cong F(\mathfrak{V}),$$

whose rank is the same as that of K. By the assumption, one factor in each of these direct products must be trivial. Without loss of generality assume $V(B) = \{1\}$ hence $V(A) = A$. Thus $A = F(\mathfrak{U}) \subseteq K$ and $B \cong F(\mathfrak{V})$, that is in K the subgroup $F(\mathfrak{U})$ is a direct factor.

If K has finite rank n, the rank of $F(\mathfrak{U})$ is definitely greater than n, so that $F(\mathfrak{U})$ cannot be a direct factor.

If K has infinite rank let $k_1, k_2, \ldots$ be a set of free generators and let $b_1, b_2, \ldots$ be their images in B under the natural epimorphism $K \twoheadrightarrow B$. Then $k_i = b_i u_i$, $u_i \in A = F(\mathfrak{U})$. As $[b_i, u] = 1$ for all i and all $u \in A$, each k_i centralizes A modulo A'. Thus reducing modulo A' we obtain the free group $L = F_\infty(\mathfrak{A}^* \mathfrak{V})$ where $\mathfrak{A}^*$ is the variety of all abelian groups in $\mathfrak{U}$, and we know that $V(L)$ is central in L. But L generates $\mathfrak{A}^* \mathfrak{V}$ which contains the wreath product $F_\infty(\mathfrak{A}^*)$ wr $F_\infty(\mathfrak{V})$ whose $\mathfrak{V}$-subgroup is the base group which is not central in the whole group. Hence the assumption $A \neq \{1\}$ leads to a contradiction. //

44.52 **Theorem** (C. H. Houghton, unpublished). *If the free groups of $\mathfrak{V}$ are torsion-free and $\mathfrak{U}$, $\mathfrak{V} \neq \mathfrak{E}$, then the free groups of $\mathfrak{U}\mathfrak{V}$ are directly indecomposable.*

Proof. By 25.63, the centralizer of an element of $K = F(\mathfrak{U}\mathfrak{V})$ that has infinite order modulo $V(K)$ has trivial intersection with $V(K)$. Assume $K = A \times B$ so that again $V(K) = V(A) \times V(B)$.

As $F(\mathfrak{V}) \cong K/V(K) \cong A/V(A) \times B/V(B)$, both factors on the right are torsion-free, and at least one is non-trivial. Let $a \in A$ not belong to $V(A)$, then it is an element of K of infinite order modulo $V(K)$; the centralizer of a contains B, but by 25.63, intersects $V(K)$ trivially; hence $V(B) = \{1\}$. If

$B \neq \{1\}$, take $b \in B$; b must have infinite order and as before A centralizes it, hence $V(A) = \{1\}$. Thus $V(K) = \{1\}$, giving $\mathfrak{U} = \mathfrak{E}$, contradicting the assumption. //

44.53 **Corollary.** *The free groups of* $\mathfrak{U}\mathfrak{N}_c$, $c \geqq 1$ *and* $\mathfrak{U} \neq \mathfrak{E}$, *are directly indecomposable.* //

Next we use the subgroup theorems of Section 2 of this chapter.

It is a trivial consequence of Theorem 42.31 that if $G = F(\mathfrak{U})$ is a non-abelian residually nilpotent free group, then two elements that are part of a basis of G modulo G' do not commute. We use this to prove:

44.54 **Theorem.** *If* $F(\mathfrak{U})$ *is non-abelian, residually nilpotent and of exponent zero or a prime-power, then it is directly indecomposable.*

Proof. Assume $G = F(\mathfrak{U}) = A \times B$. Then A and B also are residually nilpotent and so, if A and B are non-trivial, then $A' \subset A$, $B' \subset B$. Now $G/G' \cong A/A' \times B/B'$. Take elements a and b that are part of a generating set for A modulo A' and B modulo B' respectively; then a and b are part of a free generating set of G/G', hence do not commute. But this is absurd. //

44.55 **Lemma.** *If* $\mathfrak{U}$ *is non-abelian, residually nilpotent and of exponent zero, and if* $\mathfrak{U} \subseteq \mathfrak{V}$, *then two elements that are part of a basis of* $F(\mathfrak{V})$ *modulo* $F'(\mathfrak{V})$ *do not commute.*

Proof. Put $F(\mathfrak{V}) = H$; as $\mathfrak{U}$ is of exponent zero, $U(H) \subseteq H'$. Hence, if $h_1, h_2 \in H$ are part of a basis modulo H', and if $\mu\colon H \twoheadrightarrow G = F(\mathfrak{U})$ is the natural epimorphism, then $h_1\mu, h_2\mu$ form part of a basis of G modulo G'; therefore $[h_1\mu, h_2\mu] \neq 1$ and so $[h_1, h_2] \neq 1$. //

44.56 **Theorem.** *If* $\mathfrak{V}$ *is soluble and contains a non-abelian residually nilpotent subvariety of exponent zero, then the free groups of* $\mathfrak{V}$ *are directly indecomposable.*

Proof. Put $H = F(\mathfrak{V}) = A \times B$. As H is soluble, so are A and B; hence, if A and B are non-trivial, then $A' \subset A$ and $B' \subset B$. Therefore there exist elements a and b of A and B that are part of a basis of A/A' and B/B' respectively, so that a and b form part of a basis of H/H', giving the same contradiction as before by means of 44.55. //

44.57 **Corollary** *. *If the soluble variety* $\mathfrak{V}$ *contains either* $\mathfrak{A}_p\mathfrak{A}$ *or* $\mathfrak{A}\mathfrak{A}_p$, *p a prime, or* $\mathfrak{N}_2$, *then the free groups of* $\mathfrak{V}$ *are directly indecomposable.* //

C. H. Houghton has some further information, showing inter alia that the free group of infinite rank may be indecomposable in a variety

* Compare $B+3N$, Section 4, for some of these results, proved there by means of a lemma on commutators in free metabelian groups.

whose free groups of finite rank are decomposable. Some of the results mentioned above can be pushed a little further. As the story still remains incomplete, we give no further details.

Finally a word on injective groups in varieties. S. MACLANE ([*1*]) mentions in a footnote a remark due to R. BAER that the only injective group in the variety $\mathfrak{O}$ is the trivial group.

A definition of 'injective', equivalent to 44.12 in module theory, is the following:

44.61 **Definition.** *A module G is injective if to every monomorphism α: $G \rightarrowtail A$ there exists an epimorphism $\pi: A \twoheadrightarrow G$ such that $\alpha\pi$ is the identity on G.*

It is easily checked that the groups with the corresponding property are precisely the *closed groups*:

44.62 **Definition.** *A group G is closed in the variety $\mathfrak{U}$ if every system of equations possessing a solution in a supergroup of G belonging to $\mathfrak{U}$ possesses also a solution in G.*

However 44.12 implies 44.61 in the case of groups, but the converse is not true in every variety.

There is again no systematic theory of injective or of closed groups in varieties. According to L. G. KOVÁCS and M. F. NEWMAN (oral communication) there are some varieties – such as $\mathfrak{A}_3\mathfrak{A}_2$ – where an analogue of the Eckmann-Schöpf theory of injective modules (as reported for instance in CURTIS and REINER, Chapter VIII) can be developed to some extent; there are others where the analogues break down or where there are no non-trivial injective or closed groups. The finite, directly indecomposable injective groups are necessarily extensions of a cycle of prime power order by an automorphism of co-prime order, and all such groups are in fact injective in the variety they generate. In every variety finite directly indecomposable closed groups are monolithic with abelian monolith centralizer (see Chapter 5 for these terms), but some such groups are not closed in any variety. Again, any similarity to critical groups (see Chapter 5) seems to be superficial: within the class of monolithic groups with abelian monolith centralizer closed groups and critical groups are characterized by different additional properties.

While the search for projective groups in varieties has led to interesting results on complementation in free groups, the quest for injective or closed groups in varieties does not appear to have been very fruitful.

Chapter 5

The Laws of Finite Groups

1. Critical Groups and Cross Varieties

We start with some simple remarks on the finite groups of a locally finite variety, that will serve as a reminder of facts and notations introduced early on. As every variety is generated by its finitely generated groups, a locally finite variety is generated by its finite groups. By 15.73, a finite group of such a variety is a factor of a finite direct product of finite groups taken from some generating set of the variety.

51.1 *If* $\mathfrak{X}$ *is a class of finite groups,* var $\mathfrak{X}$ *is locally finite and* A *is a finite group in* var $\mathfrak{X}$, *then* $A \in$ QSD $\mathfrak{X}$. //

In this situation elementary properties of finite direct products will be used frequently and usually without explicit references: any textbook will supply the details.

We call a factor H/K of a group A a *chief factor* if K is normal in A and H/K is a minimal normal subgroup of A/K. Every group possesses chief factors; in fact if $x \neq 1$ is any element of A, there is a chief factor H/K such that $x \in H \backslash K$: Take K as a normal subgroup of A maximal with respect to avoiding x – this exists, using Zorn's Lemma – and then H as the normal closure of gp(x, K) in A. The factor H/K is called a *composition factor* of A if K is a maximal normal subgroup of the subnormal (or, subinvariant – cf. Marshall Hall, p. 123) subgroup H. In view of the widely differing terminology we stress specially that we use the term *chief series* for an unrefinable normal series and the term *composition series* for an unrefinable subnormal series. Thus in particular in finite groups, but also in much more general situations (cf. Kurosh Vol. 2, p. 171), every chief factor occurs as quotient of successive terms in some chief series of the group, and every composition factor occurs as quotient of successive terms in some composition series of the group. Every chief factor must be characteristically simple; therefore a finite chief factor is a direct product of isomorphic simple groups each of which is a composition factor of the group.

51.2 **Theorem.** *Let* $\mathfrak{X}$ *be a class of finite groups such that* var $\mathfrak{X}$ *is locally finite and* A *a finite group in* var $\mathfrak{X}$;

51.21 *if every group in $\mathfrak{X}$ has exponent e, then A has exponent e;*

51.22 *if the composition factors of every group in $\mathfrak{X}$ have orders at most k, then the composition factors of A have orders at most k;*

51.23 *if the chief factors of every group in $\mathfrak{X}$ have orders at most m, then the chief factors of A have orders at most m;*

51.24 *if the nilpotent factors of every group in $\mathfrak{X}$ have class at most c, then the nilpotent factors of A have class at most c.*

Proof. The assertion 51.21 is evident. For 51.22 and 51.23 note that every subnormal, or normal, series of a finite direct product can be refined to one whose factors occur as composition factors, or as chief factors respectively, of the constituents of the direct product. As A is a factor of a direct product of a finite number of groups in $\mathfrak{X}$, it suffices to remark that the greatest order of a composition, or chief, factor of a subgroup is at most equal to that in the whole group, and that the same applies to the composition or chief factors of an epimorphic image of the group.

Finally, for a finite group, a Sylow subgroup of an epimorphic image is the image of some Sylow subgroup of the group, and a Sylow subgroup of a subgroup is contained in some Sylow subgroup of the whole group. Hence the classes of the nilpotent factors of a finite group are at most equal to the greatest class occurring amongst its Sylow subgroups. As the Sylow p-subgroups of a direct product are direct products of Sylow p-subgroups of its constituents, 51.24 follows. //

We turn to the fundamental concepts that first arose in the context of the finite basis problem for finite groups and are still of crucial importance in its solution. The notation suggested by B. H. NEUMANN for the set of proper factors of a group A, namely (QS-1) A, is used throughout this chapter.

51.31 **Definition** (D. C. CROSS, cf. HIGMAN [*3*]). *A group A is called critical if it is finite and does not belong to the variety generated by its proper factors.*

If the requirement of finiteness is dropped, the remaining condition, $A \notin$ var (QS-1) A, makes the group finitely generated by 15.61. Some of the properties of critical groups would remain true, or remain true if suitably modified, for infinite groups A with $A \notin$ var(QS-1) A. However, the essence of the concept is in its application to finite groups; therefore finiteness is more usefully made part of the definition of a critical group.

As mentioned before, a group with a unique minimal normal subgroup ('non-trivial' is understood) is called *monolithic* and the minimal normal subgroup is the *monolith* of the group. The monolith is, of course, isomorphic to a chief factor of the group and therefore an (abelian or non-abelian) direct power of a simple group. We have at once:

51.32 **Theorem.** *A critical group is monolithic.*

Proof. Assume that A has two distinct minimal normal subgroups, M and N say; then the intersection is normal in A, hence $M \cap N = \{1\}$. But then the mapping $a \to (aM, aN)$, $a \in A$, is easily checked to be a monomorphism of A into the direct product $(A/M) \times (A/N)$. Hence $A \in \operatorname{var}(\mathrm{QS}\text{-}1)\, A$ contradicting the assumption that A is critical. //

Not every monolithic group is critical:

51.33 **Example.** Take two copies of a finite non-abelian nilpotent group B whose centre is cyclic of prime order and form the direct product of these two isomorphic groups amalgamating their centres. The result is a monolithic group which is an epimorphic image of $B \times B$, hence not critical.

On the other hand, in the extreme case of simple groups we see from 51.22:

51.34 *A finite simple group is critical.*

Proof. The only composition factors of a simple group A are the trivial group and A itself. By 51.22 a finite group in $\operatorname{var}(\mathrm{QS}\text{-}1)\, A$ has composition factors of order less than $|A|$, and so A itself can not occur. //

51.35 **Theorem.** *A critical group that is nilpotent of class c is a p-group with cyclic centre and can be generated by c elements.*

Proof. As a finite nilpotent group is the direct product of its Sylow subgroups, it must be a p-group in order to be critical. As a central subgroup is normal in the whole group, and as in a nilpotent group every non-trivial normal subgroup has non-trivial intersection with the centre, the centre contains every minimal normal subgroup. Hence if the group is monolithic, the centre must be cyclic. Finally let A be the critical group, and $\mathfrak{U} = \operatorname{var} A$. By 35.12, $\mathfrak{U}$ is generated by its c-generator groups, hence by 16.31 it is generated by the c-generator subgroups of A. As $A \notin \operatorname{var}(\mathrm{QS}-1)\, A$, not all these subgroups can be proper subgroups. //

Clearly in the case $c=1$ the converse is true; hence

51.36 *The abelian critical groups are precisely the cycles of prime power order.* //

In fact one can see that also for $c=2$ the conditions in Theorem 51.35 are sufficient, but for $c>2$ the situation is more complex. We defer a more detailed report on critical groups; this paragraph is intended to do no more than assemble the tools for the proof that the laws of a finite group are finitely based. One of the principal tools is the following much deeper result.

51.37 **Theorem** (OATES and POWELL [*1*]). *If the group A possesses a set of normal subgroups $M_1, \ldots, M_s$ and a subgroup L such that*

(i) $A = \mathrm{gp}(L, M_1, \ldots, M_s)$,

(ii) *no proper subset of the set $\{M_1, \ldots, M_s\}$ suffices, together with L, to generate A,*

(iii) *every mutual commutator group $[M_{\pi(1)}, M_{\pi(2)}, \ldots, M_{\pi(s)}]$, where π is some permutation of the integers $1, \ldots, s$, is trivial,*

then A is not critical.

Proof (L.G. KOVÁCS). We shall use 33.37 and 33.43. Let $B_j \cong M_j$ ($j=1, \ldots, s$) and $B_0 \cong L$ be copies of the given subgroups of A and put $P = B_0 * B_1 * \cdots * B_s$. The deletions ϑ_j ($j=1, \ldots, s$) are the endomorphisms of P that map B_j onto the trivial group and map B_i ($i \neq j$) identically. Put $K = \bigcap_{j=1,\ldots,s} \ker \vartheta_j$; by 33.37 every element of K can be written as a product of commutators, each of which involves every group B_j ($j \geqq 1$). Now let α be the natural homomorphism of P onto A that continues given isomorphisms from B_0 onto L and from B_j onto M_j ($j \geqq 1$). Then, as the M_i are normal, the assumption (iii) ensures that $K \subseteq \ker \alpha$.

We now recall 33.43. It states that every element $w \in P$ can be written as follows:

$$w = u\, v_1 \ldots v_t, \qquad \text{where } u \in K \subseteq \ker \alpha,$$

and each v_i is of the form $v_i = w^{\pm 1} \beta_i$ with β_i a non-empty product of deletions ϑ_j. As $P\beta_i \subset P$, $P\beta_i\, \alpha$ is defined and is, by (ii), a proper subgroup C_i of A. We consider a direct product of groups A_i which are isomorphic copies of the subgroups C_i of A, $A_i = C_i\, \gamma_i$ say for some fixed isomorphisms γ_i. Then the epimorphisms $\beta_i\, \alpha\, \gamma_i$: $P \twoheadrightarrow A_i$ may be used to define a homomorphism γ: $P \to \Pi A_i$ by setting for each $w \in P$

$$w\gamma = \Pi\, w \beta_i \alpha \gamma_i \in \Pi A_i.$$

We now show that α can be factored through γ, that is, there is an epimorphism μ: $P\gamma \twoheadrightarrow A$ such that $\gamma\mu = \alpha$. To this end it suffices to show that $\ker \gamma \subseteq \ker \alpha$. But in the direct product ΠA_i, $w\gamma = 1$ if and only if $w\beta_i\, \alpha\gamma_i = 1$ for all i. As the γ_i are isomorphisms, this means $w\beta_i\, \alpha = 1$, that is $v_i = w^{\pm 1}\beta_i \in \ker \alpha$ for all i. The representation $w = u v_1 \ldots v_t$ now shows that $w \in \ker \alpha$ as required.

The epimorphism μ, whose existence is thus assured, represents A as an epimorphic image of a subgroup of a direct product of proper subgroups of A, that is A is not critical. //

51.38 **Corollary.** *If the critical group A possesses a normal nilpotent subgroup N partially complemented by a subgroup L (that is, $A=NL$), and a set of subgroups $N_1, \ldots, N_s$ of N such that*

(i) *each N_j ($j=1, \ldots, s$) admits the elements of L (that is $N_j^x \subseteq N_j$ for $x \in L$),*

(ii) $A = \mathrm{gp}(L, N_1, \ldots, N_s)$,

(iii) *no proper subset of the set $\{N_1, \ldots, N_s\}$ together with L generates A, then s is at most equal to the class of N.*

Proof. We apply 51.37 with $M_j = N_j\,\Phi(N)$ where $\Phi(N)$ is the Frattini subgroup of N. Then we have to check that, as soon as s exceeds the class of N, the assumptions of 51.37 are satisfied.

As $\Phi(N) \supseteq N'$, $N_j\,\Phi(N)$ is normal in N. Also $\Phi(N)$ is characteristic in N, hence normal in A, N_j admits L, so that $N_j\,\Phi(N)$ admits $NL=A$. That A is generated by L and the M_i is a trivial consequence of $A=\mathrm{gp}(L, N_1, \ldots, N_s)$. Finally, if s is greater than the class of N, the condition (iii) of 51.37 is obviously satisfied. It therefore remains to check (ii) of 51.37. To this end assume without loss of generality

$$\begin{aligned} A &= \mathrm{gp}(L, M_1, \ldots, M_d) \qquad (d \leqq s) \\ &= \mathrm{gp}\big(L, N_1\,\Phi(N), \ldots, N_d\,\Phi(N)\big). \end{aligned}$$

Then in particular every element $n \in N$ has a representation

$$n = l\, m_1 \ldots m_d, \qquad l \in L, \qquad m_i \in M_i.$$

Hence $l \in N \cap L$, and thus

$$\begin{aligned} N &= (N \cap L)\,\mathrm{gp}\big(N_1\,\Phi(N), \ldots, N_d\,\Phi(N)\big) \\ &= (N \cap L)\,\mathrm{gp}\big(N_1, \ldots, N_d, \Phi(N)\big) = (N \cap L)\,\mathrm{gp}(N_1, \ldots, N_d). \end{aligned}$$

Then $A = LN = L\,\mathrm{gp}(N_1, \ldots, N_d)$ and condition (iii) of 51.38 gives $d=s$. //

Note that the case $L=\{1\}$ leads once again to 51.35.

The following remarks indicate the significance of critical groups.

51.41 *A locally finite variety is generated by its critical groups.*

Proof. Let $\mathfrak{V}$ be locally finite, hence generated by its finite groups. Let $\mathfrak{W}$ be the subvariety generated by the critical groups. If $\mathfrak{W}$ is a proper subvariety of $\mathfrak{V}$, then $\mathfrak{V}$ contains a finite group not belonging to $\mathfrak{W}$. Let A be such a group of least possible order; then every proper factor of A belongs to $\mathfrak{W}$, hence $\mathrm{var}(\mathsf{Q}\mathsf{S}-1)A \subseteq \mathfrak{W}$ and A is critical, contradicting the definition of $\mathfrak{W}$. Hence $\mathfrak{W} = \mathfrak{V}$. //

51.42 **Corollary.** *If $\mathfrak{V}$ is locally finite, and if $\mathfrak{U}$ is a proper subvariety of $\mathfrak{V}$, then $\mathfrak{V}$ contains a critical group not belonging to $\mathfrak{U}$.* //

51.43 *A finite group belongs to the variety generated by its critical factors.*

Proof. We use induction on the order. It is true for groups of prime order, as these are themselves critical. Let B be an arbitrary group; if it is not critical it belongs to the variety generated by its proper factors. These have orders dividing the order of B and so those of the factors that are not critical are generated by their critical factors using the induction assumption. If B is critical, then $B \in \text{var } B$ confirms 51.43 in that case. //

51.51 **Definition** (cf. HIGMAN [*3*]). *A variety $\mathfrak{V}$ is called a Cross variety if*

(i) *$\mathfrak{V}$ is locally finite,*

(ii) *the laws of $\mathfrak{V}$ are finitely based,*

(iii) *the number of non-isomorphic critical groups in $\mathfrak{V}$ is finite.*

Then

51.52 **Theorem.** *Every subvariety of a Cross variety is a Cross variety.*

Proof. Let $\mathfrak{W} \subset \mathfrak{V}$ be a proper subvariety of the Cross variety $\mathfrak{V}$. Clearly the properties (i) and (iii) are inherited by $\mathfrak{W}$ and only (ii) remains to be proved.

Let $\mathfrak{W} = \mathfrak{V}_k \subset \mathfrak{V}_{k-1} \subset \cdots \subset \mathfrak{V}_1 = \mathfrak{V}$ be a chain of subvarieties properly between $\mathfrak{W}$ and $\mathfrak{V}$. By 51.42, there is a critical group in $\mathfrak{V}_i$ that does not belong to $\mathfrak{V}_{i+1}$ for each $i \geqq 1$. Hence (iii) shows that k is at most equal to the number of critical groups in $\mathfrak{V}$. We may therefore assume that the chain cannot be refined. Now $\mathfrak{V}_1$ is given to be finitely based; assume that $\mathfrak{V}_i$ is finitely based and let w be a law of $\mathfrak{V}_{i+1}$ that does not hold in $\mathfrak{V}_i$. Let $\mathfrak{U}$ be the variety defined by w and the laws of $\mathfrak{V}_i$; then the laws of $\mathfrak{U}$ are finitely based, as those of $\mathfrak{V}_i$ are. Also $V_{i+1} \supseteq \{w, V_i\} \supset V_i$, hence $\mathfrak{V}_{i+1} \subseteq \mathfrak{U} \subset \mathfrak{V}_i$. As the chain is unrefinable, $\mathfrak{V}_{i+1} = \mathfrak{U}$, and so $\mathfrak{V}_{i+1}$ is finitely based. Induction completes the proof. //

51.53 **Corollary.** *The laws of every finite group are finitely based if every finite group belongs to some Cross variety.* //

Finally one more preparatory step:

51.54 *Let $\mathfrak{U} = \text{var } A$ be the variety generated by a finite group A; then for every positive integer k the variety $\mathfrak{U}^{(k)}$ defined by the k-variable laws of A is finitely based.*

Proof. The k-variable laws of $\mathfrak{U} = \text{var } A$ are given by $U(F_k) = F_k \cap U(F_\infty)$. As $F_k(\mathfrak{U})$ is finite and $F_k(\mathfrak{U}) \cong F_k / U(F_k)$, $U(F_k)$ has finite index in F_k; hence, by Schreier's Theorem, it is finitely generated. Thus certainly $U(F_k)$ is the closure of a finite set. //

Now $\mathfrak{U} \subseteq \mathfrak{U}^{(k)}$ for all k, so that it is sufficient to show that $\mathfrak{U}^{(k)}$ is a Cross variety for some positive integer k. This has the advantage that only the properties (i) and (iii) remain to be established and only for a suitable choice of the integer k.

2. The Theorem of Oates and Powell

The aim of this section is to establish the finite basis theorem for the laws of a finite group, and some related results.

52.11 **Theorem** (OATES and POWELL [*1*]). *The variety generated by a finite group is a Cross variety.*

52.12 **Corollary.** *The laws of a finite group have a finite basis.*

This answers positively the question first asked by B. H. NEUMANN [*1*]. The version of the proof here presented is due to KOVÁCS and NEWMAN [*1*].

For fixed positive integers e, m, c denote by $\mathfrak{C}(e, m, c)$ the class of all groups with exponent e, whose chief factors are of order at most m, and whose nilpotent factors have class at most c. Clearly every finite group belongs to some such class, Theorem 52.11 will therefore be an immediate consequence, by means of 51.53 and 51.54, of the following three principal lemmas.

52.21 **Lemma.** *If A is a finite group of order n, exponent e and maximum class of its nilpotent factors c, and $\mathfrak{U} = \operatorname{var} A$, then there exists a positive integer k such that $\mathfrak{U}^{(k)} \subseteq \mathfrak{C}(e, e^n, c)$.*

52.22 **Lemma.** *Finitely generated groups in $\mathfrak{C}(e, m, c)$ are finite.*

52.23 **Lemma.** *$\mathfrak{C}(e, m, c)$ contains only a finite number of (non-isomorphic) critical groups.*

Before we deal with these three lemmas, we establish a further simple lemma which is needed repeatedly. It says, loosely, that in any group a bound on the order of a chief factor determines a bound on the index of its centralizer and conversely. We use the notation $C_A(H/K)$ for the centralizer of a factor H/K of the group A; if H/K is a chief factor, we call $C_A(H/K)$ a *chief centralizer* of A.

52.24 **Lemma.** *If H/K is a chief factor of A of order at most m, then its centralizer, C say, has index at most $m!$. If conversely, C has index at most n and A has exponent e, then H/K has order at most e^n.*

Proof. The factor group A/C is faithfully represented – by conjugation, of course – on H/K; hence its order divides that of the automorphism group of H/K.

For the converse note that $C \supseteq K$ and $C \cap H/K$ is the centre of H/K. As H/K is characteristically simple, either $C \cap H = K$ or $C \supset H$ and H/K is elementary abelian. In the first case, $H/K = H/C \cap H \cong HC/C \subseteq A/C$, so that $|A/C| \leqq n$ implies $|H/K| \leqq n$. In the second case note that the images of a non-trivial element of H/K under the action of A, that is of A/C, generate H/K. If $|A/C| \leqq n$, then H/K needs at most n generators. As its exponent is a prime dividing e, its order is at most e^n. //

Clearly the estimates given are very rough and do no more than establish the possibility of estimating one in terms of the other.

The main step in the proof of 52.21 consists in providing a law which bounds the index of the chief centralizers of a group. We shall refer to it as the *chief centralizer law* and define it inductively by

52.31 $$v_2 = [x_1, x_2, (x_1^{-1} x_2)^{y_{1,2}}],$$
$$v_n = [v_{n-1}, x_n^{y_n}, (x_1^{-1} x_n)^{y_{1,n}}, \dots, (x_{n-1}^{-1} x_n)^{y_{n-1,n}}] \quad \text{if} \quad n > 2.$$

Then v_n is a word in the $\frac{1}{2}(n-1)(n+4)$ variables $x_1, \dots, x_n, y_3, \dots, y_n, y_{ij}$ $(1 \leqq i < j \leqq n)$. We remark that by using three more variables one may obtain a more symmetrically formed commutator, with entries of the form $(x_i^{-1} x_j)^{y_{ij}}$ only, that serves the same purpose.

52.32 **Theorem.** *A group of order at most n satisfies the law v_n. Conversely, if v_n is a law in the group A, then every centralizer of a chief factor of A has index at most n in A.*

Proof. Assume the group A has order at most n. Then every substitution of group elements for the variables $x_1, \dots, x_n$ gives value 1 to at least one of the x_i or at least one of the quotients $x_i^{-1} x_j$. Hence v_n takes value 1 whatever elements are substituted for the y_i and y_{ij}. This proves the first part.

For the second part we first note the following rule:

52.33 *If H/K is a chief factor of A and C its centralizer in A, let $h \in H \backslash K$ and $a \notin C$. Then there exists a conjugate a^b of a such that $[h, a^b] \in H \backslash K$.*

Proof. Clearly the commutator belongs to H; if for all b it belongs to K, then all conjugates of h centralize a modulo K. As H/K is minimal normal in A/K, this means that the whole of H centralizes a modulo K, contradicting the choice of a. //

Returning to the second part of Theorem 52.32 we assume that the group A possesses a chief factor whose centralizer C has index greater than n in A; then, whether C contains H or not, it is possible to choose n elements in distinct cosets of C such that the first is in $H \backslash K$ and all the others do not belong to C. This can be done in such a way that, moreover, the commutator of the first two elements does not fall into K. To see this, take $a' \in H \backslash K$ arbitrary and $a_2 \notin C$ and not in the same coset as a'. As in 52.33, there is a conjugate of a', $a_1 = a'^b$ say, such that $[a_1, a_2] \notin K$. Clearly $a_1 \in H \backslash K$; moreover $a_1^{-1} a_2 \notin C$, because $[a_1, a_1^{-1} a_2] = [a_1, a_2] \notin K$. Having chosen a_1, a_2, the remaining elements $a_3, \ldots, a_n$ may now be picked so that none belongs to C and all a_i are from different cosets modulo C.

To find a non-trivial value of v_n in A, start by putting $x_i = a_i$ for $i = 1, \ldots, n$. It remains to find suitable values of $y_2, \ldots, y_n$ and $y_{i,j}$. As $[a_1, a_2] \in H \backslash K$ and $a_1^{-1} a_2 \notin C$, 52.33 provides us with the existence of a conjugate, $(a_1^{-1} a_2)^{b_{1,2}}$ say, such that $[a_1, a_2, (a_1^{-1} a_2)^{b_{1,2}}] \notin K$. Hence $x_1 = a_1, x_2 = a_2, y_{1,2} = b_{1,2}$ gives a value of v_2 that is not in K, but of course in H. If $n > 2$, use induction: if values for $y_2, \ldots, y_{k-1}$ and y_{ij} for $1 \leqq i < j \leqq k-1$ have been found so that v_{k-1} takes a value in $H \backslash K$, then the definition of v_k and the choice of values for $x_1, \ldots, x_k$ show that k successive applications of 52.33 give elements which substituted for y_k and y_{ik} $(1 \leqq i \leqq k-1)$ give v_k a value not in K. Hence, inductively, one finds values for all the variables such that the resulting value of v_n is not in K, hence certainly not trivial. //

We draw attention in passing to a corollary of Theorem 52.32 although the result will not be needed here and will in any case be obtained as part of a more general criterion in the next section.

52.34 **Corollary.** *A finite monolithic group with non-abelian monolith is critical.*

Proof. Let A be finite, of order $n+1$, with non-abelian monolith. The centralizer of the monolith intersects the monolith trivially, hence is trivial; thus its index is $n+1$. Hence the law v_n does not hold in A by the second part of Theorem 52.32. But by the first part of the theorem the law v_n holds in every proper factor of A. Hence A is critical. //

One further lemma is wanted.

52.35 **Lemma.** *Let A be a finite group whose nilpotent factors have class at most c and $\mathfrak{U} = \operatorname{var} A$. If $k \geqq c+1$, then the nilpotent factors of every group in the variety $\mathfrak{U}^{(k)}$ have class at most c.*

Proof. By 51.24, every finite group in $\mathfrak{U} = \operatorname{var} A$ has nilpotent factors of class at most c. An arbitrary group is nilpotent of class c if and only if its $(c+1)$-generator subgroups are nilpotent of class c, by 34.15. But a $(c+1)$-generator group of $\mathfrak{U}^{(k)}$ belongs tb $\mathfrak{U}$, because $k \geqq c+1$ and by 16.21 $\mathfrak{U}^{(k)}$ consists of all groups whose k-generator subgroups belong to $\mathfrak{U}$. As a $(c+1)$-generator nilpotent group of finite exponent is finite, our starting remark shows that the $(c+1)$-generator nilpotent groups of $\mathfrak{U}^{(k)}$ have class at most c. //

The proof of the first of the three lemmas is now easy.

Proof of Lemma 52.21. Let A be a finite group whose order is $n>1$, whose exponent is e, and whose nilpotent factors have class at most c. Choose $k=\frac{1}{2}(n-1)(n+4)$; then the law v_n which is satisfied in A, hence in $\mathfrak{U}=\operatorname{var} A$, also holds in $\mathfrak{U}^{(k)}$. We show that $\mathfrak{U}^{(k)}$ is contained in $\mathfrak{C}(e, e^n, c)$.

Let $B\in\mathfrak{U}^{(k)}$. As x^e is a law in $\mathfrak{U}$, it is a law in $\mathfrak{U}^{(k)}$; hence B has exponent e.

As v_n is a law in $\mathfrak{U}^{(k)}$, Theorem 52.32 shows that the chief centralizers of B have index at most n, hence by 52.24 the chief factors of B have order at most e^n.

Finally $n>c$ is obviously true, hence $k>c+1$. Therefore by 52.35 the nilpotent factors of B have class at most c. //

Proof of Lemma 52.22. Let $A\in\mathfrak{C}(e, m, c)$ be finitely generated. By 52.24 the chief centralizers of A are of index at most $m!$. But a finitely generated group possesses only a finite number of distinct subgroups of given finite index (Kurosh Vol. 2, p. 56); hence in particular A has only a finite number of chief centralizers. Let F be their intersection*, then F has finite index in A, hence is finitely generated.

Now assume that N is a normal subgroup of finite index in A and contained in F. Then F/N is finite, and so there exists a chief series of the finite group A/N containing F/N as one of its terms. The chief factors contained in F/N are centralized by F/N, hence central in F/N. Thus F/N possesses a central series, therefore is nilpotent; by the assumption on A, the class is at most c. As the exponent of F/N divides e and the number of generators is at most equal to the number of generators of F, the order of F/N is bounded by some number that does not depend on N. As before, the number of normal subgroups of bounded index in a finitely generated group is finite so that there are only a finite number of such normal subgroups N of A contained in F. If M is an arbitrary normal subgroup of finite index in A, then its intersection with F is one of these subgroups N just considered, hence the index of M in A is also bounded and so A possesses only a finite number of normal subgroups of finite index. Let their intersection be G; then G has finite index in A and so is finitely generated. But a non-trivial finitely generated group possesses maximal operator subgroups for the various operator domains that arise naturally (B. H. Neumann; for a proof of this result in its natural, more general context cf. Cohn, Universal Algebra, p. 81); in particular, if G is non-trivial then it possesses proper subgroups maximal with respect to being

* F for Fitting subgroup, which it will turn out to be. No absolutely free groups will occur in this or the following sections.

normal in A. Let L be one of them; by the construction of G, L has infinite index in A, hence G/L is an infinite chief factor of A, which is impossible. Hence G is trivial and A is finite. //

The tools for the final step, the proof of Lemma 52.23, include some properties of the Frattini subgroup and the *Fitting subgroup* of a group. The latter is defined as the unique maximal nilpotent normal subgroup of the group, if this exists. It is easy to see that a finite group always possesses a Fitting subgroup. A proof of this and similar remarks can be found in Chapter 7 of SCOTT's textbook (Sections 7.3 and 7.4) where in particular also the results of WOLFGANG GASCHÜTZ quoted below (52.42) are proved.

The argument used to establish 52.22 leads to an alternative characterisation of the Fitting subgroup.

52.41 **Lemma.** *The Fitting subgroup of a finite group is the intersection of all chief centralizers of the group.*

Proof. Denote the Fitting subgroup of the finite group A temporarily by F_1, and use F as before for the intersection of the chief centralizers. Then every chief factor in F is centralized by F, that is, F is nilpotent and so $F \subseteq F_1$.

To prove the reverse inclusion, consider a chief series of A through F_1. The chief factors of A lying in F_1 are centralized by F_1, as F_1 is nilpotent. If H/K is a chief factor lying above F_1, then $F_1 \subseteq K$, hence $[H, F_1] \subseteq F_1 \subseteq K$, and so F_1 also centralizes H/K. Thus F_1 centralizes every chief factor of this series, and therefore of every chief series, since any two chief series are A-isomorphic (that is operator isomorphic with A as operator domain acting by conjugation) by the Jordan-Hölder Theorems. Hence $F_1 \subseteq F$ as required. //

As the Frattini subgroup of a finite group is nilpotent, it is contained in the Fitting subgroup. We use the following abbreviated notation throughout the rest of this section: The Frattini subgroup of A is Φ, the Fitting subgroup of A is F, the centralizer of F/Φ in A is C. Now one has:

52.42 **Lemma** (GASCHÜTZ [*1*]). *If A is finite, then*

(i) *the Fitting subgroup of A/Φ is F/Φ;*

(ii) *F/Φ is a direct product of minimal normal subgroups $M_1/\Phi, \ldots, M_s/\Phi$ of A/Φ;*

(iii) *F/Φ possesses a complement L/Φ in A/Φ;*

(iv) *the centralizer C of F/Φ in A is the intersection of the centralizers of the chief factors M_i/Φ of A.*

We need one further lemma obviously analogous to the situation of 52.42:

52.43 **Lemma** (Oates and Powell [*1*]). *If $M_1, \ldots, M_s$ are non-nilpotent normal subgroups of the finite group A which generate their direct product in A, then A possesses a subgroup L such that $A = \mathrm{gp}(M_1, \ldots, M_s, L)$, but A is not generated by L together with a proper subset of the set of groups $M_1, \ldots, M_s$.*

Proof. There certainly are subgroups of A which together with $M_1, \ldots, M_s$ generate A. Let L be a minimal such subgroup. We show that it satisfies the further condition that together with this L, no subgroup M_i is redundant. Put $M = \prod_i M_i$ and let M^* be the product where, without loss of generality, M_1 has been omitted: $M^* = \{1\}$ when $s=1$, $M^* = M_2 \times \ldots \times M_s$ when $s>1$. We assume $LM^* = A$ and derive a contradiction to the minimality of L. Put $N = L \cap M^*$, then N is normal in L. Also $M/M^* \cong M_1$ and $M = M^*(M \cap L)$ as $M^*L = A$; hence $M/M^* \cong M \cap L/M \cap L \cap M^* = M \cap L/N$, and so $M \cap L/N$ is non-nilpotent and therefore not contained in the Frattini subgroup of L/N. Hence there exists a maximal subgroup of L/N not containing $M \cap L/N$. Let L_1/N be such a maximal subgroup, then $(L_1/N)(M \cap L/N) = L/N$ so that $L_1(M \cap L) = L$; hence we obtain $A = LM^* = L_1(M \cap L)M^* = L_1 M$. But $L_1 \subset L$, contradicting the assumption. //

The proof of Lemma 52.23 will consist in showing that the order of a critical group in $\mathfrak{C}(e, m, c)$ is bounded by a function of e, m and c alone. Since there are only a finite number of non-isomorphic groups of any given order, the number of critical groups in $\mathfrak{C}(e, m, c)$ will then be finite. The procedure follows closely that used by Sheila Oates and M. B. Powell in bounding the order of a critical group with abelian monolith in terms of e, c and one other invariant—we come back to this at the end of the proof. The present modification makes the assumption that the monolith is abelian unnecessary. In fact it is worth pointing out that in the case of non-abelian monolith the whole argument reduces to something exceedingly simple:

52.5 *If $A \in \mathfrak{C}(e, m, c)$ is critical and its monolith is non-abelian, then its order is at most $m!$.*

Proof. The monolith is contained in every non-trivial normal subgroup of A; hence, if it is non-abelian, its centralizer is trivial, and so has index equal to the order of A. But the monolith is a chief factor, whose centralizer, by 52.24, has index at most $m!$. //

Proof of Lemma 52.23. We now assume that $A \in \mathfrak{C}(e, m, c)$ is critical. A 'bound' will always mean 'bound in terms of e, m and c'.

First step: If a bound for the index of Φ in A is found, then a bound for $|A|$ can be derived. For, since Φ consists of all non-generators of A, the number of elements needed to generate A can be at most $|A/\Phi|$. But from bounds for the number of generators of A and the index of Φ in A one obtains a bound for the number of generators of Φ by means of Schreier's formula. As Φ is nilpotent, of class at most c and exponent dividing e, this then leads to a bound for the order of Φ, and so for the order of A.

Second step: As $\Phi \subseteq F \subseteq C \subseteq A$, we have

$$|A/\Phi| = |A/C| \cdot |C/F| \cdot |F/\Phi|.$$

We use Lemma 51.38 to show that the number s of direct factors M_i/Φ of F/Φ in 52.42 (ii) is at most c. This is immediate since $F, M_1, \ldots, M_s$ and the subgroup L of A chosen so that L/Φ is a complement of F/Φ according to 52.42 (iii) clearly fit the assumptions of 51.38.

By assumption each M_i/Φ has order at most m, hence 52.42 (ii) shows that

$$|F/\Phi| \leqq m^c.$$

Moreover, as $|M_i/\Phi| \leqq m$, 52.24 shows that the centralizer of M_i/Φ has index at most $m!$ in A. Again, as there are at most c such centralizers, 52.42 (iv) shows that

$$|A/C| \leqq (m!)^c.$$

Thus it remains to find a bound for the order of C/F.

By 52.41, $F = \bigcap_j (C \cap C_j)$ where C_j runs through all chief centralizers of A. This representation may have superfluous terms; we omit these and assume that the number of terms is minimal, t say. Then put $C^* = \bigcap (C_j,\ 1 \leqq j \leqq t)$ so that $F = C \cap C^*$, hence $C/F \cong CC^*/C^* \subseteq A/C^*$. It therefore suffices to bound the index of C^*; as each chief centralizer has index at most $m!$, we have $|A/C^*| \leqq (m!)^t$, and it finally remains to bound t.

Third step: From now on we keep the chosen centralizers $C_1, \ldots, C_t$ fixed so that $F = \bigcap_j (C \cap C_j)$ is an irredundant representation of F as intersection of t terms. The case $t=1$ leaves nothing more to do, so that we assume $t>1$. Hence, putting $D_i = \bigcap_{j \neq i} (C \cap C_j)$, D_i contains F properly, and $D_i \cap D_k = F$ whenever $i \neq k$ so that D_i and D_k centralize each other modulo F. Moreover the D_i/F generate their direct product in C/F:

Assume that $\Pi\, d_i \in F$ and use that the factors commute modulo F; then for each j, $1 \leqq j \leqq t$, $d_j^{-1} \equiv \prod_{j \neq i} d_i$ modulo F. Each term on the right hand side is in C_j by the definition of D_i $(i \neq j)$, but $d_j \in D_j$ and $D_j \cap C_j = F$.

Hence each factor of the product Πd_i belongs to F and so $\mathrm{gp}(D_i/F) = \Pi(D_i/F)$.

Now pick out of each group D_i/F a subgroup N_i/F that is a minimal normal subgroup of A/F. By 52.42 (i), every nilpotent normal subgroup of A/Φ lies in F/Φ; therefore the groups N_i/Φ cannot be nilpotent. But each N_i is a subgroup of C which centralizes F/Φ. Hence F/Φ is central in N_i/Φ; hence N_i/F must be non-nilpotent. As $N_i/F \subseteq D_i/F$, $i=1, \ldots, t$, the groups N_i/F also generate their direct product in C/F, that is in A/F. Now Lemma 52.43 shows the existence of a subgroup L/F of A/F such that A/F is generated by the N_i/F and L/F, but no N_i/F can be omitted. Hence also $A = LN_1 \ldots N_t$, but omitting one of the groups N_i gives a proper subgroup of A.

The subgroups $N_1, \ldots, N_t, L$ now satisfy the first two of the requirements in Theorem 51.37. The last step shows that if t is too large, then the third also will be satisfied contradicting the criticality of A.

Last step: We show that for A to be critical, $t < 2 + ce\,(m!)$.

The group F is nilpotent, hence a direct product of p-groups, each characteristic in F, hence normal in A. But A is monolithic, so that only one such factor can occur; hence F is a p-group for some p dividing e. The subgroups N_i $(i=1, \ldots, t)$ are non-nilpotent, hence N_i/F possesses elements of order prime to p. More than that, each N_i/F is a non-abelian chief factor of A, hence a direct power of a non-abelian simple group which can be generated by conjugates of a single element. Thus N_i/F is generated by elements of order prime to p. We choose arbitrarily one element b_i from each N_i so that b_iF has order prime to p in N_i/F. The aim is to show that if $t \geqq 2 + ce(m!)$ then $[b_1, b_2, \ldots, b_t] = 1$. As the numbering of the N_i and the choice of $b_i \in N_i$ was arbitrary, this shows that every left-normed commutator of weight t formed with generating elements from distinct groups N_i is the identity, and so it follows that the mutual commutator groups $[N_{\pi(1)}, \ldots, N_{\pi(t)}]$, π a permutation, are trivial (by an argument used in 34.21).

We may assume that F is non-trivial, since otherwise $A \cong A/F$ is monolithic and so $t=1$. We refine the lower central series of F by interposing between any two successive terms the iterated Frattini series of the factor, that is its Frattini subgroup, then the Frattini subgroup of this, and so on. The result is a chain $F = F_0 \supset F_1 \supset \cdots \supset F_k = \{1\}$, where each term is characteristic in F, hence normal in A, and each factor group of successive terms is an elementary abelian p-group, since the Frattini factor group of a p-group is elementary abelian. Since the class of F is at most c and its exponent divides e, there are certainly less than ce steps, that is $k < ce$.

Now let $F_{\kappa-1}$ and F_κ be successive terms and take $b_1, \ldots, b_{m!}$ from distinct N_i as before. Note that $m!$ is an upper bound for the index of all chief centralizers. From this it will follow that

$$[F_{\kappa-1}, b_1, \dots, b_{m!}] \subseteq F_\kappa \quad \text{for} \quad \kappa = 1, \dots k.$$

Put $B = \mathrm{gp}(F, b_1, \dots, b_{m!})$, and let $F_{\kappa-1} = H_0 \supset H_1 \supset \cdots \supset H_l = F_\kappa$ be the part of a chief series of A through $F_{\kappa-1}$ and F_κ. We look at the representation of B on the elementary abelian factor $F_{\kappa-1}/F_\kappa$. As F centralizes this factor, this is in fact a representation of B/F. By the choice of the elements b_i, B/F is a direct product of cyclic groups of order prime to p. Using elementary representation theory, we know that Maschke's Theorem applies. It provides for each H_λ/F_κ a complementary invariant factor G_λ/F_κ in $H_{\lambda-1}/F_\kappa$. Then, for each $\lambda = 1, \dots, l$, $H_{\lambda-1}/H_\lambda$ is B-isomorphic to $G_\lambda | F_\kappa$ and, inductively, $F_{\kappa-1}/F_\kappa = \Pi\, G_\lambda/F_\kappa$. But then it suffices to show for each such factor that

$$[G_\lambda, b_1, \dots, b_{m!}] \subseteq F_\kappa.$$

By the choice of the G_λ, this is equivalent to showing

$$[H_{\lambda-1}, b_1, \dots, b_{m!}] \subseteq H_\lambda \quad \text{for} \quad \lambda = 1, \dots, l.$$

This will follow as soon as we know that at least one of the $m!$ elements b_i must lie in the centralizer, C_λ say, of the chief factor $H_{\lambda-1}/H_\lambda$. Now C_λ, like every chief centralizer, contains F. We look at the intersection of C_λ/F with the direct product of all the minimal normal subgroups N_i/F, $i = 1, \dots t$, of A/F. This intersection is normal in A/F and contained in $\Pi N_i/F$, hence is itself the direct product of some of the factors N_i/F. (To confirm this last remark, let X be the intersection, $x \in X$, and assume that x has non-trivial component bF in a factor N/F. As the latter is non-abelian, there is an element $b'F$ in it such that $[b, b']\, F \neq F$. Also $[x, b'F] \in X$ as X is normal in A/F, but this commutator has the single non-trivial component $[b, b']\, F$ in N/F and trivial component in every other factor. As N/F is minimal normal in A/F, the normal closure of $[b, b']\, F$ in A/F is the whole of N/F, and it belongs to X which is normal in A/F.) Now the direct product of the remaining factors avoids C_λ/F. But the index of C_λ in A, that is of C_λ/F in A/F, is at most $m!$; hence there are at most $m! - 1$ such factors N_j/F outside C_λ/F. As the $m!$ elements b_i are from different factors, at least one lies in C_λ/F as asserted.

Having established now that $[F_{\kappa-1}, b_1, \dots, b_{m!}] \subseteq F_\kappa$ for each κ and each choice of elements b_i from $m!$ distinct groups N_i, assume $t \geqq 2 + ce(m!)$ and form $[b_1, b_2, \dots, b_t]$. As N_1 and N_2 permute modulo F, $[b_1, b_2]$ lies in $F = F_0$. Each of the $m!$ further commutations takes the result one step further down the chain of subgroups F_κ. As $k \leqq ce$, the final result is trivial.

This completes the last step of the proof of Lemma 52.23, and so also the proof of the Oates-Powell Theorem. //

Very little further argument is needed to prove

52.6 **Theorem** (KOVÁCS and NEWMAN [*1*]). *The class* $\mathfrak{C}(e, m, c)$ *is a Cross variety.*

Proof. We first improve on Lemma 52.21 by showing that var $A \subseteq \mathfrak{C}(e, m, c)$ whenever A is a finite group in $\mathfrak{C}(e, m, c)$. We know, from 52.21, that var $A \subseteq \mathfrak{C}(e, e^n, c)$, if A has order n. Therefore, if $B \in$ var A, B has certainly only finite chief factors. Let H/K be one of them; to show that its order is at most m, we exhibit a finite group in var A with the same chief factor; then $|H/K| \leqq m$ follows from 51.23. As H/K is a chief factor of B, there exists to each proper subgroup of H/K an element in B/K that does not normalize H/K. As H/K is finite, this provides a finite number of elements which, together with H/K, generate a subgroup of B/K which is finitely generated, hence finite by Lemma 52.22. This subgroup has H/K as one of its chief factors, and it clearly belongs to var A, as required.

We now take in particular A as the direct product of one copy of each of the distinct critical groups in $\mathfrak{C}(e, m, c)$; this is possible by Lemma 52.33. We show that for this choice of A the class $\mathfrak{C}(e, m, c)$ is contained in var A; then the first part gives $\mathfrak{C}(e, m, c) =$ var A and the proof is complete.

Let $C \in \mathfrak{C}(e, m, c)$ be arbitrary; to prove that C belongs to var A, it suffices to prove that every finitely generated subgroup of C belongs to var A. We write $\mathfrak{B} =$ var A and assume that there is a finitely generated subgroup B of C not belonging to $\mathfrak{B}$. Then $V(B)$ is non-trivial, but $B/V(B)$ belongs to $\mathfrak{B}$, hence to $\mathfrak{C}(e, m, c)$ by the first part. In particular $B/V(B)$ is finite, so that by Schreier's Theorem $V(B)$ is finitely generated. Hence, using Zorn's Lemma, there is a normal subgroup N of C maximal with respect to not containing $V(B)$. Then all those normal subgroups of C which properly contain N also contain $V(B)$; if M is their intersection, then M/N is easily confirmed to be a chief factor of C, hence of order at most m. Now put $L = V(B) \cap N$, then as $V(B)N \subseteq M$, $V(B)/L$ also has order at most m. But now B/L is finite, and as $B/V(B) \in \mathfrak{C}(e, m, c)$ and $V(B)/L$ has order at most m, every chief series of B/L through $V(B)$, and so every chief series of B/L, has factors of order at most m. Also, since B/L is a factor of C, its exponent divides e and its nilpotent factors have class at most c. Thus $B/L \in \mathfrak{C}(e, m, c)$ and therefore, by the first part of the proof, var $B/L \subseteq \mathfrak{C}(e, m, c)$. By 51.41, var B/L is generated by its critical groups; hence it is generated by some of the critical groups in $\mathfrak{C}(e, m, c)$, that is by some of the direct factors of A. But then var $B/L \subseteq \mathfrak{B}$, in particular $B/L \in \mathfrak{B}$. But, as $L = V(B) \cap N$ is properly contained in $V(B)$, $V(B/L) \neq \{1\}$ giving a contradiction. //

The bounding of the order of critical groups with abelian monolith in the original proof of OATES and POWELL is modelled on POWELL's argument in the case of soluble critical groups (POWELL [1]), where the *absolute rank* is used in place of the maximum order of the chief factors. Define first the *absolute degree* of an abelian chief factor of the finite group A as the (common) degree of the absolutely irreducible components of the representation induced by A on that chief factor. Then:

52.71 *The absolute rank of A is the maximum of the absolute degrees of its abelian chief factors.*

Now it is well known that a representation is absolutely irreducible if and only if the matrix algebra spanned by it is isomorphic to a complete matrix algebra over a field. By a theorem of A. S. AMITSUR and J. LEVITZKI [1], a certain polynomial identity holds in a complete matrix algebra precisely if the number of variables is at least twice the degree of the matrix algebra. This then permits the formulation of a law, the *absolute rank law*, bounding the absolute degrees of all the chief factors of a soluble group.

52.72 *The absolute rank law is, for each integer $k \geqq 1$, defined inductively by*

$$w_0(k) = x_0,$$

$$w_{n+1}(k) = \Pi\left(w_n(k)^{x_{n,\pi(1)} \cdots x_{n,\pi(2k)}}\right)^{\operatorname{sgn} \pi}$$

where the product is extended over all $(2k)!$ permutations π of the integers $1, \ldots, 2k$ in some order and the variables x_0 and $x_{n,1}, \ldots, x_{n,2k}$ for all $n \geqq 0$ are distinct.

Then one has

52.73 **Theorem** (POWELL [1]). *The absolute rank of a finite soluble group is at most k if and only if $w_t(k)$ is a law in the group for some integer $t \geqq 1$.*

In fact, t may be taken as the length of a chief series of the group.

Thus the absolute rank law gives, in the case of soluble groups, rather more precise information on some features of the group than the chief centralizer law; on the other hand the latter describes the size of arbitrary chief factors for arbitrary groups.

3. Critical Groups and Subvarieties

Locally finite varieties are generated by their critical groups; clearly, therefore, the critical groups will contain information on the subvarieties of such a variety. The naive hope that the lattice of subvarieties is simply given by the lattice of subsets of the set of critical groups is far from being fulfilled, even in the case of Cross varieties. The object of this section is to clarify the relation between a finite group and the critical groups generating it and between the group and the varieties generated by proper factors of it. Almost all the work reported here is due to L. G. KOVÁCS and M. F. NEWMAN [*1*], [*2*], [*3*], whose analyses are close to the method used earlier by SHEILA OATES and M. B. POWELL ([*1*], Section 3), I. D. MACDONALD [*6*] and P. M. WEICHSEL [*1*], [*3*]; specific references will not always be given.

We need the concept of *similar normal subgroups;* as usual, $C_X(Y)$ is the centralizer in X of the normal subgroup Y of X.

53.11 **Definition.** *Let M be normal in A and N normal in B; M in A is similar to N in B if there exist isomorphisms μ: $M \rightarrowtail\!\!\twoheadrightarrow N$ and $\alpha: A/C_A(M) \rightarrowtail\!\!\twoheadrightarrow B/C_B(N)$ such that for all $m \in M$ and $a \in A/C_A(M)$*

$$(m^a)\,\mu = (m\,\mu)^{a\,\alpha}.$$

The element m^a is, of course, well defined, namely as the common value of all conjugates m^x, $x \in A$, where x runs through the relevant coset of the centralizer $C_A(M)$. Thus similarity requires that the normal subgroups are isomorphic, that the automorphism groups induced on them by the whole groups are isomorphic, and that moreover these two isomorphisms can be chosen so as to be compatible. If M in A is similar to N in B, we write $(M \trianglelefteq A) \sim (N \trianglelefteq B)$. Often M and N are subgroups of the same group and we may then write simply $M \sim N$, if the common supergroup is understood. By a routine check:

53.12 *Similarity is an equivalence relation.* //

We shall need some simple properties of similarity which we collect here.

53.13 *If M and N are normal in A and $M \cap N = \{1\}$, then $(M \trianglelefteq A) \sim (MN/N \trianglelefteq A/N)$.*

Proof. One has $C_A(M)/N = C_{A/N}(MN/N)$; now define the isomorphisms by

$$m\,\mu = m\,N \quad \text{for} \quad m \in M$$

$$(a\,C_A(M))\,\alpha = (a\,N)\,C_{A/N}(M\,N/N) \quad \text{for} \quad a \in A,$$

and check their compatibility. //

53.14 *Let H be a subgroup of the direct product $A \times B$ whose projection into B is the whole of B. If M is normal in H and contained in $B \cap H$, then $(M \trianglelefteq B) \sim (M \trianglelefteq H)$.*

Proof. Under the assumptions M is normal in B and one checks that $C_B(M)A \cap H = C_H(M)$. Define the isomorphisms as follows:

μ is taken as the identity on M and α is given by $(h C_H(M))\alpha = b C_B(M)$ for each $h \in H$ and b the projection of h in B. Then $b^{-1}h \in A$, and the compatibility is again a routine check. //

We shall naturally be much concerned with minimal normal subgroups of a finite group in the context of this section. The subgroup generated by all minimal normal subgroups is the *socle* of the group. It is well known (cf. Scott, Section 7.4), but can also be derived easily by an inductive argument from 53.15 below, that the socle and indeed every normal subgroup of the whole group that is contained in the socle, is a direct product of minimal normal subgroups.

53.15 *If N is a product of minimal normal subgroups of a finite group A, and M is a normal subgroup of A contained in N, then there is a normal subgroup L of A that complements M in N.*

Proof. Take L maximal with respect to being normal in A, contained in N and avoiding M. Then $LM = N$, since otherwise one can find a minimal normal subgroup K contained in N, but not in LM, hence intersecting LM trivially. Then also $LK \cap M = \{1\}$ contradicting the choice of L. //

53.16 *If M is a minimal normal subgroup of A contained in a product of similar minimal normal subgroups $M_1, \ldots, M_s$, then M is similar to all M_i, $i = 1, \ldots, s$.*

Proof. We may assume that M is not contained in the normal subgroup generated by a proper subset of the set $\{M_1, \ldots, M_s\}$. Put $N = \mathrm{gp}(M_1, \ldots, M_s)$; by 53.15 there is a complement K of M in N. Not all the groups M_i can belong to K. Without loss of generality assume $M_1 \nsubseteq K$ so that $M_1 \cap K = \{1\}$. But then $M_1 K = N$, for $M_1 K \subset N$ would give $M_1 K/K \subset MK/K \subseteq A/K$ which is impossible as MK/K is a minimal normal subgroup of A/K. Thus we have $N = MK = M_1 K$, and by 53.13

$$(M \trianglelefteq A) \sim (MK/K \trianglelefteq A/K) \quad \text{and} \quad (M_1 \trianglelefteq A) \sim (M_1 K/K \trianglelefteq A/K)$$

and the assertion follows from 53.12. //

Now 53.15, 53.16 and the remark preceding 53.15 give

53.17 *If N is a normal subgroup of the finite group A contained in a product of similar minimal normal subgroups M_i of A, then N is a direct product of minimal normal subgroups, each similar to M_1.* //

This completes the preparations.

Now consider a finite set $\mathfrak{D}$ of finite groups which is *factor closed*, that is to each factor of a group in $\mathfrak{D}$ there is a group isomorphic to it in $\mathfrak{D}$. Take a finite group A in var $\mathfrak{D}$; we know that A is a factor of a finite direct product of groups in $\mathfrak{D}$. In general there will be many ways of representing A in that way. We choose a *minimal representation of A in* var $\mathfrak{D}$ as follows: Every representation of A as a factor of a direct product of groups in $\mathfrak{D}$ determines a non-increasing sequence of integers consisting of the orders of the factors that occur. Ordered lexicographically – one sequence comes before another if its entry in the first place where they differ is the smaller of the two – the set of these sequences has a first element. The representations of A corresponding to this first sequence are the minimal representations. All subsequent statements refer to a fixed minimal representation of A in var $\mathfrak{D}$ with the following notation:

$$A = H/K \quad \text{where} \quad K \lhd H \subseteq P = \Pi D_i, \qquad i = 1, \ldots, n.$$

53.21 *Each group D_i is critical, and if any group D_i is replaced by a proper factor, the resulting direct product has no factor isomorphic to A.*

Proof. If D_k is not critical, then D_k is a factor of $\prod_j D_{k,j}$ where each $D_{k,j}$ is a proper factor of D_k, hence belongs to $\mathfrak{D}$ and has smaller order than D_k. But then A also is a factor of the direct product

$$\prod_{i \neq k} D_i \times \prod_j D_{k,j}$$

and the sequence of integers associated with this representation is earlier than that of the given one, contradicting the assumptions. Again, if one group is replaced by a smaller one, the sequence of integers is replaced by an earlier one which can no longer correspond to a representation of A. //

Denote by π_i the projection of P onto the component D_i as well as any restriction of it to a subgroup of P.

53.22 *The subgroup H of P is a subdirect product of P, that is $H\pi_i = D_i$, hence H ker $\pi_i = P$ for each i.*

Proof. If $H\pi_i$ were a proper subgroup of D_i, then $H\pi_i$ could have been chosen in place of D_i to represent A in var $\mathfrak{D}$, contradicting the minimality. As ker π_i is the product of all factors D_j other than D_i, H ker π_i contains $H\pi_i = D_i$, hence contains D_i ker $\pi_i = P$. //

53.23 *A subgroup of D_i is normal in D_i if and only if it is normalized by H; every non-trivial normal subgroup of D_i intersects H non-trivially.*

Proof. The first part is immediate from 53.22. If N is a non-trivial normal subgroup of D_i and $H \cap N = \{1\}$, then A is a factor of

$$\prod_{j \neq i} D_j \times D_i/N,$$

contrary to the minimality assumption. //

53.24 *The normal subgroup K of H intersects all factors D_i trivially.*

Proof. By 53.23, $K \cap D_i$ is normal in D_i as well as in H. But then A is a factor of

$$\prod_{j \neq i} D_j \times D_i/D_i \cap K,$$

and the minimality assumption shows that $K \cap D_i$ is trivial. //

By 53.21 and 51.32 the groups D_i are monolithic. Let M_i be the monolith of D_i for $i = 1, \dots, n$. Then we can now show:

53.25 **Lemma.** *If $A = H/K$, $H \subseteq \Pi D_i$ is a minimal representation of A in var $\mathfrak{D}$ then, for each i, D_i is critical and A contains a minimal normal subgroup N_i which in A is similar to the monolith M_i in D_i.*

Proof. From 53.23 and 53.24 we know that M_i is contained in H, that $M_i K/K$ is minimal normal in H/K and is isomorphic to M_i, and $M_i K \cap D_i = M_i$. Application of 53.14 gives $(M_i \lhd D_i) \sim (M_i \lhd H)$. But then, by 53.12 and 53.13, M_i in D_i is similar to $M_i K/K$ in $H/K = A$. //

In general, of course, not every minimal normal subgroup of H/K is contained in $(\Pi M_i)K/K$. But if A itself is monolithic, then this cannot fail to be true. This gives us:

53.26 **Lemma.** *If $A \in$ var $\mathfrak{D}$ is monolithic and $A = H/K$, $H \subseteq \Pi D_i$ is a minimal representation of A in* var $\mathfrak{D}$, *then the monolith M of A is similar in A to the monolith M_i of D_i for each i, and A/M is contained in* var $\{D_1/M_1, \dots, D_n/M_n\}$.

Proof. The first part is an immediate consequence of 53.25. For the second part note that if M^*/K is the monolith of H/K, then $M^* = M_i K$ for each i, hence $M^* = (\Pi M_i) K$. Thus $A/M \cong H/M^* = H/(\Pi M_i) K$, which shows that A/M is isomorphic to a factor group of $H/\Pi M_i$; but the latter is isomorphic to a subgroup of $\Pi D_i/\Pi M_i \cong \Pi (D_i/M_i)$. //

We now go on to apply these lemmas in a number of different directions.

53.31 **Theorem** (Kovács and Newman [2]). *If A is a critical group with non-abelian monolith contained in* var B, *where B is a finite group, then A is a factor of B.*

Proof We use Lemma 53.26 with $\mathfrak{D}$ the set of all distinct factors of B. Let $A = H/K$, $H \subseteq \Pi D_i$ be a minimal representation so that for each i, D_i is a critical factor of B whose monolith M_i is similar in D_i to the monolith M in A. As M is non-abelian, $C_A(M) = \{1\}$, so that $A/C_A(M) \cong A$. From the similarity it follows that for each D_i, M_i is non-abelian, hence $D_i/C_{D_i}(M_i) \cong D_i$, and so $D_i \cong A$ (and, of course, only one constituent D_i occurs). //

53.32 **Theorem.** *If two critical groups A and B generate the same variety, then their monoliths are similar.*

Proof. The variety var $A=$var B is generated by the critical factors of B, but not by the proper factors of B. Hence B itself occurs in a minimal representation of A in the form $A=H/K$, where $H\subseteq \Pi D_i$ and the D_i are critical factors of B. By Lemma 53.26 it follows that the monolith of B is similar to that of A. //

53.33 **Corollary.** *Two non-isomorphic critical groups that generate the same variety have abelian monoliths.*

Proof. By 53.32 their monoliths are both non-abelian or both abelian. By 53.31 the former implies that the critical groups are isomorphic. //

No more can be said, as for example the dihedral group of order eight and the quaternion group of order eight are both critical and generate the same variety. Nor is the converse of Theorem 53.32 true in general, as will be obvious from 54.11; but also non-nilpotent critical groups with abelian similar monoliths generate in general different varieties:

53.34 **Example.** The symmetric group S_3 of degree three, and the group C which is the splitting extension of the cycle C_9 of order 9 by the automorphism of order two that transforms a generator into its inverse both have monoliths isomorphic to a 3-cycle, and clearly they are similar. //

From 53.32 we have in particular:

53.35 **Corollary.** *Two non-isomorphic finite simple groups cannot generate the same variety.* //

Problem 23. *Can a variety other than $\mathfrak{D}$ contain an infinite number of non-isomorphic non-abelian finite simple groups?*

The next theorem extends to arbitrary finite groups properties observed by P. M. WEICHSEL in finite p-groups.

53.41 **Theorem.** (KOVÁCS and NEWMAN [*2*], [*3*]). *A finite group is contained in the variety generated by its proper factor groups if and only if it is not monolithic.*

A finite monolithic group that is not critical is contained in the variety generated by its proper subgroups.

53.42 **Corollary.** *If a finite group is contained neither in the variety generated by its proper subgroups nor in the variety generated by its proper factor groups, then it is not contained in the variety generated by its proper factors, that is, it is critical.*

Proof. The corollary is immediate from the theorem.

To prove the theorem, note that by the proof of 51.32 a group with more than one minimal normal subgroup is contained in the variety generated by its proper factor groups. For the converse of the first part, assume A is a finite monolithic group. If it is critical, the statement is trivial; hence assume it is not critical, that is $A \in \text{var}\,(\text{QS}-1)\,A$. Let $\mathfrak{D}$ be a finite subset of non-isomorphic groups in $(\text{QS}-1)\,A$ which is minimal with respect to being factor closed and generating A, let D be a group of maximal order in $\mathfrak{D}$ and put $\mathfrak{D}_0 = \mathfrak{D} \backslash \{D\}$. Then $A \notin \text{var}\,\mathfrak{D}_0$, but the set $\mathfrak{D}_0$ is still factor closed and every proper factor of a group in $\mathfrak{D}$ belongs to $\mathfrak{D}_0$. By 53.26 $A/M \in \text{var}\,\mathfrak{D}_0$, where M is the monolith of A. But then the variety generated by all proper factor groups of A belongs to var $\mathfrak{D}_0$ and so cannot contain A.

It remains to show that A does belong to the variety generated by its proper subgroups. This time we take $\mathfrak{D}$ as a finite subset of non-isomorphic groups in $(\text{QS}-1)\,A$ which is minimal with respect to being factor closed, generating A and containing $\mathfrak{D}_1$, the set of non-isomorphic factors of proper subgroups of A. As finite sets with these three properties exist in $(\text{QS}-1)\,A$, there certainly are minimal such sets. Now assume $A \notin \text{var}\,\mathfrak{D}_1$. Then $\mathfrak{D} \backslash \mathfrak{D}_1$ is not empty as $A \in \text{var}\,\mathfrak{D} \backslash \text{var}\,\mathfrak{D}_1$. Let D be a group of maximal order in $\mathfrak{D} \backslash \mathfrak{D}_1$ and put $\mathfrak{D}_0 = \mathfrak{D} \backslash \{D\}$, so that $\mathfrak{D}_1 \subseteq \mathfrak{D}_0 \subset \mathfrak{D}$. Again $\mathfrak{D}_0$ contains all proper factors of groups in $\mathfrak{D}$ and it is factor closed. Because of the minimality of $\mathfrak{D}$, $A \notin \text{var}\,\mathfrak{D}_0$. As before, 53.26 shows that $A/M \in \text{var}\,\mathfrak{D}_0$, so that every proper factor group of A belongs to var $\mathfrak{D}_0$, that is $\mathfrak{D} \backslash \mathfrak{D}_1$ belongs to var $\mathfrak{D}_0$. But then the inclusions $\mathfrak{D}_1 \subseteq \mathfrak{D}_0 \subset \mathfrak{D}$ imply var $\mathfrak{D}_0 =$ var $\mathfrak{D}$, which is impossible as A belongs to var $\mathfrak{D}$, but not to var $\mathfrak{D}_0$. Hence $A \in \text{var}\,\mathfrak{D}_1$ as required. //

The last part of Theorem 53.41, or rather, the argument yielding it, can be refined further so as to give, with the aid of Theorem 53.44 below, the following result:

53.43 **Theorem** (KOVÁCS and NEWMAN [3]). *If the finite monolithic group A with monolith M is not critical, then A/M is contained in the variety generated by the proper subgroups of A/M.*

We refer to the source for the proof of this theorem which confirms a conjecture by SHEILA OATES.

These theorems may be looked upon as giving implicitly conditions for a monolithic group to be critical. The information we have now also supplies some more explicit conditions:

53.44 **Theorem** (KOVÁCS and NEWMAN [3]). *A finite monolithic group is critical if either*

(i) *the monolith centralizer is contained in the monolith (hence is either trivial or equal to the monolith), or*

(ii) *its Frattini subgroup is trivial.*

Proof. Let A be finite and monolithic, and let $\mathfrak{D}_1$, as before, be the set of factors of proper subgroups of A and let $\mathfrak{D}$ this time be the set of those critical groups in $\mathfrak{D}_1$ whose monolith is similar to that of A. From 53.41, if A is not critical then $A \in \operatorname{var} \mathfrak{D}_1$, and so by 53.26, $A \in \operatorname{var} \mathfrak{D}$ and $A/M \in \operatorname{var} \{D_i/M_i \colon D_i \in \mathfrak{D}\}$.

In case (i) $C_A(M) \subseteq M$. If $C_A(M) = \{1\}$, let $D_0 \in \mathfrak{D}$, then

$$|D_0| \geqq |D_0/C_{D_0}(M_0)| = |A/C_A(M)| = |A|,$$

using that the monoliths M of A and M_0 of D_0 are similar. But every group in $\mathfrak{D}$ has order less than that of A, hence only the alternative $C_A(M) = M$ remains. Now M is abelian, hence so is M_0 and therefore $M_0 \subseteq C_{D_0}(M_0)$. Thus $|D_0| \geqq |M_0|\,|D_0/C_{D_0}(M_0)| = |M|\,|A/C_A(M)| = |A|$, contradicting again the choice of $\mathfrak{D}$ from which D_0 was taken. This completes case (i).

For (ii) we may now assume that M is abelian, since otherwise (i) applies. If the Frattini subgroup $\Phi(A)$ is trivial, then the maximal subgroups of A have trivial intersection, hence there exists some maximal subgroup B of A that does not contain M. As M is abelian, $B \cap M$ is central in M, and it is normal in B; thus it is normal in $MB = A$. As $B \cap M \subset M$, $B \cap M = \{1\}$. Now $C_A(M) = M(B \cap C_A(M))$ as $MB = A$, and $B \cap C_A(M)$ is also centralized by M and normal in B, hence normal in A and $B \cap C_A(M) \cap M \subseteq B \cap M = \{1\}$. Thus, as A is monolithic, $B \cap C_A(M)$ is trivial and $C_A(M) = M$ follows, reducing this case to (i). //

Note that (i) does not imply (ii): there exists a non-splitting extension of an elementary 5-group by the alternating group A_5 of degree five such that the A_5 acts irreducibly on the elementary abelian 5-group. Then the latter is the monolith and its own centralizer and also is the Frattini subgroup.

We further point out that neither (i) nor, therefore, (ii) give any help in deciding whether a monolithic p-group is critical or not, since in a monolithic p-group the monolith is central and the Frattini subgroup non-trivial except in the trivial case when the p-group is elementary abelian. Thus the case of non-abelian critical p-groups shows incidentally that neither condition in Theorem 53.44 is necessary. Kovács and Newman (loc. cit.) give further sufficient conditions whose proof requires more detail than we have reported here. Again none of these conditions is helpful in the case of p-groups.

Every group other than the trivial group possesses non-trivial verbal subgroups; hence a finite group possesses *minimal verbal subgroups* ('non-trivial' is again implied). It is easy to see that in the case of critical groups the monolith is verbal, and then of course it is the unique minimal verbal subgroup. SHEILA OATES conjectured that the monolith is verbal in every finite monolithic group. This can now be confirmed.

53.51 **Theorem** (KOVÁCS and NEWMAN [2]). *The monolith of a finite monolithic group is a verbal subgroup.*

Proof. Let A be the group, M its monolith as before. Let $\mathfrak{U}$ be the variety generated by its proper factor groups. By Theorem 53.41 A does not belong to $\mathfrak{U}$ whether or not A is critical. Hence $U(A)$ is non-trivial, normal in A, and so contains M. But trivially, $A/M \in \mathfrak{U}$, that is $U(A/M) = U(A)\,M/M$ is trivial in A/M, giving $U(A) \subseteq M$. //

We note specially that when A is critical, then $\mathfrak{U}$ may just as well be taken as the variety generated by all proper factors of A:

53.52 *If A is a critical group with monolith M and* $\mathfrak{U} = \operatorname{var}(\mathrm{QS}-1)\,A$, *then* $M = U(A)$. //

The next aim is to generalize these facts to arbitrary finite groups.

53.53 **Lemma.** *Let B be a finite group, $\mathfrak{V}$ a proper subvariety of* var B *and A a group belonging to* var B *but not to $\mathfrak{V}$. Then there is a subvariety $\mathfrak{U}$ of* var B *containing $\mathfrak{V}$, and a critical factor C of B whose proper factors belong to $\mathfrak{U}$, such that $A \notin \mathfrak{U}$ but $A \in \mathfrak{U} \vee$* var C.

Proof. Using 51.42 and 51.43, we arrange the critical factors $C_1, \dots, C_r$ of B that do not belong to $\mathfrak{V}$ so that $|C_1| \leqq \dots \leqq |C_r|$; by assumption $r > 0$. Let i be the first value such that $A \in \mathfrak{V} \vee \operatorname{var}\{C_1, \dots, C_i\}$ but $A \notin \mathfrak{V} \vee \operatorname{var}\{C_1, \dots, C_{i-1}\}$ – to be interpreted as $\mathfrak{V}$ when $i=1$. Then put $\mathfrak{U} = \mathfrak{V} \vee \operatorname{var}\{C_1, \dots, C_{i-1}\}$; as the critical proper factors of C_i have smaller order than C_i, it follows from 51.43 that all proper factors of C_i belong to $\mathfrak{U}$. Thus putting $C = C_i$ completes the proof. //

53.54 **Lemma.** *If A is a finite group, $\mathfrak{U}$ a variety not containing A, and C a critical group whose proper factors lie in $\mathfrak{U}$ and such that $A \in \mathfrak{U} \vee$* var C, *then $U(A)$ is a direct product of minimal normal subgroups all similar in A to the monolith of C in C.*

Proof. As A is finite, there exists a finite factor closed set $\mathfrak{D} \subset \mathfrak{U} \vee \{C\}$ such that $A \in \operatorname{var} \mathfrak{D}$. As $A \notin \mathfrak{U}$, $\mathfrak{D}$ must contain C. Let $A = H/K$, $H \subseteq \Pi\, D_i$ be a minimal representation; then all D_i are critical, and some of the factors are isomorphic to C since the proper factors of C belong to $\mathfrak{U}$, but A does not. Hence $A = H/K$, $H \subseteq D_1 \times \dots \times D_s \times C^r = P$, say, where $r \geqq 1$ and $D_1 \times \dots \times D_s \in \mathfrak{U}$. From 53.52 and the assumptions on $\mathfrak{U}$, $U(C) = M$ is the monolith of C, hence $U(P) = M^r$. But $U(H) \subseteq U(P)$, hence $U(H/K) \subseteq M^r K/K$. By 53.25, each normal subgroup MK/K of $H/K = A$ is minimal and similar in A to M in C. Now 53.17 completes the proof. //

53.55 **Theorem** (KOVÁCS and NEWMAN [*2*]). *Every minimal verbal subgroup of a finite group is a direct product of similar minimal normal subgroups of that group.*

Proof. Let $W(A)$ be minimal verbal in the finite group A; then $A \notin \mathfrak{W}$. Hence, with $\mathfrak{V} = \mathfrak{W} \wedge \operatorname{var} A$, $A \notin \mathfrak{V}$. Apply 53.53: there is a subvariety $\mathfrak{U} \supseteq \mathfrak{V}$ and a critical factor C of A in $\operatorname{var} A$ such that the proper factors of C belong to $\mathfrak{U}$ and $A \notin \mathfrak{U}$, but $A \in \mathfrak{U} \vee \operatorname{var} C$. Hence by 53.54, $U(A)$ is a direct product of minimal normal subgroups of A, all similar in A to the monolith of C in C. From the definition of $\mathfrak{V}$, $V(A) = W(A)$. As $\mathfrak{V} \subseteq \mathfrak{U} \subset \operatorname{var} A$ we have $U(A) \subseteq V(A) = W(A)$, and so $U(A) = W(A)$ because $W(A)$ is minimal. //

Perhaps we should stress that though minimal verbal subgroups exist in a finite group and every verbal subgroup contains a minimal one, the intersection of verbal subgroups need not be verbal (cf. B. H. NEUMANN [*1*] for an example). Nevertheless Theorem 53.55 ensures that all minimal verbal subgroups lie in the socle. Hence, supplementing Theorem 53.41:

53.56 **Corollary.** *No finite group belongs to the variety generated by the factor group of its socle.* //

Note, however, that the socle need not itself be verbal.

Finally, a group is *verbally simple* if every verbal subgroup is trivial or the whole group. By Theorem 53.55, a verbally simple finite group is a direct product of similar minimal normal subgroups. As a normal subgroup of a direct factor is normal in the whole group, each of these factors is simple. Hence one obtains the following result:

53.57 **Corollary.** *A finite verbally simple group is characteristically simple.* //

This generalizes a theorem of REINHOLD BAER [*1*] which draws the same conclusion for a finite fully invariantly simple group.

The discussion of the minimal representations of a group in a variety generated by a finite set of finite groups leads to some information on the number of generators of the critical groups that generate a Cross variety.

53.61 **Theorem** (BURNS [*1*]). *A Cross variety is generated by a k-generator group if and only if it is generated by its k-generator critical groups.*

Proof. The sufficiency is trivial: if k-generator groups of any kind generate a variety then so does the free group of rank k. Conversely, let $\mathfrak{D}$ be the set of all distinct critical groups and their factors in the given Cross variety, $\mathfrak{U}$ say, and let $\mathfrak{U} = \operatorname{var} A$ where A is a k-generator group. As $\mathfrak{D}$ generates $\mathfrak{U}$, we have a minimal representation of A in the form $A = H/K$ where $H \subseteq \Pi D_i$, $D_i \in \mathfrak{D}$. Now use 53.21 and 53.22: as A is a

k-generator group we may assume H to be a k-generator group—possibly after replacing H by a proper subgroup. The minimality of the representation ensures that the projections will still be onto the factors D_i. But then these factors are critical and, as projections of H, k-generator groups. //

53.62 **Theorem.** *If a variety is generated by a single critical group that can be generated by k, but by no less than k elements, then every group generating the variety needs at least k generators.*

Proof. Let A be the k-generator critical group and B such that $\operatorname{var} B = \operatorname{var} A$. As B is a factor of a direct power of A, that is $B \cong H/K$ with $H \leqq \Pi A(i)$, the projections of H into the factors $A(i)$ also generate the variety. If B can be generated by l elements, so can these projections. But A is critical, hence not every projection can be a proper subgroup of the factor $A(i)$, hence $l \geqq k$. //

It is possible that a Cross variety that is generated by its k-generator groups contains critical groups that need more than k generators. This is a common occurrence in more general varieties. For example the metabelian variety $\mathfrak{A}^2$ is generated by $F_2(\mathfrak{A}^2)$, but it contains critical groups that need k generators for arbitrary large k, obtainable as factors of wreath products of a p-cycle by an elementary abelian p-group. To describe what seems to be the only known instance of this situation in a Cross variety, we refer back to the statements 24.64 and 24.66 on the conditions for a product variety to be a Cross variety. We can now see why $\mathfrak{U}\mathfrak{A}_n$, where $\mathfrak{U}$ is nilpotent of class c and of exponent m prime to n, is a Cross variety. In any group $B \in \mathfrak{U}\mathfrak{A}_n$, the verbal subgroup $A_n(B)$ is in the Fitting subgroup and nilpotent of class c. The fundamental lemma 51.37, used in conjunction with Schreier's formula, bounds the number of generators of a critical group in $\mathfrak{U}\mathfrak{A}_n$ and then only a much simplified version of the arguments in Section 2 of this chapter is needed to bound the order of such critical groups. The argument may then be completed in many ways, possibly even using that the laws are already known to be finitely based by 34.24. It is a by-product of these arguments that all critical groups in $\mathfrak{U}\mathfrak{A}_n$ have at most $c+1$ generators, but other tools are needed to provide the following precise information reported here without proof.

53.63 (Burns [1].) *If $\mathfrak{U}$ is a variety of groups that are nilpotent of class $c > 1$ and of exponent m prime to n, then $\mathfrak{U}\mathfrak{A}_n$ is generated by its c-generator groups, but not by its $(c-1)$-generator groups; its critical groups need at most $c+1$ generators and when $c=2$, $m=p$, and $n=q$ is a prime dividing $p-1$, then 3-generator critical groups exist in the variety.*

Problem 24. *Does there exist, for a given integer $n > 0$, a Cross variety that is generated by its k-generator groups and contains $(k+n)$-generator* *critical groups? In such a variety, is every critical group that needs more than k generators a factor of a k-generator critical group, or at least of the free group of rank k?*

We turn to the relation between a critical group and the variety generated by its proper factors.

53.64 **Theorem.** *If A is critical and the variety of its proper factors can be defined by n-variable laws, then A can be generated by n elements.*

Proof. Put $\mathfrak{U} = \text{var}\,(\text{Qs}-1)\,A$; by assumption $\mathfrak{U} = \mathfrak{U}^{(n)}$, which means by 16.21 that a group belongs to $\mathfrak{U}$ if all its n-generator subgroups belong to $\mathfrak{U}$. If all n-generator subgroups of A were proper, they would belong to $\mathfrak{U}$ by the definition of $\mathfrak{U}$, and so A would be in $\mathfrak{U}$. Hence an n-generator subgroup of A must be the whole of A. //

53.65 **Theorem.** *If the critical group A can be generated by n elements, then there is a law requiring n variables that holds in* var (Qs − 1) *A, but not in A. If A cannot be generated by less than n elements then all the laws that hold in* var (Qs − 1) *A, but not in A, involve at least n variables.*

Proof. Use again 16.21: if A satisfies all n-variable laws of $\mathfrak{U} = \text{var}\,(\text{Qs}-1)\,A$, then $A \in \mathfrak{U}^{(n)}$, that is the n-generator subgroups of A belong to $\mathfrak{U}$ and so, by the assumption, A itself is in $\mathfrak{U}$.

Further, assume all $(n-1)$-generator subgroups of A are proper subgroups and consider an $(n-1)$-variable law of $\mathfrak{U}$, that is an $(n-1)$-variable law that holds in all proper subgroups of A. A group satisfies an $(n-1)$-variable law if all its $(n-1)$-generator subgroups satisfy it; hence A satisfies this law, and so the laws of $\mathfrak{U}$ not satisfied in A must involve more than $n-1$ variables. //

The n-variable words that are laws in all proper factors of the n-generator critical group A, but not in A itself, are called *A-critical words* ('critical functions' in P. M. WEICHSEL [*3*]).

The ideas evolved here, especially the simple remark 53.64, have been used by SHEILA OATES and M. B. POWELL, in different ways, to obtain results on the number of generators of a finite simple group.

For example:

53.66 (OATES [2]): *If A is simple and* $\mathfrak{U} = \text{var}\,(\text{Qs}-1)\,A$ *contains a simple d-generator group B that is contained in every generating set of critical groups for* $\mathfrak{U}$, *then A can be generated by* $2d+1$ *elements.*

By means of a set of two-variable laws that bound the p-length of a finite soluble group, M. B. POWELL (unpublished) has shown:

53.67 *A minimal simple group can be generated by at most three elements.*

It is a trivial consequence of 53.32 and 53.33 that if two critical groups with non-abelian monolith generate the same variety, then the varieties generated by their proper factors also coincide. The same can be established in the other extreme case, that of critical p-groups.

53.71 **Theorem** (MACDONALD [6]). *If two critical p-groups generate the same variety, then the varieties generated by their proper factors also coincide.*

Proof. Let A and B be critical p-groups with var A = var B and put $\mathfrak{U} = \text{var}\,(\text{QS}-1)\,A$. The idea of the proof is to show that the laws of $\mathfrak{U}$ are determined only by the laws of var A and the fact that a single critical group generates var A. Then it is immaterial whether A or B was used to generate the variety.

Assume that A has class c, exponent p^α and that it can be generated by n, but not by fewer elements. Then, by Theorem 53.62, the same is true of B, that is these integers c, p^α and n are invariants of the variety and do not depend on the choice of the critical group generating it. Now let w be a word in m variables; it is a law in $\mathfrak{U}$ if and only if it is a law in the monolith factor group of A and in every maximal subgroup of A. We deal with the two conditions in turn.

53.72 *The word w is a law in the monolith factor group of the critical p-group A if and only if $[w, x_{m+1}]$ and w^p are laws in A, that is in* var A.

This is an immediate consequence of the fact that by 51.35 the monolith of a critical p-group is central and of order p.

To deal with the case of maximal subgroups of A, let v be a word in variables $y_1, \ldots, y_n$ of the following form:

$$v = y_1^{\gamma_1} \ldots y_{n-1}^{\gamma_{n-1}} y_n^{p\,\gamma_n} B(y_1, \ldots, y_n),$$

where

$$0 \leqq \gamma_i < p^\alpha \quad \text{for} \quad i = 1, \ldots, n-1, \qquad 0 \leqq \gamma_n < p^{\alpha-1},$$

and $B(y_1, \ldots, y_n)$ is a product of distinct commutators of weight at most c in $y_1, \ldots, y_n$, occurring in some order given by an ordering of all distinct commutators of weight at most c, and each with exponent at most $p^\alpha - 1$. Clearly the set, $\mathfrak{v}$ say, of such words is finite. Now we show

53.73 *The m-variable word w is a law in each maximal subgroup of the critical p-group A if and only if $w(v_1, \ldots, v_m)$ is a law in A, that is in* var A, *for every substitution of words $v_1, \ldots, v_m$ from $\mathfrak{v}$.*

Proof. Assume w is a law in each maximal subgroup of A, and let $a_1, \ldots, a_n$ be arbitrary elements of A. Substituting these for the variables y_i in each word $v \in \mathfrak{v}$ gives a value

$$v(a_1, \ldots, a_n) \in \text{gp}(a_1, \ldots, a_{n-1}, a_n^p, A') = \text{gp}(a_1, \ldots, a_{n-1}, \Phi(A)),$$

where $\Phi(A)$ is the Frattini subgroup. But $\text{gp}(a_1, \ldots, a_{n-1}, \Phi(A))$ is a proper subgroup of A, hence contained in some maximal subgroup, the same for every choice of $v \in \mathfrak{v}$. In this maximal subgroup w is a law, hence $w(v_1, \ldots, v_m)$ is a law in A.

Conversely, assume that all the words $w(v_1, \ldots, v_m)$ are laws in A, and let M be a maximal subgroup of A. Choose a generating set $a_1, \ldots, a_n$ of A so that $M = \text{gp}(a_1, \ldots, a_{n-1}, \Phi(A))$. This is always possible. Then every element of M can be written in the form $v(a_1, \ldots, a_n)$ for a suitable word $v \in \mathfrak{v}$. Hence, if $b_1, \ldots, b_m$ are arbitrary elements of M, there exist words $v_1, \ldots, v_m$ in $\mathfrak{v}$ such that $b_i = v_i(a_1, \ldots, a_n)$, and so $w(b_1, \ldots, b_m) = w(v_1(a), \ldots, v_m(a)) = 1$ by assumption. Thus w is a law in M.

From 53.72 and 53.73 it is immediate that w is a law in $\mathfrak{U}$ if and only if $[w, x_{m+1}]$, w^p and all $w(v_1, \ldots, v_m)$, $v_i \in \mathfrak{v}$, are laws in A, that is in B, hence if and only if w is a law in $\text{var}(\text{QS}-1)\,B$. Thus $\text{var}(\text{QS}-1)\,A = \text{var}(\text{QS}-1)\,B$. //

There remains the case of two non-nilpotent critical groups with abelian monolith that generate the same variety:

Problem 25. *Prove that whenever A and B are critical groups such that* $\text{var}\,A = \text{var}\,B$, *then* $\text{var}(\text{QS}-1)\,A = \text{var}(\text{QS}-1)\,B$.

Incidentally, the variety of proper factors of a critical group is not in general maximal in the variety generated by the critical group. WARREN BRISLEY [*1*] has constructed examples to show

53.74 *To every positive integer $n > 1$ and every prime $p > n+2$ there is a critical metabelian p-group A such that there exists a properly descending chain, of length n, of subvarieties between* $\mathfrak{U}_0 = \text{var}\,A$ *and* $\mathfrak{U}_n = \text{var}(\text{QS}-1)\,A$.

Compare also GRAHAM HIGMAN [*6*], where the existence of such varieties is established by entirely different means.

Finally we mention that the converse of Theorem 53.71 is false; as a consequence of Theorem 5.4 of WEICHSEL [*3*] one has:

53.75 *There exist critical p-groups of different classes whose varieties of proper factors coincide.*

4. Critical p-Groups and Locally Finite Varieties; a Summary of Developments

Every variety whose free groups are residually finite p-groups for some prime p is generated by its finite p-groups. Thus the investigation of critical p-groups may be expected to have a bearing on a wide range of problems. The tools developed in the preceding section lose some of their power when applied to p-groups. The reason is simple:

54.11 *Any two critical p-groups for the same prime p have similar monoliths.*

Proof. By 51.35, the monolith of every critical p-group is a p-cycle, contained in the centre. Thus the group acts trivially on the monolith. //

In fact the subsets of the set of critical groups in a Cross variety of p-groups are as unsuitable for describing the lattice of subvarieties as they could be. Notice that to substantiate this claim, it is quite sufficient to look at metabelian groups only.

54.12 (MACDONALD [*6*]): *To each integer* $n>1$ *and every prime* $p>n$ *there exist n non-isomorphic critical metabelian p-groups that generate the same variety.*

The construction is explicit; the groups have class $n+2$ and are *regular* (cf. MARSHALL HALL, Section 12.4); when $p>n+2$, the groups have exponent p and so are explicit examples of a situation like that described by GRAHAM HIGMAN:

54.13 (HIGMAN [*6*]): *If* $c>6$, *the number of distinct critical groups, each generating the variety of metabelian groups of exponent p and class c, tends to infinity with p.*

On the other hand a Cross variety of p-groups need not be generated by any one critical group:

54.14 (HIGMAN [*6*]): *There are Cross varieties of groups of exponent p that cannot be generated by a critical group.*

An explicit example of a variety of 2-groups exhibiting the same feature is also available:

54.15 (MACDONALD [*6*]): *There is a metabelian 2-group of class six, generated by two elements, such that the variety it generates cannot be generated by a single critical group.*

Since these varieties must be generated by their critical groups, they are joins of proper subvarieties. We call a variety *join-irreducible* if it is not the join of proper subvarieties. In order to handle the superabundance of critical groups, P. M. WEICHSEL [*3*], [*4*] singles out those that, in the light of 54.14 and 54.15, are the only ones needed to generate a Cross variety: a *basic p-group* is a critical p-group that generates a join-irreducible variety. Then one sees easily

54.21 *The join-irreducible Cross varieties of p-groups are precisely those generated by a basic p-group.*

There exist, of course, critical p-groups that are not basic; this is shown by the relation between the two non-abelian groups of order p^3, $p>2$, a simple example which is worth knowing.

54.22 **Example.** Let A be the non-abelian group of order p^3 which is of exponent p^2, let B be the non-abelian group of order p^3 and exponent p. Both are critical. One verifies that A is a factor of the direct product $B \times C$, where C is the cycle of order p^2. Moreover $\operatorname{var} B \subseteq \operatorname{var} A$, and the inclusion is clearly proper. Hence $\operatorname{var} A = \mathfrak{A}_{p^2} \vee \operatorname{var} B$ showing that $\operatorname{var} A$ is not join-irreducible. //

We point out at once that basic p-groups still do not provide the whole answer to the problem of classifying varieties of p-groups. In the first place, the situation described by 54.12 and 54.13 also arises when basic p-groups only are involved:

54.23 *The two non-abelian groups of order eight are both basic and generate the same variety.*

Moreover, and more disturbing:

54.24 (HIGMAN [*6*]): *There exist three distinct join-irreducible metabelian varieties of exponent p whose joins in pairs coincide.*

Hence any attempt to characterize Cross varieties of p-groups by means of sets of basic p-groups will, in general, have to select further from the set of all basic p-groups. Nevertheless basic p-groups have proved useful. Their structure is comparatively simple, due to some extent to the following property. We have to introduce the concept of a *marginal subgroup* (P. HALL [*1*], STROUD [*1*]): If V is a set of words, then the marginal subgroup $M_V(A)$ of a group A consists of all $a \in A$ such that

$$v(x_1, x_2, \ldots, x_n) = v(a\,x_1, x_2, \ldots, x_n) = \cdots = v(x_1, x_2, \ldots, a\,x_n)$$

holds identically in A for every word v in V.

54.25 (WEICHSEL [*3*]): *If B is a basic p-group then $M_V(B) \subseteq \Phi(B)$ whenever $V(B) \neq \{1\}$.*

Using this, one obtains:

54.26 (WEICHSEL [*4*], [*5*] and oral communication). *If $p > c$, the exponents of all terms of the lower central series of a basic p-group are equal. There are such basic p-groups to every pair of exponent p^α and class c. In the metabelian case, the exponent and the class determine the group uniquely to within isomorphism.*

If $c \geq p$ and the group is regular, the exponents of the terms of the lower central series drop at most every $p-1$ steps going down the lower central series.

A *p-group of small class*, that is $p > c$, is regular and regularity here, just as elsewhere in the theory of p-groups, plays a prominent role. It is not a varietal property (WEICHSEL [*6*]); this causes a certain amount of trouble. However, for most commutator calculations regularity can be dispensed with when the groups are metabelian, because the rule 34.51

for left-normed commutators aids computation as much as regularity does*. Even then the condition $c<p$ is more than a mere convenience: the sequence of exponents of the lower central series is affected by it. In the case of metabelian p-groups a direct attack on the problem of classification can be made by finding a basis for the laws of the group. These calculations (WEICHSEL [5], BRISLEY [2]) show

54.27 *A metabelian variety generated by a p-group of small class is completely determined by the sequence of exponents of its lower central terms. It is generated by its two-generator groups.*

In fact they have more detail:

54.28 (WEICHSEL [5]): *Every metabelian critical p-group of small class can be generated by two elements.*

54.29 (BRISLEY [2]): *The laws of a metabelian p-group of small class follow from two-variable laws together with the metabelian and the nilpotency law.*

It is evident from this brief but, I believe, essentially complete account of the present knowledge on varieties of p-groups, that a systematic theory is lacking. In the case of exponent p, at least, it should be possible to make headway using the representation theoretical methods outlined for the case of small class by GRAHAM HIGMAN [6].

Denote by $\mathfrak{B}_{p,c}$ the variety of all groups of exponent p and class c, and put $G_n = F_n(\mathfrak{B}_{p,p-1})$. Then $G_n/\Phi(G_n)$ is a vector space, E say, over the field of p elements, and so is each factor group of the lower central series, E_c say, where $1 \leqq c \leqq p-1$ and $E_1 = E$. The correspondence L_c: $E \rightarrow E_c$ is a functor on the category of vector spaces over the prime field and as such corresponds to a representation of the general linear group $GL(n, p)$ in $GL(n_c, p)$, where n_c is the dimension of E_c given by Witt's formula. As the commutators which form a basis of E_c are multilinear functions of the generators of G_n which, modulo $\Phi(G_n)$, form a basis of E, L_c is in fact a 'quotient functor' of the functor $E \rightarrow E^{(c)}$ where $E^{(c)}$ denotes the c-fold tensor power of E. As $c<p$, one has complete reducibility and the irreducible components can be worked out (I have adhered to Higman's notation, L_c, for this functor, chosen because the functor can be thought of as the homogeneous component of degree c in the free Lie ring generated by E). Now the varieties between $\mathfrak{B}_{p,c-1}$ and $\mathfrak{B}_{p,c}$ are in one-one correspondence with the subfunctors of L_c; in particular also the claim that such a variety is generated by a single critical group can be expressed in this framework and this leads to the applications quoted above.

---

* For cross-connections between regularity and the metabelian property see in particular ALPERIN [1] and MACDONALD [7].

A first step in the investigation of non-Cross varieties is to look at varieties all whose proper subvarieties are Cross varieties. These minimal non-Cross varieties have been called *just-non-Cross varieties* by KOVÁCS and NEWMAN. The variety $\mathfrak{A}$ of all abelian groups is obviously an example of a just-non-Cross variety. In order to describe more significant instances, we need some notation. The group B of example 54.22, of order p^3 and of exponent p, $p>2$, generates a variety of class two all whose subvarieties are abelian. We write var $B=\mathfrak{B}_{p,2}$ in agreement with the notation used above. In the case of prime 2, the corresponding variety is that generated by the dihedral group of order eight, as this also has the property that it is minimal nilpotent. We denote it by $\mathfrak{B}$ so that $\mathfrak{B}=\text{var } D_8=\text{var } Q_8$.

54.31 (KOVÁCS and NEWMAN [*4*]): *The following are just-non-Cross varieties:* $\mathfrak{A}$, $\mathfrak{A}_p^2$, $\mathfrak{A}_p\,\mathfrak{B}_{q,2}$, $\mathfrak{A}_p\mathfrak{B}$ $(p\neq 2)$ *and* $\mathfrak{A}_p\,\mathfrak{A}_q\,\mathfrak{A}_r$, *where* p, q, r *are any three distinct primes.*

In fact every proper subvariety of $\mathfrak{A}_p^2$ is nilpotent. This is a consequence of certain relations, due to N. D. GUPTA and M. F. NEWMAN [*1*], between commutator laws in a nilpotent factor group of a metabelian group and the exponents of some central factors. The laws in question are of the form $[x_1, x_2, n_1 x_1, \dots, n_s x_s]$, $s\geqq 2$, in the notation used before.

Related arguments show

54.32 *If* $[x_1, x_2, n_1 x_1, \dots, n_s x_s]$ *is a law in the metabelian group* A, *then* $A_{(m)}$, *where* $m=2+n_1+\dots+n_s$, *has finite, explicitly bounded, exponent.*

Using the arithmetic properties of the exponents of $A_{(m)}$ and $A_{(m+1)}$ obtainable from 54.32, this leads to

54.33 (GUPTA and NEWMAN [*1*]): *If a metabelian p-group satisfies the law* $[x_1, (p-1)\,x_2, (p-1)\,x_1, (p-1)\,x_3, \dots, (p-1)\,x_s]$ *with* $s\geqq 2$, *then it is nilpotent of class at most* $s(p-1)$.

Moreover

54.34 (KOVÁCS and NEWMAN [*5*]): *In every proper subvariety of* $\mathfrak{A}_p^2$, $[x_1, (p-1)\,x_2, (p-1)\,x_1, (p-1)\,x_3, \dots, (p-1)\,x_s]$ *is a law for some* $s\geqq 2$.

Therefore every subvariety of $\mathfrak{A}_p^2$ is a Cross variety.

It follows from remarks in HIGMAN [2] that the proper subvarieties of $\mathfrak{A}_p\,\mathfrak{B}_{q,2}$ and $\mathfrak{A}_p\mathfrak{B}$ $(p\neq 2)$ are Cross varieties. That these varieties themselves are not Cross varieties is a consequence of 24.64. This same theorem of ŠMEL'KIN, or 24.62 directly, confirms that $\mathfrak{A}_p\mathfrak{A}_q\mathfrak{A}_r$ is not a Cross variety. That all its proper subvarieties are Cross varieties follows from

54.35 (COSSEY [*1*]): *Every infinite set of non-isomorphic monolithic groups in* $\mathfrak{A}_p\mathfrak{A}_q\mathfrak{A}_r$ *generates the whole variety.*

This theorem arises out of an investigation of varieties that consist of soluble *A-groups*, that is soluble locally finite groups all whose Sylow subgroups are abelian. P. J. COSSEY finds:

54.36 *Every variety of soluble A-groups that is not a Cross variety contains a product* $\mathfrak{A}_p\mathfrak{A}_q\mathfrak{A}_r$ *for some distinct primes* p, q, r.

KOVÁCS and NEWMAN conjecture that every soluble non-Cross variety contains one of the just-non-Cross varieties mentioned in 54.31. The question what other just-non-Cross varieties might exist is also open.

The classification of metabelian varieties is proceeding. The subvariety lattice of $\mathfrak{A}_p\mathfrak{A}_n$, where n is prime to p, is known.

54.41 (HIGMAN [2]): *The proper subvarieties of* $\mathfrak{A}_p\mathfrak{A}_n$ *containing* A_{pn} *are characterized by a law of the form*

$$[x^n, y^{d_1}, \dots, y^{d_k}], \qquad d_1 > d_2 > \dots > d_k \geqq 1,$$

where each d_i *divides* n *but no* d_i *divides* d_j *for* $i > j$.

Hence the lattice of subvarieties between $\mathfrak{A}_{pn}$ and $\mathfrak{A}_p\mathfrak{A}_n$ is clearly isomorphic to the lattice of these sets of divisors $\{d_1, \dots, d_k\}$ ordered in the obvious way. This result also serves to classify the subvarieties of $\mathfrak{A}_m\mathfrak{A}_n$ as long as m and n are prime to each other.

54.42 (C. H. HOUGHTON, unpublished): *Each subvariety of* $\mathfrak{A}_m\mathfrak{A}_n$ *containing* $\mathfrak{A}_{mn}$ *is characterized in* $\mathfrak{A}_m\mathfrak{A}_n$ *by a law of the form* $[x^n, y^{d_1}, \dots, y^{d_k}]^{m'}$, *where the divisors* $d_1, \dots, d_k$ *of* n *are restricted as before and* m' *divides* m.

Every subvariety of $\mathfrak{A}_m\mathfrak{A}_n$ *is a variety between* $\mathfrak{A}_{rs}$ *and* $\mathfrak{A}_r\mathfrak{A}_s$ *for some* r *dividing* m *and* s *dividing* n.

Recently KOVÁCS and NEWMAN [5] have determined completely the lattice of subvarieties of the products $\mathfrak{A}_p^2$, $\mathfrak{A}_{p^n}\mathfrak{A}_p$ and hence of $\mathfrak{A}\mathfrak{A}_p$. They, too, describe the lattice of subvarieties of $\mathfrak{A}_{p^n}\mathfrak{A}_p$ by the additional laws they possess. Here, in fact in $\mathfrak{A}_p^2$, one finds instances of subvarieties that cannot be defined by a single (power of a) commutator, but need a product of distinct commutators to describe them. These results have been some help in dealing also with the cases $\mathfrak{A}_p\,\mathfrak{A}_{pm}$ and $\mathfrak{A}_{p^r}\mathfrak{A}_{pm}$ (R. A. BRYCE, unpublished), and the general case $\mathfrak{A}_m\mathfrak{A}_n$ seems within reach.

Finally we mention that GRAHAM HIGMAN [5] has started a systematic enquiry into the growth of the orders of free groups of a locally finite variety taking up PETER M. NEUMANN's idea to relate the growth of the order of the free groups, as the rank increases, to other significant properties of the variety. I shall attempt a brief report, although it is not at this stage possible to do justice to the results obtained so far and the potentialities of the idea.

Let $\mathfrak{V}$ be locally finite and put $f(n)=|F_n(V)|$ for all $n \geqq 1$. It is easy to see from the fact that $f(n+1)=f(n)\,|\ker \pi_n|$, where π_n is the natural projection of $F_{n+1}(\mathfrak{V})$ onto $F_n(\mathfrak{V})$, that $\log f$ is 'totally convex'.

We saw (cf. 24.52 and 24.53) that the rate of growth of f is markedly different for different varieties. The question whether there is an upper bound to the rate of growth is tied up with a number of unsolved problems, for example the problem whether locally finite, locally soluble varieties are soluble, or whether there are only a finite number of simple groups of given exponent, or whether the minimum number of generators of a finite simple group is bounded. Certain features of the rate of growth of f had been noticed (Chapter 2, loc. cit); for example $\log f$ grows like a polynomial function if and only if $\mathfrak{V}$ is nilpotent; if $\mathfrak{V}$ is not nilpotent, $\log f$ grows at least exponentially. Hence varieties such that $\log f(n)$ grows as $n \log n$ or as $\sqrt{n}$, when n tends to infinity, do not exist. These gaps in the possible rate of growth are, of course, likely to correspond to significant changes in the group theoretical properties of the varieties. Higman conjectures that every function f that can occur belongs to a fairly restricted class of functions, namely the functions that are CREAM, that is are obtained by *C*losure under *R*epeated *E*xponentiation, *A*ddition and *M*ultiplication from the identity function on the set of positive integers. The evidence presented in the paper in support of that conjecture gives an indication of the scope of these ideas.

References

ALPERIN, J. L.: [1] On a special class of regular p-groups. Trans. Amer. Math. Soc. **106,** 77—99 (1963).

AMITSUR, A. S., and J. LEVITZKI: [1] Minimal identities for algebras. Proc. Amer. Math. Soc. **1**, 449—463 (1950).

ANDREADAKIS, S.: [1] On the automorphisms of free groups and free nilpotent groups. Proc. London Math. Soc. (3) **15**, 239—268 (1965).

AUSLANDER, MAURICE, and R. C. LYNDON: [1] Commutator subgroups of free groups. Amer. J. Math. **77**, 929—931 (1955).

BACHMUTH, S.: [1] Automorphisms of free metabelian groups. Trans. Amer. Math. Soc. **118**, 93—104 (1965).

— [2] Induced automorphisms of free groups and free metabelian groups. Trans. Amer. Math. Soc. **122,** 1—17 (1966).

—, and I. HUGHES: [1] Applications of a theorem of Magnus. Arch. Math. **17,** 380—382 (1966).

—, and J. LEWIN: [1] The Jacobi identity in groups. Math. Z. **83**, 170—176 (1964).

BAER, REINHOLD: [1] Group elements of prime power index. Trans. Amer. Math. Soc, **75**, 20—47 (1953).

BATES, GRACE E.: [1] Free loops and nets and their generalizations. Amer. J. Math. **69,** 499—550 (1947).

BAUMSLAG, G.: [1] Wreath products and p-groups. Proc. Cambridge Philos. Soc. **55**. 224—231 (1959).

— [2] Wreath products and extensions. Math. Z. **81**, 286—299 (1963).

— [3] Some subgroup theorems for free $\mathfrak{v}$-groups. Trans. Amer. Math. Soc. **108,** 516—525 (1963).

— [4] On the residual nilpotence of some varietal products. Trans. Amer. Math. Soc. **109**, 357—365 (1963).

— [5] A subgroup theorem for some product varieties. Arch. Math. **6**, 337—341 (1965).

—, and N. BLACKBURN: [1] Groups with cyclic upper central factors. Proc. London Math. Soc. (3) **10**, 531—544 (1960).

—, B. H. NEUMANN, HANNA NEUMANN, and PETER M. NEUMANN: [1] On varieties generated by a finitely generated group. Math. Z. **86**, 93—122 (1964).

BIRKHOFF, GARRETT: [1] On the structure of abstract algebras. Proc. Cambridge Philos. Soc. **31**, 433—454 (1935).

BRISLEY, WARREN: [1] A problem of D. W. BARNES. Proc. Internat. Conf. Theory of Groups. Austral. Nat. Univ. Canberra 1965. Gordon and Breach 1967.

— [2] On varieties of metabelian p-groups and their laws. J. Austral. Math. Soc. (in print).

BURNS, R. G.: [1] Verbal wreath products and certain product varieties of groups. J. Austral. Math. Soc. (in print).

BURROW, MARTIN: [1] Invariants of free Lie rings. Comm. Pure Appl. Math. **11**, 419—431 (1958).

COHEN, D. E.: [1] On the laws of a metabelian variety. J. Algebra (in print).

COSSEY, P. J.: [1] On varieties of A-groups. Proc. Internat. Conf. Theory of Groups. Austral. Nat. Univ. Canberra 1965. Gordon and Breach 1967.

DUNWOODY, M. J.: [1] On verbal subgroups of free groups. Arch. Math. **16**, 153—157 (1965).

FOX, R. H.: [*1*] Free differential calculus I: Derivation in the free group ring. Ann. Math. (2) **57**, 547—560 (1953).

GASCHÜTZ, W.: [*1*] Über die Φ-Untergruppe endlicher Gruppen. Math. Z. **58**, 160—170 (1953).

GOL'DINA, N. P.: [*1*] Free nilpotent groups [Russian]. Dokl. Akad. Nauk S.S.S.R. **111**, 528—530 (1956).

— [*2*] Free nilpotent groups: Corrigenda [Russian]. Dokl. Akad. Nauk S.S.S.R. **126**, 694 (1959).

—, and O. N. GOLOVIN: [*1*] Subgroups of free metabelian groups [Russian]. Mat. Sbornik **37**, (**79**), 323—336 (1955).

GOLOD, E. S.: [*1*] Nil-algebras and residually finite p-groups [Russian]. Izvestiya Akad. Nauk S.S.S.R., Ser. Mat. **28**, 273—276 (1964).

—, and I. R. ŠAFAREVIČ: On the class field tower [Russian]. Izvestiya Akad. Nauk S.S.S.R., Ser .Mat. **28**, 261—272 (1964).

GOLOVIN, O. N.: [*1*] Nilpotent products of groups [Russian]. Mat. Sbornik **27**, (69), 427—454 (1950). Amer. Math. Soc. Transl. (2) **2**, 89—115 (1956).

— [*2*] Metabelian products of groups [Russian]. Mat. Sbornik **28**, (**70**), 431—444 (1951). Amer. Math. Soc. Transl. (2) **2**, 117—132 (1956).

GRUENBERG, K. W.: [*1*] Two theorems on Engel groups. Proc. Cambridge Philos. Soc. **49**, 377—380 (1953).

— [*2*] Residual properties of infinite soluble groups. Proc. London Math. Soc. (3) **7**, 29—62 (1957).

— [*3*] The Engel elements of a soluble group. Illinois J. Math. **3**, 151—168 (1959).

— [*4*] The residual nilpotence of certain presentations of finite groups. Arch. Math. **13**, 408—417 (1962).

GUPTA, CHANDRA KANTA: [*1*] A bound for the class of certain nilpotent groups. J. Austral. Math. Soc. **5**, 506—511 (1965).

GUPTA, N.D.: [*1*] Some group-laws equivalent to the commutative law. Arch. Math. **17**, 97—102 (1966).

— [*2*] Groups with Engel-like conditions. Arch. Math. **17**, 193—199 (1966).

—, and M. F. NEWMAN: [*1*] On metabelian groups. J. Austral. Math. Soc. **6**, 362—368 (1966).

HALL JR., MARSHALL: [*1*] A basis for free Lie rings and higher commutators in free groups. Proc. Am. Math. Soc. **1**, 575—581 (1950).

HALL, P.: [*1*] Verbal and marginal subgroups. J. Reine Angew. Math. **182**, 130—141 (1940).

— [*2*] The splitting properties of relatively free groups. Proc. London Math. Soc. (3) **4**, 343—356 (1954).

— [*3*] Finiteness conditions for soluble groups. Proc. London Math. Soc. (3) **4**, 419—436 (1954).

— [*4*] Some word problems. J. London Math. Soc. **33**, 482—496 (1958).

— [*5*] The Frattini subgroup of finitely generated groups. Proc. London Math. Soc. (3) **11**, 327—352 (1961).

HEINEKEN, H.: [*1*] Eine Bemerkung über Engelsche Elemente. Arch. Math. **11**, 321 (1960).

— [*2*] Engelsche Elemente der Länge drei. Illinois J. Math. **5**, 681—707 (1961).

— [*3*] Über ein Levisches Nilpotenzkriterium. Arch. Math. **12**, 176—178 (1961).

— [*4*] Bounds for the nilpotency class of a group. J. London Math. Soc. **37**, 456—458 (1962).

HIGMAN, GRAHAM: [*1*] Ordering by divisibility in abstract algebras. Proc. London Math. Soc. (3) **2**, 326—336 (1952).

— [*2*] Some remarks on varieties of groups. Quart. J. Math. Oxford (2) **10**, 165—178 (1959).

HIGMAN, GRAHAM: [*3*] Identical relations in finite groups. Conv. Internaz. di Teoria dei Gruppi Finiti, Firenze 1960, 93—100. Rome: Cremonese 1960.
— [*4*] Amalgams of *p*-groups. J. Algebra **1**, 301—305 (1964).
— [*5*] The orders of relatively free groups. Proc. Internat. Conf. Theory of Groups. Austral. Nat. Univ. Canberra 1965. Gordon and Breach 1967.
— [*6*] Representations of general linear groups and varieties of groups. Proc. Internat. Conf. Theory of Groups. Austral. Nat. Univ. Canberra 1965. Gordon and Breach 1967.
KALOUJNINE, L., and MARC KRASNER: [*1*] Produit complete des groupes de permutations et le problème d'extension des groupes III. Acta Sci. Math. Szeged **14**, 69—82 (1951).
KNOPFMACHER, J.: [*1*] Extensions in varieties of groups and algebras. Acta Math. **115**, 17—50 (1966).
KOGALOVSKI, S. P.: [*1*] Structural characteristics of universal classes [Russian]. Sibirsk Mat. Ž. **4**, 97—119 (1963).
KOSTRIKIN, A. I.: [*1*] On Burnside's problem [Russian]. Izvestiya Akad. Nauk S.S.S.R., Ser. Mat. **23**, 3—34 (1959).
KOVÁCS, L. G.: [*1*] Varieties and the Hall-Higman paper. Proc. Internat. Conf. Theory of Groups. Austral. Nat. Univ. Canberra 1965. Gordon and Breach 1967.
—, and M. F. NEWMAN: [*1*] Cross varieties of groups. Proc. Roy. Soc. (London) A **292**, 530—536 (1966).
— — [*2*] Minimal verbal subgroups. Proc. Cambridge Phil. Soc. **62**, 347—350 (1966).
— — [*3*] On critical groups. J. Austral. Math. Soc. **6**, 237—250 (1966).
— — [*4*] Just-non-Cross varieties. Proc. Internat. Conf. Theory of Groups. Austral. Nat. Univ. Canberra 1965. Gordon and Breach 1967.
— — [*5*] On non-Cross varieties (to be published).
LAZARD, M.: [*1*] Sur les groupes nilpotentes et les anneaux de Lie. Ann. Sci. Ecole Norm. Sup. (3) **71**, 101—190 (1954).
LEVI, F. W.: [*1*] Über die Untergruppen der freien Gruppen. II. Math. Z. **37**, 90—97 (1933).
— [*2*] Groups in which the commutator relation satisfies certain algebraic conditions. J. Indian Math. Soc., New Ser. **6**, 87—97 (1942).
—, and B. L. VAN DER WAERDEN: [*1*] Über eine besondere Klasse von Gruppen. Abhandl. Math. Sem. Univ. Hamburg **9**, 154—158 (1932).
LEVIN, FRANK: [*1*] On some varieties of soluble groups I. Math. Z. **85**, 369—372 (1964).
LIEBECK, HANS: [*1*] Concerning nilpotent wreath products. Proc. Cambridge Philos. Soc. **58**, 443—451 (1962).
LYNDON, R. C.: [*1*] Two notes on nilpotent groups. Proc. Amer. Math. Soc. **3**, 579—583 (1952).
MACDONALD, I. D.: [*1*] On certain varieties of groups. Math. Z. **76**, 270—282 (1961).
— [*2*] On certain varieties of groups. II. Math. Z. **78**, 175—188 (1962).
— [*3*] Generalisations of a classical theorem about nilpotent groups. Illinois J. Math. **8**, 556—570 (1964).
— [*4*] Another law for the 3-metabelian groups. J. Austral. Math. Soc. **4**, 452—453 (1964). Correction to appear in J. Austral. Math. Soc.
— [*5*] Some metabelian-like varieties of groups. Amer. Math. Monthly **72**, 159—162 (1965).
— [*6*] A theorem on critical *p*-groups. Proc. Intern. Conf. Theory of Groups. Austral. Nat. Univ. Canberra 1965. Gordon and Breach 1967.
— [*7*] The variety of regular *p*-groups. Arch. Math. (in print).
MACLANE, SAUNDERS: [*1*] Duality for groups. Bull. Amer. Math. Soc. **56**, 485—516 (1950).

MAGNUS, WILHELM: [*1*] Beziehungen zwischen Gruppen und Idealen in einem speziellen Ring. Math. Ann. **111**, 259—280 (1935).
— [*2*] Über Beziehungen zwischen höheren Kommutatoren. J. Reine Angew. Math. **177**, 105—115 (1937).
— [*3*] On a theorem of Marshall Hall. Ann. Math. **40**, 764—768 (1939).
— [*4*] Über Gruppen und zugeordnete Liesche Ringe. J .Reine Angew. Math. **182**, 142—147 (1940).
MAL'CEV, A. I.: [*1*] On some classes of infinite soluble groups [Russian]. Mat. Sbornik **28**, (**70**), 567—588 (1951). Amer. Math. Soc. Transl. (2) **2**, 1—22 (1956).
— [*2*] Two remarks on nilpotent groups [Russian]. Mat. Sbornik **37**, (79), 567—572 (1955).
— [*3*] On free soluble groups [Russian]. Dokl. Akad. Nauk S.S.S.R. **130**, 495—498 (1960). Transl.: Soviet Math. Dokl. **1**, 65—68 (1960).
MEIER-WUNDERLI, H.: [*1*] Über die Gruppen mit der identischen Relation $[x_1, x_2, \ldots, x_n] = [x_n, x_1, \ldots, x_{n-1}], n \geqq 3$. Vierteljahresschr. Naturforsch. Ges. Zürich **94**, 211—218 (1949).
— [*2*] Über endliche p-Gruppen, deren Elemente der Gleichung $x^p = 1$ genügen. Comment. Math. Helvet. **24**, 18—45 (1950).
— [*3*] Metabelsche Gruppen. Comment. Math. Helvet. **25**, 1—10 (1951).
— [*4*] Note on a basis of P. HALL for the higher commutators in free groups. Comment. Math. Helvet. **26**, 1—5 (1952).
— [*5*] Über die Struktur der Burnsidegruppen mit zwei Erzeugenden und vom Primzahlexponenten $p > 3$. Comment. Math. Helvet. **30**, 144—174 (1956).
MORAN, S.: [*1*] Associative operations on groups. I. Proc. London Math. Soc. (3), **6**, 581—596 (1956).
— [*2*] Associative operations on groups II. Proc. London Math. Soc. (3), **8**, 548—568 (1958).
— [*3*] Unrestricted verbal products. J. London Math. Soc. **36**, 1—23 (1961).
— [*4*] A subgroup theorem for free nilpotent groups. Trans. Amer. Math. Soc. **103**, 495—515 (1962). Errata and Addenda. Trans. Amer. Math. Soc. **112**, 79—83 (1964).
— [*5*] Unrestricted nilpotent products. Acta Math. **108**, 61—88 (1962).
MOSTOWSKI, A. W.: [*1*] Nilpotent free groups. Fund. Math. **49**, 259—269 (1961).
— [*2*] Automorphisms of relatively free groups. Fund. Math. **50**, 403—411 (1962).
NEUMANN, B. H.: [*1*] Identical relations in groups I. Math. Ann. **114**, 506—525 (1937).
— [*2*] Ascending derived series. Compositio Math. **13**, 47—64 (1956).
— [*3*] On a conjecture of HANNA NEUMANN. Proc. Glasgow Math. Ass. **3**, 13—17 (1957).
— [*4*] Lectures on topics in the theory of infinite groups. Lecture Notes prepared by M. PAVMAN MURTHY. Tata Institute of Fundamental Research. Bombay 1960.
— [*5*] Special topics in algebra: Universal algebra. Lecture notes prepared by PETER M. NEUMANN. Courant Institute of Mathematical Sciences, New York University 1962.
— [*6*] On a theorem by AUSLANDER and LYNDON. Arch. Math. **13**, 4—9 (1963).
— [*7*] Twisted wreath products of groups. Arch. Math. **14**, 1—6 (1963).
—, and HANNA NEUMANN: [*1*] Embedding theorems for groups. J. London Math. Soc. **34**, 465—479 (1959).
— —, and PETER M. NEUMANN: [*1*] Wreath products and varieties of groups. Math. Z. **80**, 44—62 (1962).
—, and TEKLA TAYLOR: [*1*] Subsemigroups of nilpotent groups. Proc. Roy. Soc. (London) A **274**, 1—4 (1963); A **281**, 436 (1964).
NEUMANN, HANNA: [*1*] On varieties of groups and their associated near-rings. Math. Z. **65**, 36—69 (1956).

NEUMANN, HANNA: [2] On a theorem by AUSLANDER and LYNDON. Arch. Math. **13**, 1—3 (1962). A correction: Arch. Math. **14**, 367—368 (1963).
— [3] On a theorem by GASCHÜTZ. J. Reine Angew. Math. **212**, 109—112 (1963).
— [4] Varieties of groups. Lecture notes prepared by I. M. S. DEY and C. H. HOUGHTON. Manchester College of Science and Technology 1963.
NEUMANN, PETER M.: [1] Some indecomposable varieties of groups. Quart. J. Math. Oxford (2), **14**, 46—50 (1963).
— [2] On the structure of standard wreath products of groups. Math. Z. **84**, 343—373 (1964).
— [3] On word subgroups of free groups. Arch. Math. **16**, 6—21 (1965).
—, and M. F. NEWMAN: [1] Schreier varieties of groups (submitted to Math. Z.).
—, and JAMES WIEGOLD: [1] Schreier varieties of groups. Math. Z. **85**, 392—400 (1964).
NOVIKOV, P. S.: [1] On periodic groups [Russian]. Dokl. Akad. Nauk S.S.S.R. **127**, 749—752 (1959).
OATES, SHEILA: [1] Identical relations in groups. J. London Math. Soc. **38**, 71—78 (1963).
— [2] Identical relations in a small number of variables. Proc. Internat. Conf. Theory of Groups. Australian Nat. Univ. Canberra 1965. Gordon and Breach 1967.
—, and M. B. POWELL: [1] Identical relations in finite groups. J. Algebra **1**, 11—39 (1964).
POWELL, M. B.: [1] Identical relations in finite soluble groups. Quart. J. Math. Oxford (2) **15**, 131—148 (1964).
REMESLENNIKOV, V. N.: [1] Two remarks on nilpotent groups of class three [Russian]. Algebra i Logika Seminar **4**, 59—65 (1965).
ŠMEL'KIN, A. L.: [1] The semigroup of varieties [Russian]. Dokl. Akad. Nauk S.S.S.R. **149**, 543—545 (1963). Transl.: The semigroup of group manifolds. Soviet Math. Dokl. **4**, 449—451 (1963).
— [2] Free polynilpotent groups [Russian]. Dokl. Akad. Nauk S.S.S.R. **151**, 73—75 (1963). Transl.: Soviet Math. Dokl. **4**, 950—953 (1963). Izvestiya Akad. Nauk S.S.S.R., Ser. Mat. **28**, 91—122 (1964).
— [3] Wreath products and varieties of groups [Russian]. Dokl. Akad. Nauk S.S.S.R. **157**, 1063—1065 (1964). Transl.: Soviet Math. Dokl. **5**, 1099—1101 (1964). Izvestiya Akad. Nauk S.S.S.R., Ser. Mat. **29**, 149—170 (1965).
— [4] On soluble products of groups [Russian]. Sibirsk Mat. Ž. **6**, 212—220 (1965).
— [5] On free polynilpotent groups. Dokl. Akad Nauk S.S.S.R. **169**, 1024—1025 (1966).
STROUD, P. W.: [1] On a property of verbal and marginal subgroups. Proc. Cambridge Philos. Soc. **61**, 41—48 (1965).
STRUIK, RUTH R.: [1] On associative products of groups. Trans. Amer. Math. Soc. **81**, 425—452 (1956).
— [2] On verbal products of groups. J. London Math. Soc. **34**, 397—400 (1959).
— [3] On nilpotent products of cyclic groups. I. Canad. J. Math. **12**, 447—462 (1960).
— [4] On nilpotent products of cyclic groups. II. Canad. J. Math. **13**, 557—568 (1961).
TAKAHASI, M.: [1] Note on word subgroups in free products of groups. J. Inst. Polytech. Osaka City Univ. A **2**, 13—18 (1951).
TOBIN, S.: [1] On a theorem of BAER and HIGMAN. Canad. J. Math. **8**, 263—270 (1961).
TURNER-SMITH, R. F.: [1] Marginal subgroup properties for outer commutator words. Proc. London Math. Soc. (3) **14**, 321—341 (1964).
WARD, M. A.: [1] Basic commutators for polynilpotent groups. Proc. Internat. Conf. Theory of Groups. Austral. Nat. Univ. Canberra 1965. Gordon and Breach 1967.
WEICHSEL, PAUL M.: [1] A decomposition theory for finite groups with applications to p-groups. Trans. Amer. Math. Soc. **102**, 218—226 (1962).

WEICHSEL, PAUL M.: [*2*] On isoclinism. J. London Math. Soc. **38**, 63—65 (1963).
— [*3*] On critical *p*-groups. Proc. London Math. Soc. (3) **14**, 83—100 (1964).
— [*4*] Critical and basic *p*-groups. Proc. Internat. Conf. Theory of Groups. Austral. Nat. Univ. Canberra 1965. Gordon and Breach 1967.
— [*5*] On metabelian *p*-groups. J. Australian Math. Soc. (in print).
— [*6*] Regular *p*-groups and varieties. Math. Z. **95**, 223—231 (1967).
WEVER, FRANZ: [*1*] Über Invarianten in Lieschen Ringen. Math. Ann. **120**, 563—580 (1949).
— [*2*] Über Regeln in Gruppen. Math. Ann. **122**, 334—339 (1950).
WIEGOLD, JAMES: [*1*] Nilpotent products of groups with amalgamations. Publ. Math. Debrecen **6**, 131—168 (1959).
— [*2*] Some remarks on generalised products of groups with amalgamations. Math. Z. **75**, 57—78 (1961).
WIELANDT, H., and B. HUPPERT: [*1*] Arithmetical and normal structure of finite groups Proc. Symposia in Pure Math. Amer. Math. Soc. **6**, 17—38 (1962).
WITT, E.: [*1*] Treue Darstellung Liescher Ringe. J. Reine Angew. Math. **117**, 152—160 (1937).
WRIGHT, C. R. B.: [*1*] On the nilpotency class of a group of exponent four. Pacific J. Math. **11**, 387—394 (1961).

Author Index

Alperin, J. L. 177
Amitsur, A. S. 161
Andreadakis, S. 111
Auslander, Maurice 126

Bachmuth, S. 99, 111
Baer, Reinhold 41, 144, 170
Bates, Grace E. 13
Baumslag, G. 27, 32, 45, 53, 54, 58, 60, 61, 65, 68, 69, 70, 72, 75, 78, 82, 107, 117, 118, 120, 122, 123, 143
Birkhoff, Garrett 15
Blackburn, N. 78
Brisley, W. 174, 177
Bruck, R. C. 98
Bryce, R. A. 22, 179
Burns, R. G. 64, 170, 171
Burrow, M. 102

Cohen, D. E. 22, 104
Cohn, P. M. 154
Cossey, P. J. 178, 179
Cross, D. C. 22, 146
Curtis, C. W. 144

Dunwoody, M. J. 40, 58, 75, 128, 133

Eckmann, B. 144

Fox, R. H. 48, 104
Frobenius, G. 46

Gaschütz, W. 155
Gol'dina, N. P. 123
Golod, E. S. 98
Golovin, O. N. 33, 37, 123
Gruenberg, K. W. 14, 30, 73, 75, 76, 80, 98
Gupta, N. D. 178

Hall, Jr., Marshall 2, 19, 33, 42, 43, 77, 79, 80, 93, 118, 129, 133, 145, 175
Hall, P. 1, 9, 29, 30, 78, 79, 80, 84, 114, 115, 136, 137, 138, 140, 141, 176
Heineken, H. 93, 98
Higman, Graham 18, 22, 26, 43, 61, 64, 68, 88, 89, 90, 91, 92, 105, 146, 150, 174, 175, 176, 177, 179
Hirsch, K. A. 80
Houghton, C. H. 41, 64, 142, 143, 179
Huppert, B. 46

Kaloujnine, L. 46
Kogalovski, S. P. 17
Kostrikin, A. I. 19, 113, 134
Kovács, L. G. 19, 79, 144, 148, 151, 160, 162, 165, 166, 167, 168, 169, 170, 178, 179
Krasner, M. 46
Kurosh, A. G. 2, 33, 41, 43, 58, 118, 145, 154

Levi, F. W. 25, 41, 43, 44, 92, 93
Levin, F. 99
Levitzki, J. 161
Lewin, J. 99
Liebeck, H. 25
Lyndon, R. C. 22, 89, 126

Macdonald, I. D. 93, 99, 162, 173, 175, 177
MacLane, S. 136, 137, 144
Magnus, W. 102, 104, 107
Mal'cev, A. I. 105, 123
Meier-Wunderli, H. 99
Moran, S. 33, 37, 123
Mostowski, A. W. 110, 111, 115, 116, 121

Neumann, B. H. 5, 15, 18, 21, 27, 32, 33, 40, 42, 43, 45, 53, 57, 65, 68, 70, 72, 82, 83, 105, 107, 114, 126, 135, 143, 146, 151, 154, 170
Neumann, Hanna 7, 27, 32, 40, 43, 45, 53, 57, 65, 66, 68, 70, 72, 82, 107, 114, 127, 143
Neumann, Peter M. 27, 32, 40, 45, 53, 57, 59, 60, 61, 62, 65, 68, 69, 70, 72, 82, 107, 113, 114, 117, 124, 125, 127, 128, 133, 134, 143, 179

Newman, M. F. 22, 25, 97, 105, 134, 139, 144, 151, 160, 162, 165, 166, 167, 168, 169, 170, 178, 179
Novikov, P. S. 19, 113

Oates, Sheila 22, 41, 42, 141, 148, 151, 156, 160, 162, 167, 172

Powell, M. B. 22, 87, 148, 151, 156, 160, 161, 162, 172

Rédei, L. 42
Reiner, I. R. 144

Šafarevič, I. R. 98
Schmidt, O. J. 42
Schöpf, A. 144
Schreier, O. 42
Scott, W. R. 83, 155, 163
Šmel'kin, A. L. 45, 54, 57, 63, 64, 70, 123, 124
Stroud, P. W. 176
Struik, Ruth R. 33

Taylor, Tekla 105, 132, 133
Turner-Smith, R. F. 84

Van der Waerden, B. L. 25, 93

Ward, M. A. 101
Weichsel, M. 162, 166, 172, 174—177
Wiegold, J. 43, 97, 114, 133
Wielandt, H. 46
Witt, E. 80

Subject Index

Abelian relatively free 11
— variety 13
absolute degree 161
— rank 161
— rank law 161
absolutely free 11
A-groups 179
amalgam 42
automorphisms of relatively free groups **4.1**
— of absolutely free groups 3
— of free abelian groups 3
— of free metabelian groups 111
— of free nilpotent groups 111

Basic commutators 79
— *p*-groups 175
Bates-free 13
bound, greatest lower 20
— least upper 20
Burnside problem, the restricted 19
Burnside variety 13

Canonical generators 9
cartesian power 14
— product 14
— subgroup 34
central series, iterated lower 8
— —, lower 8, 77
— —, upper 77
— — of metabelian nilpotent free groups 101
chain, ascending, of varieties 24
—, descending, of varieties 21
chief centralizer 150
— centralizer law 152
— factor 145
— series 145
class, nilpotency 14
—, small 176
— row 14
closed class of groups 15, **1.5**
— group 144
— set of words 6
closure of a set of words 6
— of a class of groups 15
collecting process 79, 101
composition factor 145
— series 145
commutator, basic 79
— collecting process 79, 101
— identities 85
— law 98
—, left-normed 4
—, mutual 8
—, outer 84
—, special 84
—, weight of 4, 84
— word 4
consequence 4
constituent of a cartesian or direct product 14
— of a free product 33
— of a verbal product 35
coordinate subgroup 14
critical function 172
— group 146
— word 172
Cross variety 150, **5.1**

Degree, absolute 161
deletion of a free generator 84
— of a free factor 84
derivative, Fox- 48
derived series 8
diagonal 17
direct factor of a relatively free group 41, 141, **4.4**
— power 14
— product 2, 14
discriminating group 28
— set of groups 27
discrimination **1.7**, **2.2**

Endomorphism 2
—, induced 3
Engel group 98
— law 98

equivalent sets of words 4
exponent 13
extension 38

Factor 1
— closed 163
—, proper 1
— of cartesian, direct, verbal or free product *see* constituent
—, free 33
—, lower central 77
—, upper central 77
factorization of varieties 43, **2.3**
finite basis problem 22
— relatively free group 18
Fitting subgroup 155
Fox derivative 48
Frattini subgroup 78
free abelian 11
— abelian of exponent *m* 11
—, absolutely 11
—, Bates- 13
— Burnside group 14
— generating set 2, 9
— group 2
— — of a product variety 38
—, Hall- 9
— factor 33
— metabelian 14
— — nilpotent **3.6**
— nilpotent 14, **3.5**
— polynilpotent 14
—, reduced 9
—, relatively 9
— soluble 14
— subgroup **4.2**
—, $\mathfrak{V}$- 13
fully invariant 5
— invariantly simple 58

Generating groups of finite rank 18, **2.5**, **3.5**, **3.6**
generators, canonical 9
—, free 2, 9

Hall-free 9
Hopf group 111
— property 111, **4.1**

Identical relation 4
identity, commutator 85
—, Witt 86
indecomposable variety 43, **2.4**
induced automorphism 3, 110, 111
— endomorphism 3
injective group 136
iterated lower central series 8

Join-irreducible variety 175
just-non-Cross variety 178

Kostrikin variety 19

Lattice of varieties 20
law 4, **1.2**
—, absolute rank 161
—, chief centralizer 152
laws of a finite group 151
— of a metabelian variety 104
— of a nilpotent variety 89, **3.4**
— of a product variety 90
left-normed 4
length, of a subset of a free group 43
—, solubility 14
locally finite variety 19
lower central factor 77
— central series 8, 77
— nilpotent series 122
— *p*-series 139

Marginal subgroup 176
metabelian critical groups 171, 174—177
— groups 21
— —, automorphisms of 111
— —, free 104, 109, **4.2**
— —, laws of 104, 178
— —, matrix representation of 104
— —, nilpotent 97, 101, 104, **3.6**
— —, of exponent four 24, 25, 97, 98
— —, of exponent *p* 99, 175, 176
— —, prime power exponent 175—177
— —, special examples of 60, 98, 121
metabelian product varieties, discriminating groups 68
— — —, generating groups 68
— — —, lattice of subvarieties 178, 179
— — —, residual properties of free groups 109, **2.6**
metabelian nilpotent varieties 97, **3.6**
— *p*-group varieties 174—177
— varieties, laws of 97, 99, 104, 178
— —, special examples of 21, 24, 25, 27
— —, three variable laws 21, 99
— —, two variable laws 21
minimal representation 164
— verbal subgroup 168

monolith 147
monolithic 144, 146
monotone 126
mutual commutator subgroup 8

n-generator group 20, **1.6**
n-variable law 21, **1.6**
— word 4, 21
Nielsen reduced 44
— system 43
nilpotent groups **3.1**
— series 122
— variety 14, Chapter 3
normal form 33

Order of finite relatively free group 18, 62, 179
outer commutator 84

p-groups, critical 173, **5.4**
polycyclic 80
polynilpotent 14
power, cartesian 14
— direct 14
powers, group of n-th 8
problems 6, 22, 23, 42, 60, 69, 72, 92, 101, 102, 113, 114, 125, 128, 133, 141, 142, 166, 171, 174
product, cartesian 14
—, direct 14
—, free 33
—, subcartesian 17, 30
—, subdirect 30
—, varietal 35
—, verbal 35, **1.8**
—, $\mathfrak{V}$- 35
— variety 38, Chapter 2
projection 30
projective group 136

Rank 2, 12
—, absolute 161
reduced free 9
regular p-group 175, 176
— variety 122
relation 2
—, identical 4
relatively free 9, **1.3**
relator 2
residual properties 30, **1.7**, **2.6**, **3.2**
— — of $F/U(R)$ 54, 75
residually a k-generator group 69

Schreier's formula 3
— theorem 3
Schreier property 126, **4.3**
— variety 114, 133
semigroup of varieties 58
series, chief 145
—, composition 145
—, derived 8
—, iterated lower central 8
—, lower central 8, 77
—, lower nilpotent 122
—, lower p-series 139
—, normal 77
—, subnormal 80
—, upper central 77
—, upper nilpotent 122
similar normal subgroups 162
similarity 162
simple, verbally 170
small class 176
socle 163
soluble 14
solubility length 14
solubility length 14
special commutator 84
splitting group 137
— property 136, **4.4**
subcartesian 17, 30
subdirect 30
subgroup, cartesian 34
—, coordinate 14
—, free 114, **4.2**
—, fully invariant 5
—, mutual commutator 8
—, of n-th powers 8
—, verbal 5
subnormal 80
subvariety 13
supersoluble 77
support 14
syllable 33

Three-metabelian 99
translation 84
twisted wreath product 65

Upper central factor 77
— central series 77
— nilpotent series 122

Value 4
variable 4
varietal product 35

variety 12, **1.4**, **1.5**
—, abelian 13
—, abelian of exponent *m* 13
—, Burnside 13
—, Cross 150, **5.1**
— defined by 12
— determined by 26
—, factorization of 43
—, free groups of 13
— generated by 18
—, indecomposable 43, **2.4**
—, join-irreducible 174
—, just-non-Cross 178
—, Kostrikin 19
—, lattice of varieties 20
—, locally finite 19
—, monotone 126
—, nilpotent 14, Chapter 3
— of proper factors 146, 172
—, polynilpotent 14
—, product 38, Chapter 2
—, regular 122
—, Schreier 133
—, semigroup of varieties 58
—, soluble 14
verbal product 35, **1.8**
— product with amalgamation 42
— subgroup 5
— subgroup, minimal 168
— subgroup of a free product 34
— wreath product 54
verbally simple 170
$\mathfrak{V}$-free 13
$\mathfrak{V}$-product 35

Weight 4, 84
Witt's formula 80
— identity 86
word 4
—, commutator 4
— in *n* variables 4
— subgroup *see* verbal subgroup
—, value of 4
words **1.2**
—, closed set of 6
—, equivalence of 4
wreath product 45, **2.2**
— —, restricted 45
— —, twisted 65
— —, unrestricted 45
— —, verbal 54